DATE		

REAL-TIME
SYSTEM
DESIGN

McGraw-Hill Computer Science Series

Ahuja: *Design and Analysis of Computer Communication Networks*
Barbacci and Siewiorek: *The Design and Analysis of Instruction Set Processors*
Collins: *Intermediate Pascal Programming: A Case Study Approach*
Donovan: *Systems Programming*
Filman and Friedman: *Coordinated Computing: Tools and Techniques for Distributed Software*
Goodman and Hedetniemi: *Introduction to the Design and Analysis of Algorithms*
Hayes: *Computer Architecture and Organization*
Hutchison and Just: *Programming Using the C Language*
Katzan: *Microprogramming Primer*
Keller: *A First Course in Computer Programming Using Pascal*
Kohavi: *Switching and Finite Automata Theory*
Levi and Agrawala: *Real-Time System Design*
Liu: *Elements of Discrete Mathematics*
Liu: *Introduction to Combinatorial Mathematics*
MacEwen: *Introduction to Computer Systems: Using the PDP-11 and Pascal*
Madnick and Donovan: *Operating Systems*
Manna: *Mathematical Theory of Computation*
Milenkovic: *Operating Systems: Concepts and Design*
Newman and Sproull: *Principles of Interactive Computer Graphics*
Payne: *Introduction to Simulation: Programming Techniques and Methods of Analysis*
Rice: *Matrix Computations and Mathematical Software*
Salton and McGill: *Introduction to Modern Information Retrieval*
Schalkoff: *Artificial Intelligence: An Engineering Approach*
Shooman: *Software Engineering: Design, Reliability, and Management*
Tremblay and Bunt: *An Introduction to Computer Science: An Algorithmic Approach*
Tremblay, DeDourek and Bunt: *An Introduction to Computer Science: An Algorithmic Approach, Pascal Edition*
Tremblay and Manohar: *Discrete Mathematical Structures with Applications to Computer Science*
Tremblay and Sorenson: *Introduction to Data Structures with Applications*
Tremblay and Sorenson: *The Theory and Practice of Compiler Writing*
Tucker: *Programming Languages*
Tucker: *Computer Science: A Second Course Using Modula-2*
Wulf, Levin, and Harbison: *Hydra/C.mmp: An Experimental Computer System*

REAL-TIME
SYSTEM
DESIGN

Shem-Tov Levi

Ashok K. Agrawala

McGraw-Hill Publishing Company

New York St. Louis San Francisco Auckland Bogotá Caracas Hamburg
Lisbon London Madrid Mexico Milan Montreal New Delhi Oklahoma City Paris
San Juan São Paulo Singapore Sydney Tokyo Toronto

This book was set in Times Roman by Publication Services, Inc.
The editor was David M. Shapiro;
the production supervisor was Friederich W. Schulte.
The cover was designed by John Hite.
Project supervision was done by Publication Services, Inc.
R. R. Donnelley & Sons Company was printer and binder.

REAL-TIME SYSTEM DESIGN

3 4 5 6 7 8 9 0 DOC DOC 9 5 4 3 2 1 0

ISBN   0-07-037491-0

Library of Congress Catalog Card Number: 90-60025.

To Tova and Radhika

CONTENTS

Part III   Real-Time Operating Systems

14   Resource Allocation   218

15   Communication   238

Part IV   Operating System Implementation

16   The MARUTI Operating System   257

LIST OF FIGURES

PREFACE

Computers have been used for real-time applications for a long time. The design and implementation of such systems has usually been carried out as an extension of the system design principles used for general purpose computer systems. In particular, real-time systems have often been designed as interrupt-driven systems with priority-based scheduling. Priority structures are used to accomplish the real-time processing by assigning higher priority to critical tasks. In this approach *time* is not treated explicitly in resource management or in scheduling of tasks.

The hard real-time applications of tomorrow must provide support for reliable distributed operation. The past design methodologies may not be adequate to meet these challenges. In this book we have attempted to present a comprehensive approach to the design of the next generation of real-time systems.

We believe that it is essential for the next generation of hard real-time systems to use time directly and explicitly. The approach taken here is to make a uniform representation and use of time. Using an object-oriented approach, we consider time to be an integral property of every entity in the system. In addition, a hard real-time system has to have a deterministic and predictable behavior. The techniques useful for making the system behavior deterministic are also presented.

It has often been noted that the maintenance of a complex real-time system becomes a major problem. Any change usually requires extensive testing to assure functional as well as temporal correctness. The approach we propose is to carry out a verification of the resource allocation. In this way we can reduce significantly the testing requirements. The ideas presented in this book are realistic, they have been implemented, and they are therefore practical.

We present a detailed discussion of the current state of the art of real-time systems and application methodologies along with some major recent advances.

This includes a complete presentation of the design, implementation, verification, and testing issues of the real-time problems. Both the application level and the system level view are taken.

This book is aimed at the professional in the field who has to deal with real-time systems from different perspectives. It is useful to the researchers as it presents many novel ideas, not only for real-time systems but also for distributed, reliable systems. The complete treatment of real-time systems makes it well suited for a graduate or advanced undergraduate course on the subject.

This book reflects our experience in building and implementing real-time systems that are in use extensively, as well as our backgrounds in academic research. The main motivation for this work was to explore ways of improving the current design methodologies to meet the challenges of tomorrow. As we found no adequate text on the subject, we started compiling our notes, which resulted in this book.

While writing the book we found many issues we wanted to share with our readers. Some of these issues concern general subjects such as fault tolerance or complexity, while others concern practical issues such as debugging. A detailed presentation of all these topics would make the book unwieldy. The more information we add the more difficult it would be to focus. We therefore decided on this version of the book, in order to present a discussion of all relevant topics, with suitable references for further study.

As the book is aimed at various types of professionals in the field of real-time systems, let us suggest a structure of the book according to reading interests.

The book has sections that are common to all readers, as they include basic information as well as notation and semantic definitions. These sections are: Section 2.1, Section 2.2, Section 2.3, Section 3.1, Section 4.1, Section 5.2, Section 6.1, Section 6.2, Chapter 11, Chapter 12, Section 13.1, Section 14.1, Section 15.1, Section 15.4, Section 16.1, and Section 17.1. The information introduced in these sections is essential for understanding the rest of the book.

Readers who are more engineering-oriented may want to read the following sections: Section 2.4, Section 2.5, Section 3.2, Section 3.3, Section 4.2, Section 5.1, Section 7.1, Chapter 9, Chapter 10, Section 13.2, Section 13.3.1, Section 13.4.1, Section 14.2, Section 14.4, Section 15.2, Section 15.3, Section 16.2, Section 17.2, and Section 17.3.

Readers who are more research-oriented may find further interest in the following sections: Section 4.3, Section 6.3, Chapter 7, Chapter 8, Section 13.2, Section 13.3, Section 13.4, Section 14.2, Section 14.3, Section 14.4, and Section 17.3.

We hope that the above suggested structure will help each professional to focus easily where he or she finds interest.

ACKNOWLEDGMENTS

A project of this magnitude is clearly the result of a lot of support from many friends. Members of the Systems Design and Analysis Group of the Department of Computer Science, University of Maryland have actively contributed to the development of the material in the book and are implementing the **MARUTI** operating system, which is based on the ideas presented in this book. We would like to gratefully acknowledge the support for our research that has contributed to the development of this book. Our research was supported by the Office of Naval Research and Rome Air Development Center through the Army Strategic Defense Command through grants and contracts to the Department of Computer Science at the University of Maryland. We would also like to acknowledge the Israel Aircraft Industries, Ltd., for contributing to the making of this work.

Shemi-Tov Levi
Ashok K. Agrawala

CHAPTER
1

INTRODUCTION

The ever-increasing use of computer systems is clear evidence that the functional capabilities provided by them can be used very effectively for a variety of purposes and in a large number of fields. In many of these applications, the performance of the computer system is measured with metrics such as response time or turnaround time, the implication being that the faster the better with no specific requirement being placed on the timing behavior of the system. *Real-time applications* are different from this paradigm of computation in that they impose strict requirements on the timing behavior of the system. The systems that support the execution of real-time applications and ensure that the timing requirements are met are often referred to as *real-time systems*. Traditionally, the correctness of many computer systems has been taken to imply their logical and functional behavior. For real-time systems correctness depends on the temporal properties of this behavior as well.

As the price and performance of digital computers continue to improve and their size, weight, and power requirements continue to decrease, there has been a steady increase in the use of computer-based real-time systems in a wide variety of fields. Application domains such as military, industry, and medicine indicate a wide spectrum of possible implementations. Current real-time system examples include nuclear power plant control, industrial manufacturing control, medical monitoring, digital fly-by-wire avionics, weapon delivery systems, space navigation and guidance, and reconnaissance systems. As the use of real-time systems has spread, the timing requirements have become more stringent and the reliability requirements more difficult to achieve.

In general, we call a system a real-time system when it can support the execution of applications with time constraints on that execution. A variety of systems clearly meet this definition. Note that no assumptions are made about the structure or the architecture of the computer system used. A particular class of such systems comprises embedded computer systems.

1.1   EMBEDDED COMPUTER SYSTEMS

Many complex systems in use today require a very elaborate control and computational facility to support their continued proper functioning. Such systems often use dedicated hardware as controllers. Clearly, all the computations and control functions can also be carried out by an appropriate computer system. When a computer system is used in a large system to provide control and computation functions, it is often referred to as an *embedded computer system.* Currently we find such systems in almost every aspect of our lives, with computers being introduced into new systems at an ever-increasing rate.

An embedded computer system has to manage and control the rest of the system. It collects data through sensors and issues control commands to mechanical, electromechanical, and electronic actuators. Figure 1.1 illustrates a typical system of this class. Note that this figure could also depict any process control system; we are using it to convey the idea of a computer as a controller in such a system.

A distinguishing feature of embedded computer systems is that they usually provide an execute-only environment, in which no program development goes on. The processing requirements in these systems do not change as they handle a fixed and well-defined workload. Although some embedded systems are designed

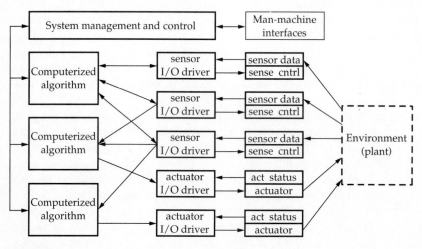

FIGURE 1.1
Embedded computer system.

to handle transient inputs, the processing requirements for such transient requests are predefined. For example, the embedded computer system used in automobiles to control the fuel injection and spark ignition executes one fixed program that may adjust its parameters as its sensors provide it with new information about environmental conditions.

When we study embedded computer systems, their close interaction with mechanical, electromechanical, and electronic components requires that such components be considered as a part of the system and that the expressions and modeling tools used in the study have the capability of representing the interdisciplinary properties of the system. We cannot describe the performance of a robot arm without reference to its mechanics, electronics, and control software. Furthermore, each discipline must maintain consistency with the others. We want the system description to resolve interdisciplinary contradictions when they exist. For example, consider a control system with high-bandwidth control software and control hardware that is very slow. The system description of this example must allow for combining the hardware and its control software. The description must reflect the overall slow response time of this system.

Specifying a system that makes use of techniques from several disciplines starts at the level of the whole system. Out of this high-level specification, we specify the subsystems up to single-discipline components. Derivation of subsystem specifications based on the high-level specification must be consistent and unambiguous. Budgeting software subsystem specifications must, therefore, not only support the performance description of the whole system; it must also be derivable from a whole system description and allow verification of the system properties.

1.2 HISTORICAL PERSPECTIVE

Real-time systems developed from embedded computer systems are still an important family of real-time systems. The use of digital computers in such systems started with the replacement of analog processing sections of control systems during the 1950s. A major step in this direction was taken in March 1956. TRW engineers were contracted by Texaco to computerize a process control system in a polymerization unit of a refinery in Port Arthur, Texas [11]. The process controller employed an RW-300 computer, which controlled 26 flows, 72 temperatures, and 3 pressures. It was announced to be operational in March 1959. In 1962, another major step was taken in the chemical industry, at ICI in England, where a single Ferranti computer replaced complete analog instrumentation that controlled 129 valves and measured 224 nodes.

Other examples of the early use of embedded systems exist. Airborne controllers were needed for missile and aircraft applications. NASA engineers developed many flight control systems during the 1960s for the Mercury, Gemini, and Apollo projects. Other military projects employed time-driven sequencers, digital comparators, and adders for flight control subsystems.

The development of minicomputers brought a major acceleration in the use of computer systems for real-time applications. The PDP family of Digital Equipment, Data General's Nova family, the Microdata 800, Hewlett-Packard's 2100, Texas Instruments' 960, and other systems provided a small package with a powerful computing machine, based on MSI and LSI logic devices. These machines and their successors have provided an environment for designing real-time systems based on their user-interrupt systems, their real-time clock and timer services, and mainly on their operating system software that supported such applications. These systems provided the foundation for and the promise of redundant computation nodes that compensate for each other's failures.

Distributed computing in real-time applications has started spreading. The Space Shuttle project architecture is a well-known example in which several computers are used to provide each critical function to ensure the reliability of operations. Microcomputers and VLSI devices accelerated the use of distributed computing power in real-time applications. Specialization of tasks in conjunction with an inexpensive and very small-sized redundancy provided the incentive for this generation of distributed real-time systems.

Development of real-time systems has been aided by various catalysts. These were the process control systems during the 1950s and early 1960s, the space programs during the 1960s, minicomputers during the 1970s, and microcomputers during the 1980s. Accordingly, tools and environments that support designing of such systems have evolved with time. Current real-time systems are found in a variety of system architectures: from the simple controller that replaces an analog instrument to multiple-machine, fault-tolerant, distributed battle management control.

1.3   DISTRIBUTED REAL-TIME SYSTEM ENVIRONMENT

Let us consider a multiple-machine, distributed computing environment, in which autonomous machines communicate via various communication media. The real-time system, both of today and tomorrow, has to operate in this environment. Processing requests can originate at any node in this network. The actual processing of the requests uses the resources of this environment.

A real-time system must be able to handle time-constrained processing of requests. We call such requests *on-line*, or *time-constrained*. We distinguish these from *off-line*, or *unconstrained*, requests also processed by the distributed system. Because the off-line, or unconstrained, requests do not have the time constraints associated with them, there is significant flexibility in scheduling them.

Hard real-time systems are those real-time systems in which the time constraints of the processing requests play a major role; that is, not meeting the constraints of an accepted processing request is considered a system failure. A *soft* constraint, on the other hand, may be desirable to meet, but failure to do so does not cause a system failure.

The distributed real-time operating system has to manage the distributed processing environment. It must provide the necessary processing services to the on-line, or time-constrained, and off-line, or unconstrained, jobs. In addition to providing for the timely execution of jobs, the distributed real-time system must meet its fault-tolerance requirements.

The execution of real-time systems is controlled by their software. Programming of real-time jobs poses a number of significant problems of its own. Use of special languages and compilers may become necessary when the general purpose languages do not provide enough capabilities to program the real-time systems.

In this book we consider a variety of issues associated with design, implementation, and verification of distributed, hard real-time, fault-tolerant systems. These issues originate in the needs that arise from real-time systems design in general and real-time programming in particular. We do not assume any specific hardware architecture, and the results presented are applicable to a wide range of systems. We can build this spectrum with computing nodes as a multiprocessor, multimemory unit or as a single memory and processor unit, on either a homogeneous or a heterogeneous basis.

We present some innovations in this book. The methodology we use employs *objects* as the system's elements and assigns time properties to them with *calendars*, which are data structures used to keep track of all known time events for this object in the future. This object-oriented architecture achieves objectives set for both fault containment and predictable temporal behavior. Another innovation is the achievement of *guaranteed* future execution of an object. We achieve it through a *schedule feasibility verification* scheme that controls both the object and its resources. A fault-tolerance–motivated *resource allocation* scheme ensures specified resilience to failures. This allocation scheme supports both *temporal redundancy* and *physical redundancy* requirements.

1.4   REAL-TIME PROGRAMMING

The major distinguishing feature of real-time programming arises from the requirement of handling time in all aspects of the application's specification, design, development, testing, verification, and execution. New language features have to be added to permit the expression of the timing requirements for the individual tasks. New techniques are required to verify the correctness of programs that meet the timing properties, and new approaches are required to ensure the timing properties of the programs during testing.

Later in this book, we discuss the issue of producing a predictable temporal behavior of the system we design and implement. The temporal behavior of a program depends on the operating system that supports its execution. Interactions with other executing programs, with which the program shares data or resources, may violate time constraints. Figure 1.2 illustrates these interactions.

Current techniques allow correctness verification of concurrent modules, say module 1 and module 2 in a parallel program A. However, these techniques ignore the effects of module 3 and module 4 in program B on the execution of program A. Such effects are due to interactions with the operating system and the execution environment, which share resources and control mechanisms with the modules. Such effects cannot be treated at the programming language level

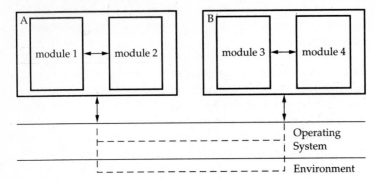

FIGURE 1.2
Computation interactions with operating system and environment.

unless these interactions are forced to obey specific restrictions. To overcome these unpredictabilities in the use of resources, new operating systems and run-time environments that eliminate them are necessary.

1.5 REAL-TIME OPERATING SYSTEMS

Real-time operating systems have to create, maintain, and support the execution environment in which real-time applications can execute. Clearly, one of the major functions of the operating system is that of resource management. The timing behavior of the applications depends crucially on the way the resources are managed and made available to the applications. Traditional approaches to the design of operating systems, aimed at the time-sharing systems for general-purpose computing, do not address the problems of real-time systems.

One way of structuring operating systems is to design them in a hierarchical organization. One such organization, using object encapsulation, is shown in Figure 1.3.

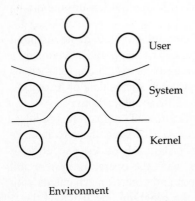

Environment

FIGURE 1.3
System's layers of objects.

Real-time operating systems must provide solutions to timing and interaction problems, in addition to providing the support given by the conventional, general purpose operating systems. Resource management must therefore relate to time explicitly. Time services must support application requirements for accuracy and granularity. Failure modes and recovery mechanisms must take into account timing correctness as well as containment problems. Every access mechanism in the system, including communication channels, must support these timing and interaction issues. Clearly, these complex requirements must be achieved with minimal invasiveness and overhead costs.

1.6 BOOK ORGANIZATION

This book is organized in four parts. The first chapter of the first part (Chapter 2) deals with the principles of time and architecture of real-time systems. The following chapters introduce principles of time-handling in real-time systems, from definitions of temporal relations to ways in which the knowledge of time is acquired and enhanced. Chapter 3 suggests a way in which the "building blocks" of the system support the objectives of temporal guarantees and fault tolerance. Chapter 4 shows a methodology through which time is attached to these blocks.

Part II deals with problems commonly related to applications implementation. Chapter 5 opens this discussion with an introduction of the system life cycle. Chapters 6, 7, and 8 present major system design approaches. Chapter 9 deals with the implementation and expression of solutions, and Chapter 10 discusses the verification of the design and the implementation.

Part III introduces aspects of real-time operating systems. Chapters 11 and 12 discuss required properties of real-time operating systems as well as review allocation and scheduling approaches. Chapters 13 and 14 show how the system management can guarantee the time constraints, by schedule feasibility verification before job acceptance, and the fault-tolerance constraints, by the proper allocation approach, respectively. Chapter 15 discusses issues of distribution and communication.

The final part of the book gives a description of an experimental project in which the above methodology is implemented. This project, called MARUTI after a god in the Hindu mythology, implements an operating system whose concepts are based on those introduced in Part III. Chapter 16 describes the principles and parts of the project, and Chapter 17 expands on the user's view of the system. Chapter 18 contains some concluding remarks.

PART
I

REAL-TIME
ISSUES

CHAPTER
2

TIME
HANDLING

Time is probably the most important entity in a real-time system. The way in which a system handles time characterizes the system's temporal behavior, and thereby its correctness. Time handling by the system includes various issues including time representation, temporal reasoning, the way the system gains knowledge of time, and the management of temporal properties. The system architecture unites all these aspects through the mechanisms it adopts.

This chapter discusses temporal problems that exist in real-time systems. The first section discusses the expression of temporal properties and conditions. The following section introduces the model we use in order to constrain executing objects in the time domain. The next three sections provide descriptions of ways in which the system gains the knowledge of time.

2.1 REPRESENTATION OF TIME

A real-time system is a set of concurrently executed computations (in some models called *processes*) which interact with each other and adhere to some timing constraints. The specification of each of the computations and the interactions is based on logical properties (safety and liveness), as in other systems, but it also includes timing properties. These timing properties enforce time bounds on states of the computations and the relations (or interactions) between them. *Hard real-time* systems are those for which not meeting the time constraints to which they are subjected is considered a fatal failure. Thus, hard real-time systems have to adhere to timing constraints and to maintain a certain degree of accuracy in the knowledge of time. The correctness in the knowledge of time depends on the source of this knowledge and on the discretization imposed by the digital computation. Although time is continuous in real life, it is highly segmented in the view of a digital computation. Nevertheless, many applications use continuous-time properties in their models. For example, navigation systems integrate twice the measured acceleration along the time axis to obtain the state coordinates. The computation assumes a continuous integration path, or else the segmentation would introduce inaccuracies. Clearly, time discretization in such cases may have a strong effect on the results of the integration.

The way in which we represent time has many consequences in real-time systems. Here are some of the major issues:

- Ability to express temporal properties.
- Mechanisms employed to detect such properties.
- Ways of assigning properties to programs or program parts.
- Mechanisms employed to plan future activities.
- Support for predictability of future temporal behavior.

The literature on time representation contains a long and conflicting debate, full of contradictory theories. The debate is between those who prefer a time-point–based representation and those who are for a time-interval–based representation. In a time-point–based representation the world view of the system consists of events that occur at some time instant, take zero time to occur, and result in changing the state of the system. In time-interval–based representation the world view consists of activities that take a finite amount of time and have start and stop times associated with them.

A major disadvantage of a time-point representation of events arises from the atomicity of a point. Since instantaneous events are not decomposable, time-point–presented events cannot be decomposed into sub-events while maintaining an ordering [6]. Furthermore, an event that seems to be instantaneous in one scope may be decomposable in another scope. For example, the act of recognizing an

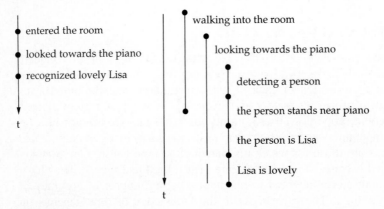

FIGURE 2.1
Point-based versus interval-based representation.

object in a certain field of view can be broken down to detection of the object, spotting its location, identifying it, and determining the proper attitude towards it. Figure 2.1 illustrates the differences between the two time representations (point-based versus interval-based), emphasizing the decomposition of the recognition event into four sub-events. In addition, partially overlapping relations are demonstrated in the time-interval approach, relations which the time-point cannot describe. On the other hand, the use of intervals exclusively may allow a cumulative loss of time under some circumstances. Such an approach requires timer manipulations to generate a time service for the system. Setting an interval timer by a "store" operation [152] is an example of a possible source of a cumulative loss of time. The time from the clock interrupt to the actual store is lost. One usually solves this problem by replacing the "store" with an "add." The overhead of clock update and the overhead of checking the task table after each interrupt establish a lower bound on the clock granularity as well.

On the other hand, an interval can be represented by its endpoints and an interval of zero duration can represent a point. Therefore, representing both points and intervals while supporting a variable granularity seems a good way to solve these representation problems. A real-time system needs both time-interval and time-point representations. Reasoning about a deadline requires both absolute and relative time-point representations, and the specification of computation requirements clearly requires time-interval representations.

2.2 TIME CONSTRAINTS

Let us consider the arrival of a request for a specific object invocation at a hard real-time reactive operating system. The operating system has to allocate (in cases where it is feasible) resources required to guarantee meeting the object's time constraint. Informally speaking, a time constraint is a requirement to start executing a particular executable object, after satisfying any necessary starting conditions, and to complete the execution before its deadline. In this model we assume that the bounds on execution time of an object are deterministic and may be derived from requirements external to the object. On the other hand, the actual execution time for every particular resource allocation (systemwide) may vary. However, we can express any finite bound of a computation interval as an interval that may contain gaps. Constraining this finite interval with begin-time and end-time requirements is proper if we introduce no contradiction. However, some computation objects require more than simple finite intervals. Since we cannot put bounds on infinite intervals, we extend the constraints expressible in our model to include periodic executions of objects. Each such execution instance is finite, and thus has bounds on execution times.

Formally, we define a time constraint that obeys this model as the quintuple

$$(Id, \ Taft(condition_1), \ c_{Id}, \ f_{Id}, \ Tbef(condition_2))$$

where

Id is the name of the executable object (process) in the proper context.

Taft(condition₁) states the event after which the execution of object *Id* should begin.

c_{Id} is the bound on the computation time of each instance of object *Id*.

f_{Id} is the frequency with which the computation has to be carried out.

Tbef(condition₂) states the deadline before which the execution of object *Id* must terminate.

The time interval defined by *Taft(condition₁)* and *Tbef(condition₂)* is the *occurrence interval*, which delimits the time domain in which the executable object is allowed to execute.

A special case of computation is that for which there is no deadline constraint. In this case

$$condition_2 \equiv C_{Id} = \infty$$

and we denote this case as an *off-line* computation. Accordingly, we denote a computation with a finite deadline constraint as *on-line*.

2.3   TIME SERVICE AND SYNCHRONIZATION

We call the source of the knowledge of time a *clock*. We assume that each site has an access to a clock, local to that site. In the following paragraphs we describe some properties of the knowledge of time, ways to characterize the quality of this knowledge, and ways to spread this knowledge.

2.3.1   Definitions

Let us define some properties of a source of the knowledge of time. In order to have an optimal reference of that knowledge we define the standard clock. We compare the quality of any other clock to the reference clock and define its correctness and accuracy. Let $C_i(t)$ denote a function that maps real time to the time at clock *i*.

Definition 1. *A* standard *clock i is one for which* $\forall t : C_i(t) = t$.

The standard clock is often called the reference clock.

The correctness of the clock, at any point of time, depends on the difference between its readout and that of the standard clock, at that point of time. The quality of this correctness is one characteristic of the quality of knowledge of time at the localities for which this clock is the source of this knowledge.

Definition 2. *A clock i is* correct *at time* t_0 *if* $C_i(t_0) = t_0$.

Another characteristic of the quality of knowledge of time at the localities for which some clock is the source of this knowledge is the quality of this clock's rate.

Definition 3. *A clock i is* accurate *at time* t_0 *if the first derivative of* $C_i(t)$ *is 1 sec/sec at* t_0.

If a clock is inaccurate at some point of time, we say that the clock *drifts* at that point of time.

2.3.2 Clock Synchronization

Clock synchronization is used for ordering purposes, as well as for enhancement of the knowledge of the time. We consider such a synchronization as a clock update, which we express in the following form:

$$C_i(t_i) \leftarrow F(C_{i1}(t_{i1}), C_{i2}(t_{i2}), \ldots, C_{ik}(t_{ik}))$$

where the function F depends on the algorithm we use. $C_{i1}()$, $C_{i2}()$, $\ldots$, $C_{ik}()$ are k clocks that synchronize with $C_i()$ and derive their time values at different times. Note that F must be monotonic in order to prevent ambiguity in local ordering of events. In later sections of this chapter, we review solutions to the clock synchronization problem.

In real-time systems, reasoning about events requires ordering mechanisms and time knowledge. We model an *event* in our system concept as a detectable, instantaneous, and atomic change in a system state. In a real-time system, the state of the system includes the set of clocks $\{C_i(t)\}$. Let $\{C_i(t) = C_0\}$ be the set of system states in which the readout of clock i is C_0. Hence, we can define the following predicates on system states. The predicate *Taft*(C_0) is *true* for $C_i(t) \geq C_0$ and *false* otherwise. The predicate *Tbef*(C_d) is *true* for $C_i(t) \leq C_d$ and *false* otherwise. Using these predicates allows defining the *occurrence interval* with *Taft*(*condition*₁) and *Tbef*(*condition*₂), which delimit the allowed execution time-domain of an executable object.

2.3.3 Types of Clock Systems

We divide clock systems into three categories: central clock systems, centrally controlled clock systems, and distributed systems. A brief description of each category follows.

CENTRAL CLOCK SYSTEMS. This category is characterized by the following properties.

- One accurate clock provides the time knowledge to the whole system. The existence of other clocks in the system is "ignored" as long as there is no detectable failure of the central clock.
- For fault tolerance a standby redundancy for the central clock is used.
- The method is accurate (within nanoseconds to milliseconds, depending on the central clock) and expensive.

- This method needs special purpose hardware integrated into the processor. The central clock sets this hardware to the proper value and any executing process can read it.
- The communication cost of this category is very low: Only one message is required for synchronizing a clock at any site. In a broadcasting environment, one message is required for synchronizing a group of sites.
- An example of this category is the GPS (Global Position System), which uses four broadcasting satellites and achieves a clock synchronization with correctness within a few nanoseconds.

CENTRALLY CONTROLLED CLOCK SYSTEMS. In this category we distinguish between two types of nodes: master nodes and slave nodes. The following properties characterize this category.

- A nominated master clock polls slave clocks.
- Clock differences are measured, and the master dictates corrections to the slaves.
- If the master clock fails, an election of a new master (from the slaves) is initiated (for an example, see [125]).
- Transmission times and delays are estimated, since they affect significantly the clock difference measured.

Examples of this category are Tempo [57, 58], Etempo [148, 56], and DCNet [102].

DISTRIBUTED CLOCK SYSTEMS. Various examples of this category have been published, first by L. Lamport [80] and followed by later enhancements [97, 84, 101, 134]. A distributed clock system can be characterized as follows.

- All the sites are homogeneous and each runs the same algorithm.
- Each site updates its own clock after receiving the time from other clocks and after estimating their correctness.
- The fault tolerance is protocol based. If a site fails, the other sites are not affected; they only detect the failure and ignore the failed site thereafter.
- Generally, relatively heavy communication traffic is involved in this category, especially when robustness in the presence of malicious faults is required [84, 134].

2.4 MASTER-SLAVE ALGORITHMS

Centrally controlled clock systems are often called *master-slave systems*. Let a master clock i begin a clock synchronization procedure, at a time T_1. It reads its current clock value $C_i(T_1)$ with an error e_1, and it sends this clock value to a slave. The message travels for μ_i^j time units, and is received by the slave at T_2.

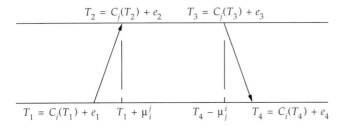

FIGURE 2.2
Master-slave synchronization principle.

At that time, the slave clock has the value of $C_j(T_2)$ with an error e_2. The slave can now compute the difference

$$d_1 = C_j(T_2) - C_i(T_1)$$

Comparing the receiving time and the sending time

$$C_i(T_1) + e_1 + \mu_i^j = C_j(T_2) + e_2$$

yields

$$C_j(T_2) - C_i(T_1) = \mu_i^j + (e_1 - e_2)$$

If we model the error difference such that ξ_j is the clock j skew and E_j^k ($k = 1, 2, \ldots$) is a noise,

$$d_1 = \mu_i^j + \xi_j - E_j^1$$

Now we can repeat the process in the opposite direction. The slave reads its current clock value at a time T_3, $C_j(T_3)$, with an error e_3. It sends this clock value to the master, attaching d_1 to it. The message travels for μ_j^i time units, and the master receives it at T_4. At that time, the master clock has the value of $C_i(T_4)$ and an error e_4. The master can now compute the difference

$$d_2 = C_i(T_4) - C_j(T_3)$$

Comparing the receiving time and the sending time

$$C_j(T_3) + e_3 + \mu_j^i = C_i(T_4) + e_4$$

yields

$$C_i(T_4) - C_j(T_3) = \mu_j^i - (e_4 - e_3)$$

and as above

$$d_2 = \mu_j^i - \xi_j - E_j^2$$

From the equations on d_1 and d_2 we receive

$$\frac{d_1 - d_2}{2} = \xi_j + \frac{1}{2}(\mu_i^j - \mu_j^i) - \frac{1}{2}(E_j^1 - E_j^2)$$

Therefore, we can use the subtraction of d_2 from d_1 to estimate ξ_j and correct $C_j()$.

However, this estimate hides some implicit assumptions. Assuming $\mu_i^j \approx \mu_j^i$ reduces significantly the error term in the subtraction equation, we can further reduce this term if E_j^k is symmetrically distributed with a zero mean. We can use this principle to perform a number of polls and average the results [57, 56] using the average message delays $\overline{\mu}_i^j$ and $\overline{\mu}_j^i$.

2.4.1   Tempo: A Master-Slave Example

Tempo is a clock synchronization algorithm used by the distributed Berkeley Unix [57]. The DCNET [102] provides a similar algorithm, and so does the ICMP protocol [118], with messages for time stamp and time stamp reply. An extension of the algorithm to hierarchical networks, ETempo [148], supports the same principle.

ALGORITHM FOR MASTER P_i. The master node in Tempo obeys three rules. The first is the initiation rule, in which a master sends its current clock value to its slaves. In the second rule, the final reception rule, the master receives from a slave j a message that contains the difference d_1^j and the transmission time of this message, T_B. Upon reception, the master calculates the second difference, d_2^j. The master estimates clock-j's skew (Δ_j) for this poll using the two differences. The third rule is the correction rule. After N polls for slave j, the master calculates the average skew found in these polls, Δ, and sends it to j for correcting clock-j. The three rules are given below.

- Upon Initiation of Clock Skew Measurement:

    do

    $\quad T_A \leftarrow C_i(now)$

    $\quad \forall j \neq i$: Send (T_A) to j

    endo

- Upon Receiving (T_B, d_1^j) from Slave j:

    do

    $\quad d_2^j \leftarrow C_i(now) - T_B$

    $\quad\quad /^* d_2^j = \mu_j^i - \xi_j - E_j^2 \ ^*/$

    $\quad \Delta_j \leftarrow \frac{1}{2}(d_1^j + d_2^j)$

    $\quad\quad /^* = \xi_j + \frac{1}{2}(\mu_j^i + \mu_i^j) - \frac{1}{2}(E_j^1 - E_j^2) \ ^*/$

    endo

- $\forall j \neq i$: Upon Complete Receiving All Polls:

  do

  $$\Delta \leftarrow \frac{1}{N} \sum_{k=1}^{N} \Delta_j[k]$$
  $$/* = \overline{\xi_j} + \frac{1}{2}(\overline{\mu_i^j} - \overline{\mu_j^i}) - \frac{1}{2}(\overline{E_j^1} - \overline{E_j^2})*/$$
  Send(Δ) to j

  endo

ALGORITHM FOR SLAVE P_j. Each slave node obeys two rules. The first is the reception of an initialization message from the master. When such a message arrives, the slave j calculates the difference d_1^j. Later, it samples its clock to get T_B and sends the calculated difference and T_B to the master. The second rule of the slave is the clock update, as dictated by the master correction.

- Upon Receiving (T_A) from Master i:

  do

  $$d_1^j \leftarrow C_j(now) - T_A$$
  $$/*d_1^j = \mu_i^j + \xi_j - E_j^1*/$$
  $$T_B \leftarrow C_j(now)$$
  Send(T_B, d_1^j) to i

  endo

- Upon Receiving (Δ) from Master i:

  do

  $$C_i(t) \leftarrow C_i(t) + \Delta$$

  endo

PERFORMANCE. We have shown above that the estimate of the clock skew ξ_j is obtained by

$$\hat{\xi}_j = \frac{d_1 - d_2}{2} = \xi_j + \frac{1}{2}(\mu_i^j - \mu_j^i) - \frac{1}{2}(E_j^1 - E_j^2)$$

Recall that if $\mu_i^j \approx \mu_j^i$, we reduce the error term due to communication. In addition, if E_j^k is symmetrically distributed with a zero mean, we can use a number of polls for averaging the result [57, 56], thereby reducing the error in the estimate. The above estimate is changed to

$$\hat{\xi}_j = \xi_j + \frac{1}{2}(\overline{\mu_i^j} - \overline{\mu_j^i}) - \frac{1}{2}(\overline{E_j^1} - \overline{E_j^2})$$

The granularity of the clocks significantly influences the error E_j^k. The result of the averaging procedure on $\frac{1}{2}(\overline{E_j^1} - \overline{E_j^2})$ is that the "worst" participant dominates the granularity and thus the associated error.

We find the assumption unrealistic that $\mu_i^j \approx \mu_j^i$ (or $\overline{\mu_i^j} \approx \overline{\mu_j^i}$). A better knowledge of the communication times μ_i^j and μ_j^i, along with a reduction of these times, significantly improves the estimate of the clock skew $\hat{\xi}_j$.

To derive the bound on synchronization error between updates, one can use the following model for clock j:

- The clock synchronized at $t = \rho_j$ with a synchronization error of ϵ_j.
- ϵ_j is the error of the above algorithm

$$\frac{1}{2}(\overline{\mu_i^j} - \overline{\mu_j^i}) - \frac{1}{2}(\overline{E_j^1} - \overline{E_j^2})$$

- The clock has a constant maximal drift rate, δ_j.
- The above algorithm is executed at least every τ time units.

Hence, a bound on the maximal clock difference [58] is

$$|2\tau \times \max_j(\delta_j)| + |4 \times \max_j(\epsilon_j)|$$

The frequency of updates (τ^{-1}) therefore controls the bounds on synchronization correctness between updates.

Now, let us examine the load this algorithm imposes on the communication network. The communication cost of each slave update is two messages for a poll and one for the update. Therefore, n processors updated after p polls require $(2p + 1) \times n$ messages.

2.4.2   Master-Slave Enhancements

We can enhance the synchronization algorithm by compensating for known ingredients of the communication duration μ_i^j and μ_j^i, instead of assuming equality of the two. Figure 2.3 describes an example of the delay breakdown in a typical local area network (LAN). In this example, one can express an estimate of the communication duration in a LAN architecture as

$$\mu_i^j = t_{\text{algorithm}} + \sum_{k=1}^{n} (t_{\text{comp}}^{(k)} + t_{\text{attempt}}^{(k)} + t_{\text{xmit}}^{(k)} + t_{\text{propagate}}^{(k)} + t_{\text{decomp}}^{(k)} + t_{\text{signal}}^{(k)}) + \Delta\mu$$

where

- $t_{\text{algorithm}}$ represents the execution time of the algorithm, and we assume it is not interrupted [57] and therefore predictable.

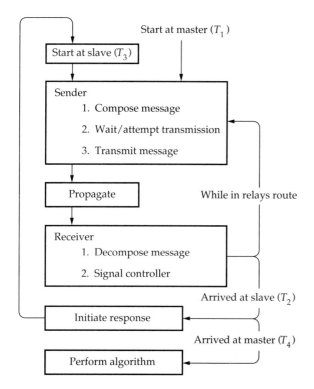

Start at master (T_1)

Start at slave (T_3)

Sender
    1. Compose message
    2. Wait/attempt transmission
    3. Transmit message

Propagate   While in relays route

Receiver
    1. Decompose message
    2. Signal controller

Arrived at slave (T_2)

Initiate response

Arrived at master (T_4)

Perform algorithm

FIGURE 2.3
Breakdown of communication
delay in Tempo.

- $t_{comp}^{(k)}$ represents the time required for composing a message that is to be sent by communication node k.
- $t_{attempt}^{(k)}$ represents the time that elapses from the moment a message is composed by node k, until its successful transmission starts (e.g., bus contention or wait for a token).
- $t_{xmit}^{(k)}$ represents the message successful transmission time, a very predictable term when the network bandwidth and the message length are known.
- $t_{propagate}^{(k)}$ represents the propagation delay from node k to node $k + 1$, a term that can be estimated accurately from the message route.
- $t_{decomp}^{(k)}$ represents the time required by node k to decompose the message in order to route it, a term we assume to be predictable when the message route is known and the resources reserved.
- $t_{signal}^{(k)}$ represents the time from routing decision to delivery attempt, a term we assume to be predictable when the message route is known and the resources reserved.
- $\Delta\mu$ represents the uncertain elapse-time in the communication delay.

We can distinguish two parts in the above delay summation: the predictable part $\hat{\mu}_i^j$ and the uncertainty $\Delta\mu_i^j$,

$$\mu_i^j = \hat{\mu}_i^j + \Delta\mu_i^j$$

Since most of the terms in the delay summation are highly predictable, we can assume that the major ingredient of the duration uncertainty is

$$\Delta\mu \approx \sum_{k=i}^{j-1} t_{attempt}^{(k)}$$

All the other terms are predictable and compensated for. For example, with IP [117] and ICMP [118], the compensation may use the routing information that is contained within the timestamp option field.

We propose the following enhancement for a master that polls each of its slaves p times. The major benefit of the following approach is the compensation for the known ingredients of the communication durations, in the bidirectional message traffic. Due to this compensation, the uncertainties are reduced and thus the correctness is enhanced.

do

for $k = 1$ to p:

$T_1 \leftarrow C_i(now)$;

Send(T_1);

Receive(T_2, T_3) at $T_4 \leftarrow C_i(now)$;

Read(T_4) and message routing through relays;

Estimate μ_j^i and μ_i^j from the message routing:

$$\hat{\mu}_i^j = t_{algorithm} + \sum_{k=i}^{j}(t_{comp}^{(k)} + t_{attempt}^{(k)}$$
$$+ t_{xmit}^{(k)} + t_{propagate}^{(k)} + t_{decomp}^{(k)} + t_{signal}^{(k)})$$
$$\hat{\mu}_j^i = t_{algorithm} + \sum_{k=j}^{i}(t_{comp}^{(k)} + t_{attempt}^{(k)} + t_{xmit}^{(k)} + t_{propagate}^{(k)}$$
$$+ t_{decomp}^{(k)} + t_{signal}^{(k)});$$

Compute C_j skew $\Delta_j[k]$;

/* $d_1^j = T_2 - T_1 - \hat{\mu}_i^j$ */

/* $d_2^j = T_4 - T_3 - \hat{\mu}_j^i$ */

/* $\Delta_j[k] \leftarrow \frac{1}{2}(d_1^j + d_2^j)$ */

Compute C_j skew Δ_j from $\Delta_j[1..p]$;

endo

2.5   DISTRIBUTED CLOCK ALGORITHMS

The major advantage of the distributed approach is the higher degree of fault tolerance it achieves. This achievement increases the cost mainly in communication rather than in special hardware. The load imposed on the communication network by the distributed approach is therefore expected to be higher than that of the master-slave approach.

In the distributed clock systems all the time servers use a uniform approach, whose characteristics are listed below.

- Each server polls the rest of the clocks or a subset of them.
- Each applies a specific algorithm to the responses of the poll.
- Each server updates the local clock accordingly.

We have chosen the following algorithms as examples that represent the ideas of ordering, accuracy enhancement, and fault tolerance. However, in addition to the algorithms introduced below, there are many others that deal with fault tolerance enhancement [83, 97, 134].

2.5.1   A Fundamental Ordering Approach

A set of computation localities $\mathcal{V}_L = \{L_1, \ldots, L_m\}$ are related to each other through a set of physical links $\mathcal{E}_L$, to form a graph

$$\mathcal{G}_L = (\mathcal{V}_L, \mathcal{E}_L)$$

Let us assume that each locality L_i is a vertex in our graph model that includes a clock C_i. These clocks run a distributed algorithm, exchanging messages via $\mathcal{E}_L$, according to which they update their readouts. The graph can be closely connected, so that every vertex can send synchronization messages to the rest of the vertices, or it can be loosely connected. In the latter case, each synchronization forum is a subset of $\mathcal{V}_L$, described as a subgraph of $\mathcal{G}_L$.

Let us consider an ordering approach based on message *timestamping* [80] with the following properties:

- The *accuracy* of clock i is bounded by a drift rate δ

$$\forall t : \left|1 - \frac{d}{dt}C_i(t)\right| < \delta_i \ll 1$$

- The communication graph of the algorithm is closely connected with a diameter d.
- The network imposes an unpredictable (yet bounded) message delay D. In other words, $\mu < D < \eta$ holds, where μ and η are the lower and upper bounds on D.

Each clock implements the following algorithm [80]:

- On every local event occurrence, increment the local clock

$$C_i(t) \leftarrow C_i(t) + 1$$

- Each process with a clock sends messages to the others at least every τ seconds. Each message includes its timestamp T_m.
- Upon reception of an external T_m, the receiver sets its clock

$$C_i(t) \leftarrow max(C_i(t), T_m + \mu)$$

Now we can examine the performance of a population of n clocks that synchronize. The communication cost of one update of the whole network is $n \times (n - 1)$ messages.

The correctness of each clock due to this synchronization algorithm is

$$\forall i : \forall j : |C_i(t) - C_j(t)| < d(2\delta\tau + \eta)$$

for all t. This algorithm achieves only the ordering goal, bounding clock differences between sites. It does not achieve any enhancement with respect to the correctness of the clocks (the knowledge of time as compared to the standard clock). The algorithm results in updates according to the fastest clock in the system, and not necessarily the most accurate one.

2.5.2 Time Intervals Approach

Now let us consider two algorithms [101] that take advantage of the bounds on the error of the clock. Requiring knowledge of the bounds is a fairly easy restriction because the necessary information is provided in the manuals of the equipment in use.

These algorithms have a communication traffic of $O(n^2)$. However, it is not the traffic characteristic we want to emphasize here. The following algorithms provide a good example of the tradeoff between robustness and accuracy.

ASSUMPTIONS AND ERROR MODEL. Every clock i "knows" it is correct within the interval

$$[C_i(t) - E_i(t), C_i(t) + E_i(t)]$$

where $E_i(t)$ is a bound on the error of clock i. The error interval is constructed from the following contributors:

- The error that comes into effect right on the clock *reset* time (ρ_i), as discretization and other constant errors (ϵ_i).
- The *delay* from the time this clock (i) is read until another clock (j) uses the readout for its update (μ_i^j).
- The *degradation* of time-counting that develops between consecutive resets (δ_i).

ALGORITHM: MINIMIZE MAXIMUM ERROR. The algorithm consists of two rules: a response rule and a synchronizer rule. A request transmitted by the synchronizer rule at node j activates i's response. In this response, node i first updates its bound on the error, $E_i(t)$. It then replies its clock value $C_i(t)$ and the above bound on that clock's error. This message expresses a time interval within which the clock is correct.

The synchronizer rule is periodic, performed at least every τ time units. Its first step is a request for responses which it sends to the rest of the nodes. Then, for each of these nodes, it performs a response reception and a conditional clock reset. Two conditions must hold for a reset:

1. The interval $[C_i(t) - E_i(t), C_i(t) + E_i(t)]$ that expresses the local knowledge of time must be consistent with the incoming interval $[C_j(t) - E_j(t), C_j(t) + E_j(t)]$. The consistency requires a nonempty intersection of these two intervals.
2. The error of the response, $E_j(t)$, plus the error of the response delay, $(1 + \delta_i)\mu_j^i$, generate an error smaller than the local one.

If these two conditions hold, the node can reset its clock and enhance its knowledge of time. The reset involves three parameters. The local clock $C_i(t)$ is set to the value of the response clock. The error at local clock reset, ϵ_i, is set to the value of the response error and the delay combined. The time-of-reset record, ρ_i, is also set to the value of the response clock.

If on the other hand one of these conditions does not hold, the algorithm ignores the response. The algorithm's two rules are given below.

- Upon receiving a time Request from $j \neq i$:

  do

  $\quad E_i(t) \leftarrow \epsilon_i + [C_i(t) - \rho_i]\delta_i;$

  $\quad \text{Send}[C_i(t), E_i(t)] \text{ to } j$

  endo

- At least once every τ time units:

  do

  $\forall j \neq i: \text{Request}[C_j(t), E_j(t)];$

  $\quad \text{for } j \neq i \text{ do begin}$

  $\quad\quad \text{Receive}[C_j(t), E_j(t)];$

  $\quad\quad \text{if } [C_j(t), E_j(t)] \text{ is consistent with } [C_i(t), E_i(t)]$

  $\quad\quad\quad \text{then if } E_j(t) + (1 + \delta_i)\mu_j^i \leq E_i(t)$

  $\quad\quad\quad\quad \text{then begin } /\text{* update */}$

  $\quad\quad\quad\quad\quad C_i(t) \leftarrow C_j(t);$

  $\quad\quad\quad\quad\quad \epsilon_i \leftarrow E_j(t) + (1 + \delta_i)\mu_j^i;$

$$\rho_i \leftarrow C_j(t)$$

end

    else *ignore it*

end

endo

ALGORITHM: INTERSECTION OF TIME INTERVALS. This algorithm also consists of two rules: a response rule and a synchronizer rule. The response rule is identical to the response of the previous algorithm. The synchronizer rule here is also periodic, performed at least every τ time units.

The first step of the synchronizer rule is a request for responses, which the algorithm sends to the rest of the nodes. The similarity to the previous algorithm ends here. The second step of this algorithm is to receive all the responses. Each response interval has a left boundary $\mathcal{L}_j(t)$ and a right boundary $\mathcal{R}_j(t)$ and the algorithm calculates both of them. Then the algorithm selects the highest left boundary in the responses, α, and the lowest right boundary, β. If the responses are consistent, there must be a nonempty intersection of them all, and thus $\alpha < \beta$. Otherwise the responses are considered inconsistent and therefore ignored. If they are consistent, we can conclude that the real-time clock is within the interval $[\alpha, \beta]$. Therefore, the algorithm sets its error to equal half this interval and the local clock to equal the interval's midpoint.

- Upon receiving a time Request from $j \neq i$:

do

    $E_i(t) \leftarrow \epsilon_i + (C_i(t) - \rho_i)\delta_i;$

    Send$(C_i(t), E_i(t))$ to j

endo

(exactly as in the previous algorithm).

- At least once every τ time units:

do

    $\forall j \neq i$: Request$[C_j(t), E_j(t)];$

    $\forall j \neq i$: Receive$[C_j(t), E_j(t)];$

    $\forall j \neq i$: $\mathcal{L}_j(t) \leftarrow [C_j(t) - E_j(t)] - C_i(t);$

    /* $\mathcal{L}_j$, the left boundary of j */

    $\forall j \neq i$: $\mathcal{R}_j(t) \leftarrow [C_j(t) + E_j(t)] + (1 + \delta_i)\mu_j^i - C_i(t);$

    /* $\mathcal{R}_j$, the right boundary of j */

$\alpha \leftarrow max(\mathcal{L}_j); \; \beta \leftarrow min(\mathcal{R}_j)$

/* intersect all boundaries */

if $(\alpha < \beta)$ /* consistent boundaries */

then begin

$\epsilon_i \leftarrow \frac{1}{2}(\beta - \alpha);$

$C_i(t) \leftarrow \frac{1}{2}(\beta + \alpha);$

$\rho_i \leftarrow \frac{1}{2}(\beta + \alpha)$

end

else *ignore them all*

endo

PERFORMANCE. Figure 2.4 compares the above minimize-maximum-error algorithm and intersection algorithm. The minimize-maximum-error algorithm produces an error that can be expressed [101] as

$$|C_i(t) - C_j(t)| < 2E_M(t) + 2\mu + (\delta_i + \delta_j) \cdot (\tau + 2\mu)$$

where E_M is the smallest error interval of the participants and μ is a bound for the communication time. The intersection of time intervals results in an error

$$[C_i(t) - C_j(t)] < \mu + (\delta_i + \delta_j) \cdot \tau$$

when no inconsistencies occur [101].

We can observe from the above equations and from Figure 2.4 that the intersection algorithm is superior in its accuracy. However, it is less robust; it may ignore the responses of all the participants because of an erroneous response from one participant. Although the clock system does not fail upon an erroneous response, its fault tolerance performance is poor. An erroneous response may prevent the algorithm execution.

Both algorithms require good knowledge of the communication time. They use this knowledge to update the intervals and to examine the responses. Furthermore, even the time-stamp ordering algorithm in [80] requires this knowledge. A good estimate is often sufficient, but in many applications precautions must be taken to ensure proper confidence in the estimate. Note that

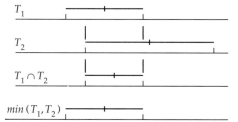

FIGURE 2.4
Comparison of synchronization algorithms.

here a good estimate for the communication time is different from the estimate required by the master-slave approach. In that approach, we made an assumption on the equality $\mu_i^j \approx \mu_j^i$, which requires both communication times to be the same, without necessarily knowing any of them.

2.5.3 Fault-Tolerant Algorithms

In a comprehensive approach to constructing a fault-tolerant time-server, one must start with providing the means for a local resynchronization of each time server in the system. This resynchronization updates the server's parameters, and thus the interpretation of the local clock. However, one must introduce additional facilities such as clock broadcasts and participant-forum establishment. This additional support serves the requirements for fault tolerance. Combining the above facilities results in a comprehensive solution to a system-wide distributed time service. Let us consider an example of such facilities: the local resynchronization, the distributed clock-exchanges, and the construction of a complete service [83].

Algorithm I: Local Resynchronization

Consider using the following algorithm to resynchronize time-server clock $T_p(t)$, constructed from the clock $C_p(t)$ by the linear combination $a_p(t)C_p(t) + b_p(t)$. The resynchronization algorithm updates the coefficients of the linear combination while maintaining a monotonic behavior of $T_p(t)$. In this mechanism, we can regard $a_p(t)$ and $b_p(t)$ as the interpretation of p-clock $C_p(t)$ by a time-server clock $T_p(t)$. The update is done according to an "ideal" clock $C_p^{(i)}(t)$, an improved version of $C_p(t)$, generated and maintained according to the protocols described later in this chapter. Updating $a_p(t)$ is really changing the pace of $T_p(t)$. Let us define formally this interpretation.

- Let $T^{(0)}, T^{(1)}, \ldots$ be an unbounded increasing sequence of times such that

$$\forall j : T^{(j+1)} - T^{(j)} \leq J$$

  In other words, we resynchronize at least every J time units.

- Let $C_p^{(0)}, C_p^{(1)}, \ldots$ be a sequence of p-clocks.
- for $i > 0$ let $t_p^{(i)}$ be the Universal Time, such that $C_p^{(i-1)}(t_p^{(i)}) = T^{(i)}$.
- Let $t_p^{(0)}$ be the Universal Time, such that $C_p^{(0)}(t_p^{(0)}) = T^{(0)}$.

The service clock T_p, for $t \geq t_p^{(0)}$, is calculated by

$$T_p(t) = a_p(t)C_p(t) + b_p(t)$$

where $a_p(t)$ and $b_p(t)$ are coefficients defined as

- $t_p^{(0)} \leq t \leq t_p^{(1)}$ (initial coefficients)

$$a_p(t) = 1, b_p(t) = T^{(0)} - C_p(t_p^{(0)})$$

- $t_p^{(i)} < t \leq t_p^{(i+1)}, i > 0$ (coefficients update)

$$a_p(t) = 1 + \frac{C_p^{(i)}(t_p^{(i)}) - T_p(t_p^{(i)})}{J}$$

$$b_p(t) = b_p(t_p^{(i-1)}) + (a_p(t_p^{(i-1)}) - a_p(t_p^{(i)}))C_p^{(i)}(t_p^{(i)})$$

This algorithm shows a bounded error of the time service clock $T_p(t)$, if the "ideal clock" it is using $[C_p^{(i)}(t)]$ has a bounded correction property [85]. In other words, if $C_p^{(i)}(t)$ satisfies $\forall j, k$ with $j < k$ and $t_p^{(k)} - t_p^{(j)} < J$:

$$\sum_{i=j}^{k-1} |C_p^{(i+1)} - C_p^{(i)}| < \sigma_p$$

then for $t_p^{(i)} \leq C_p^{(i)}(t) \leq t_p^{(i+1)}$

$$|C_p^{(i)}(t) - T_p(t)| < \frac{e}{e-1}\sigma_p$$

EXAMPLE. Let us consider the case of an inaccurate p-clock, $C_p(t)$, whose rate at $t = t_p^{(0)}$ is c. $C_p(t)$ drifts from this rate linearly. Thus, it generates the clock rate

$$\frac{d}{dt}C_p(t) = c + \rho(t - t_p^{(0)})$$

where c and ρ are constants. Using this clock drift model, let us examine the behavior of the above resynchronization algorithm. We assume in our example that the "ideal" clock, $C_p^{(i)}(t)$, is the universal time. In other words, we assume a perfect correction of an imperfect clock, and examine the resynchronization behavior.

The algorithm starts with

$$a(t) = 1$$

$$b(t) = T_p^{(0)} - C_p(t_p^{(0)})$$

and holds these values for $t_p^{(0)} < t \leq t_p^{(1)}$. With these assumptions we have continuity in the initial conditions $T_p(t_p^{(0)}) = T_p^{(0)}$.

Let us now consider the behavior of the clock error between resynchronizations. During the period that precedes the first resynchronization at $t_p^{(1)}$, the local clock drifts from correctness. Just prior to the resynchronization, it shows

$$C_p(t_p^{(1)}) = c(t_p^{(1)} - t_p^{(0)}) + \frac{1}{2}\rho(t_p^{(1)} - t_p^{(0)})^2 + C_p(t_p^{(0)})$$

The server at that time provides

$$T_p^{(1)} = 1 \cdot [c(t_p^{(1)} - t_p^{(0)}) + \frac{1}{2}\rho(t_p^{(1)} - t_p^{(0)})^2 + C_p(t_p^{(0)})]$$
$$+ t_p^{(0)} - C_p(t_p^{(0)})$$
$$= t_p^{(1)} + E(t_p^{(1)})$$

The error term $E(t_p^{(1)})$ can be expressed as

$$E(t_p^{(1)}) = (c - 1) \cdot [t_p^{(1)} - t_p^{(0)}] + \frac{1}{2}\rho[t_p^{(1)} - t_p^{(0)}]^2$$

This error includes both the linear and the quadratic terms that result from our drift model.

The first update of coefficients occurs at $t_p^{(1)}$. Having assumed a perfect clock correction, we have $C_p^{(i)}(t_p^{(1)}) = t_p^{(1)}$. Then

$$a(t) = 1 + \frac{t_p^{(1)} - T_p^{(1)}}{J} = 1 + \frac{E(t_p^{(1)})}{J}$$

$$b(t) = T_p^{(0)} - C_p[t_p^{(0)}] - \frac{E(t_p^{(1)})}{J}t_p^{(1)}$$

Notice that the correction of $a(t)$ compensates for the clock-rate inaccuracy in the following way: If no update occurs in the following J time units, then

$$T_p(t_p^{(1)} + J) = C_p^{(i)}[t_p^{(1)}] + J$$

Substituting the error term in the new values of the coefficients, yields

$$a(t) = 1 + \frac{(c - 1) \cdot (t_p^{(1)} - t_p^{(0)}) + \frac{1}{2}\rho(t_p^{(1)} - t_p^{(0)})^2}{J}$$

$$b(t) = T_p^{(0)} - C_p(t_p^{(0)}) - \frac{(c - 1) \cdot (t_p^{(1)} - t_p^{(0)}) + \frac{1}{2}\rho(t_p^{(1)} - t_p^{(0)})^2}{J}t_p^{(1)}$$

for $t_p^{(1)} < t \le t_p^{(2)}$. We note that with $t_p^{(1)} = t_p^{(0)} + J$ and $\rho = 0$, we have $a(t) = c$.

Figure 2.5 describes a particular[1] implementation of the above resynchronization example. We note the property of resynchronizing such that equality to the ideal clock (the diagonal in this figure) is obtained J time units after the resynchronization.

Algorithm II: Byzantine Clock-Broadcast

Let us now consider the construction of a local "ideal clock" reference for a synchronizing process p, $C_p^{(i)}$. Our computations are modeled as a set of processes $\mathcal{V}_p = \{p_1, \dots, p_n\}$ and are related to each other through a set of logical links $\mathcal{E}_p$, to form a graph

$$\mathcal{G}_p = (\mathcal{V}_p, \mathcal{E}_p)$$

---

[1]In this example resynchronization takes place at the same time we update the local clock, exactly every J time units. The ideal clock is the real-time, denoted as the diagonal in the figure. Further resynchronization cycles are identical to the last two presented in the figure.

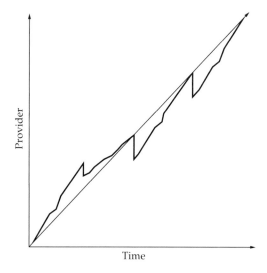

Time

FIGURE 2.5
Resynchronization example.

A set of processors $\mathcal{V}_P = \{P_1, \ldots, P_m\}$ are related to each other through a set of physical links $\mathcal{E}_P$, to form a graph

$$\mathcal{G}_P = (\mathcal{V}_P, \mathcal{E}_P)$$

The concept described in this section presents the idea of *time providers* as a preferable alternative to time servers. Members of the intersection of the sets $\mathcal{E}_p$ and $\mathcal{E}_P$ are the paths through which we can synchronize $\mathcal{V}_p$. Time providers send information to synchronizing processes through these paths. The providers employ a broadcast discipline to distribute this information. Receiving processes derive from this broadcast, if it is adequate, the necessary parameters to construct locally their "ideal clock".

Let Γ_p represent the set of p-clocks received by a synchronizing process p. Each Γ_p is of course initially empty, having received no messages. Time providers broadcast the information for these p-clocks to their neighbors. Each broadcast contains an interval out of which the ideal p-clock is derived. We denote the left end point of a time interval U by $\triangleleft (U)$, and the right end point by $\triangleright (U)$. In addition to the interval, each broadcast contains information about the path through which the message has traveled so far.

A time provider j broadcasts to every p-clock, using the following restricted diffusion for the broadcast:

1. j sends an interval $U^{(j)}$ to all its neighbors. Let $U_p^{(j)}$ denote $U^{(j)}$ as obtained by process p. We show later (Algorithm III) how j constructs[2] the set of $U_p^{(j)}$ it broadcasts.

---

[2] If both j and p are nonfaulty, $U_p^{(j)}(t_p^{(i)})$ contains the "universal time" of $t_p^{(i)}$.

2. Let p receive a broadcast with an interval R along a path π at time t. After the reception, p sets the p-clock I_p^π to a value R^π at time t. Since I_p^π is a p-clock, its pace equals that of the local clock. Then, p adds I_p^π to Γ_p. After updating its own Γ_p, p relays R to each of its neighbors (say q), unless one of the following restrictions holds.

- q is on the path π.
- $\exists U \in \Gamma_p : \lhd (U) \geq \lhd (R_p^\pi) \wedge \exists V \in \Gamma_p : \rhd (V) \geq \rhd (I_p^\pi)$.
- The length of π exceeds a given k.

The first restriction prevents unnecessary duplication. The second prevents sending intervals that will not add to what is already known. The third restriction eliminates outdated information.

3. The above steps are repeated until a time after which no more useful messages can arrive. Then, p sets $UT_p^{(j)}$ to be the p-clock whose $\lhd$ and $\rhd$ are the left-most and the right-most maxima of all the p-clocks I_p^π.

Algorithm III: Complete Time-Service

Now we can construct the complete time server using the previous two algorithms for resynchronization and broadcast. The following time-service algorithm starts with an agreement between the participants on the set of providers they are going to choose. Then, once this set is established, a sequence that constructs the time service follows. The providers broadcast and the receivers accept, forward, filter faults, and resynchronize.

1. The members $p \in \Pi_i$ use an agreement protocol (e.g., [79, 81]) to choose a set of time providers $\{j_i\}$, numbered from 1 to m. Let the following assumptions describe the clock synchronization environment.

- Let τ be the delay of the broadcast algorithm.
- Let $UT_p{}^{(j_i)}$ denote an interval for a p-clock broadcast by j_i.
- Let χ be a bound on the provided interval, such that $\chi \geq \frac{1}{2}\|UT_p{}^{(j_i)}\|$.
- Let ρ denote an upper bound on the provider's clock drift-rate, $\rho \geq |1 - \frac{d}{dt}C_{j_i}(t)|$.
- Let H be the minimal time between consecutive broadcasts of $UT^{(j_i)}$ by all j_i's.
- Let k be the maximal path length allowed for the broadcast algorithm (Algorithm II).

2. For a sequence of *predetermined* times $T^{(i)}$ and time providers j_i:

   (a) Provider j_i executes Algorithm II when $\rhd (UT^{(j)}) = T^{(i)} - \tau - k(\chi + \rho H)$ The algorithm uses $U^{(j_i)}$ that is equal to the current value of $UT^{(j_i)}$ in order to broadcast an interval for a p-clock $UT_p^{(j_i)}$ to every $p \in \Pi_i$.

(b) Each $p \in \Pi_i$ screens the faulty intervals out of the m it should have received with a defined function A^f. It uses the nonfaulty intervals to set an "assumed to be correct" p-clock

$$C_p^{(i)} \leftarrow A^f(UT_p^{(1)}, \ldots, UT_p^{(m)})$$

For example [83], $A^f(UT_p^{(1)}, \ldots, UT_p^{(m)})$ can be the average of the multiset of $m - 2f$ numbers obtained by taking the *midpoints* of all the $UT_p^{(i)}$ $(i = 1, 2, \ldots, m)$, and omitting the f lowest and f highest of them.

(c) Each p uses Algorithm I (resynchronization) to compute T_p.

Achievement of Fault Tolerance

There are two major contributors to the achievement of fault-tolerance objectives in this algorithm. The first is the agreement on the forum set $\{j_i\}$, a subset of Π_i, out of which we synchronize the local time provider. The second is the selection of the sufficient quorum, through $A^f(UT_p^{(1)}, \ldots, UT_p^{(m)})$, which we use to synchronize the p-clock. However, these two contributors have strong effects on the cost involved in executing the algorithm.

The larger the forum $\{j_i\}$ is, the smaller the effect of a single faulty provider becomes. Note that in these cases we can use a larger quorum by increasing m. Thus, the effect of a faulty provider is reduced by the averaging process. However, a large forum increases the communication traffic significantly, especially in a broadcast discipline.

The quorum selection function, $A^f(UT_p^{(1)}, \ldots, UT_p^{(m)})$, influences the fault-tolerant properties in some ways. The criterion of selection characterizes some of these properties. Let us consider the selection chosen above, in omitting the f lowest and f highest of the m $UT_p^{(i)}$'s. This selection[3] assumes a symmetric distribution of the erroneous providers. In that case, we can ignore the lowest and highest $UT_p^{(i)}$'s, since they are expected to be symmetrically distributed. In case of a strongly biased population, this selection performs weakly. For example, when all the faulty providers (say $2f$) are low, half of them are considered and f correct providers are ignored.

The parameters m and f also influence significantly the characteristics of the quorum selection function. We note that when we increase m, we can increase f and still retain an averaging population of the same size. Hence, additional robustness can be derived from increasing these parameters, but this increase causes a higher communication cost. Furthermore, a larger quorum may require a longer time to collect enough broadcasts from the forum members.

---

[3]The selection in the algorithm [85] has been chosen mainly due to its simplicity.

CHAPTER
3

OBJECTS

Significant research effort has been invested in the use of objects to establish a concurrent programming development environment [21]. In this context, one views an object as an entity whose behavior is characterized by the operations it is subjected to and the operations it carries out on other objects. The external view of an object that consists of these operations constitutes its specification. On the other hand, the internal view of an object is its implementation.

We introduce here a slightly different point of view. We consider the use of object architecture in a system context. This context expands the above object definitions to support a more general description of elements and entities. Some of the properties that characterize objects in a software development context are valid in the system architecture context as well.

- An object has a state.
- There is a set of operations to which an object is subjected and a set of operations it requires from other objects.
- An object is denoted by a name.
- An object has restricted visibility of (as well as by) other objects.

3.1 BASIC CONCEPTS

3.1.1 Objects: Justification and Manipulation

An object is a distinct and selectively accessible software element that resides on one of the storage resources of the system. Software elements may hide hardware elements which they control or serve. The object architecture defines the objects as the elements that construct the system, their classification, and the relations between them. It also defines the set of operations they are subjected to and execution parameters that permit scheduling them for execution and access. An object-based architecture is an implementation of a system based on object entities.

Current object architectures deal with object creation, deletion, access and protection in ways that often become cumbersome for real-time applications. The major inadequacy we find in current architectures is the uncertainty they introduce in assigning time to object execution. Such an inadequacy becomes serious in a real-time system that manages its resources according to specified deadlines. The predictability of objects' temporal behavior is the most important property a real-time system must demonstrate.

We propose an architecture in which we handle object manipulation (creation, deletion, access, and protection) such that access-time behavior supports the objectives of real-time constraints. In addition, the architecture supports achievement of fault tolerance goals through architectural damage containment. Furthermore, this proposed architecture demonstrates high determinism in object execution time, a property that enables predictability of its behavior.

We must answer two major questions before considering ways for object manipulation. The first question concerns the mechanisms of creation and deletion of objects in a distributed system. The second question regards the way objects are accessed while considering requirements for unique identification and protection. We discuss these questions in detail in the following sections. Let us distinguish in the discussion two classes of objects: executable objects and nonexecutable objects. We assume all the objects are addressable by the machines used in the distributed system. We also assume local treatment for representation problems, even in heterogeneous environments.

3.1.2   Creation and Deletion of Objects

To create and delete objects that are shared in a multiple-user environment, we must consider some properties that do no exist in the single-user environment. While in the single-user case each user is also the object's owner, in the multiuser case a user may have no ownership rights. For a distributed multiple-user environment there are even more properties to consider. A user that is remotely linked to an object may be loaded to execute and "find out" that the object had been deleted earlier. In order to derive the justification for the existence of an object, let us first consider the existential justification of a logical assertion in a database. Such justification takes the form of a mechanism often used in data dependency control. An assertion sometimes depends on the existence of one or more other assertions, hence producing a strong data dependency. In such cases, modifications must consider all dependency relations (e.g., in case of deletion).

The justificand is pointed to by a justification that exists as long as its justifiers support it. One must be cautious and verify that a directed cycle does not exist, or else a justificand may become its own justifier. To understand this relationship, consider Figure 3.1. Let one JUSTIFIER be the assertion $p \Rightarrow q$, and let the second JUSTIFIER be the assertion p. A trivial JUSTIFICATION

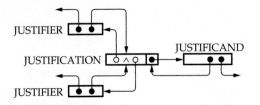

FIGURE 3.1
Justifier-justification-justificand relations.

can be inferred, and the JUSTIFICAND is then the assertion q. The above JUSTIFICATION requires two JUSTIFIERs. If we delete one of them, we must delete the JUSTIFICAND too. The doubly-linked relationship shown in the figure is very convenient for a search procedure, which one expects to move within the network of assertions to manage the data dependencies. For example, it is sufficient for a garbage collection process to examine the JUSTIFICATION in order to mark an object for deletion.

The above justification scheme demonstrates the benefits of the introduction of an additional entity: the JUSTIFICATION. Every creation (assertion addition) or deletion (assertion removal) can verify the proper relationships before being carried out. However, we can extend the relation between justifiers to other relations, rather than the AND relation in the data dependency model.

We propose here a similar mechanism for the existential justification of an object in a distributed system. We find two types of JUSTIFIERs: a user of the object and the owner of an object. Figure 3.2 demonstrates this mechanism.

In order to delete such an object, its justification should be unlinked from its owner and have no users linked to it. Initially, an owner of an object creates it and this owner is the only justifier for its existence. When another user shares the object with the owner, the owner cannot delete it until the user completes the usage. A user that is not the owner of an object can never delete it without the owner's permission. One can easily expand this relationship to one owner and multiple sharing users. We note that one can use the JUSTIFICATION to implement mutual exclusion, authorization control, and many other tasks.

3.1.3   Accessing Objects

For an object to be accessible, the object must be properly identified and the access should be properly authorized. We distinguish *identification* from *authorization* because identification is for reaching purposes while authorization depends also on the type of manipulation required (as in read permission and write denial).

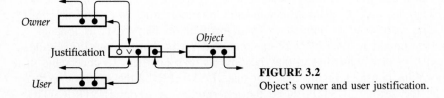

FIGURE 3.2
Object's owner and user justification.

IDENTIFYING OBJECTS. Identification of an object requires the ability to distinguish it from other members of the set of accessible objects. This ability is based on a property of uniquely naming each of the accessible objects at each level of the system operation. The term *name*, therefore, has more than just an appellative nature. It may be better interpreted as a precise pointer to the object.

Each name is always interpreted with respect to a particular *context* [127]. The context is a set of bindings of names to objects. In the following section we describe how we propose to attach properties to contexts.

In distributed systems we find different types of names at different layers of the system architecture [20]. Each layer must maintain a uniform view [153] at its distributed partitions when referring to an object. Therefore, there is a need to manage mappings for the name spaces used, keeping each name unique for all accessibility levels [116]:

1. Character *string* names are used in the file system and in user programs.
2. Segment *numbers* are used by a running process to refer to an active segment.
3. A segment table (of a user) provides physical *addresses* for the page table of a corresponding segment.

Context initialization (also called binding, or linking, or loading) is the bridge between the high-level names that are human-oriented and the low-level addresses that are machine-oriented. Furthermore, conversion of human identifiers to machine identifiers requires the use of a catalog that maps the two finite spaces. Allowing access possibility to multiple users extends the above requirement to a multiple catalog system. Here, we can view each catalog as a context in which the identifiers are interpreted. In other words, different catalogs can use the same "name" for different objects but the objects can still be distinguished. The ability to selectively share a context exists if catalogs appear as named objects in other catalogs. We call the resulting network a *naming network* [127].

When we share a context, there is a need to distinguish between the name given to an object by its owner, and the name by which an external user refers to this object. A trivial but impractical solution is to impose global uniqueness of names. A better solution is to connect an object that contains other objects' names to the proper contexts in which these names are bound. The simplest way to do it is to use the catalogs. In most cases, however, we would like to allow the use of different names at different contexts when referring to the same shared object and therefore the catalogs are insufficient. Hence, one needs dedicated pointer constructs (*closures* in [127]) that serve as *joints* between objects accessed and the contexts (catalogs) that attempt to access them.

Recalling the scheme discussed in section 3.1.2, the *joint* is the JUSTIFICATION, the catalogs (also called directories) are the JUSTIFIERS, and the accessed object is the JUSTIFICAND.

As an example, let us consider the situation shown in Figure 3.3. An object *a* of context1 refers to an object whose name according to this context is *b*. But this object is named *c* according to context2, which owns it. Furthermore, when the latter refers to *a*, it is *a* according to context2. Object *a of 1* is justified by the catalog of context1, while object *a of 2* is justified by the catalog of context2. The object *c of 2* is justified by two catalogs. Its *joint* points forward to *c* and backward to its two justifiers. The knowledge of "who's the owner?" is also kept within the joints, denoted by hollow circles in the figures.

The overall scheme is called the *name service* and is supported by the operating system. When no bridge between different naming levels exists, we activate a context initialization procedure. A context initialization procedure usually consists of resolving actions and installing actions. The resolution of a name involves searching an existing object identified by a given name in a given context.

The unpredicted time involved in such a search disqualifies it as a possible run-time procedure in a real-time system. In a real-time system the context initializer must be allowed only as an off-line task,[1] probably executed before running a real-time job. Execution of parts of the context initialization as early as possible is a desired property in real-time systems [25] because it leaves fewer unpredicted activities to near-execution time. In addition, in order to adhere to timing constraints, the response time of a name service should always be bounded and short. In order to achieve such bounds, systems may limit name servers to small-size names which are locally unique and thereby reduce search time. This restriction is relatively simple to implement in cases where local "nicknames" are employed [24].

---

[1]See Section 2.2 for the definition of *off-line*.

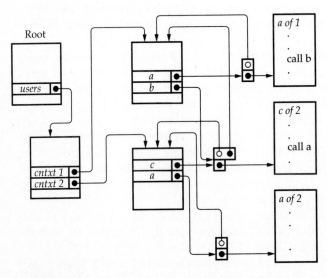

FIGURE 3.3
Example: different contexts sharing an object.

Such a restriction raises issues of reusability of names, recalling the need to maintain the uniqueness of names in a given context. We further emphasize the reusability and uniqueness issues regarding the selectively shared contexts objective. We note that implementing such a service correctly allows any user to disconnect itself from external objects. However, it requires some additional tools for deletion of objects because other users may be linked to these objects.

The search rules in a name service of a real-time operating system should emphasize efficiency. As such, a direct entry in a directory should point to a joint of an object. An indirect entry should specify the whole access path through the shared context to the desired joint. Applying such an approach allows limiting the number of directories that are searched for an access. For example, we may limit the search to the user's working directory, a language library, and a system library. The language and system libraries can be maintained, ordered, and balanced, thereby reducing search time to a minimal bounded time.

We note that increasing the predictability with restrictions on binding dynamics has its disadvantages. For example, on-line creation of objects may become limited and migratability of objects may require special mechanisms. However, an on-line update of the naming structure, with which we may overcome the above drawbacks, requires complicated means with unpredictable temporal properties.

PROTECTING OBJECTS. Real-time embedded systems usually neglect protection mechanisms. However, a real-time operating system cannot. Stringent real-time constraints, being the dominant ones, require the time taken by the protection mechanism to be as low as possible. For example, consider a case in which users are given a direct access to required resources on remote sites. The access time is reduced but the availability of potentially-restricted information is increased. Most of today's systems cannot allow such a liberal approach from the point of view of protection.

We divide protection systems into two categories: list–oriented systems and ticket-oriented systems (as capabilities [46]). Access control lists imply search procedures that are not adequate for real-time systems. A capability system, in which one grants authorization before run time, provides a better real-time environment.

The *joint* introduced above is suitable for maintaining a ticket-oriented protection scheme. Its advantage is in its authorization test being carried out before run time, before binding it to the user's context. Furthermore, a user needs a backward link from the joint in order to gain access to an object, and thus the joint acts as an information hiding module. Embedding an access control process in it may support mutual-exclusion mechanisms.

In a distributed system, an application program does not have explicit knowledge about the storage locations it uses. The operating system must therefore provide a service that maintains links to remote sites. Furthermore, timing properties of different allocation instances may differ significantly. Therefore, the efficiency of such a service is very significant.

3.1.4   Object Architecture

Let us consider an architecture for hard[2] real-time operating systems. We base this architecture on the use of the above highly encapsulated entities, called *objects*. The object-oriented architecture provides means to construct systems with a high degree of deterministic and predictable timing properties. This determinism, together with the required fault tolerance schemes, are major principles in our time-constraint–oriented system. We have defined above a classification of object types, the set of operations each of the object types is associated with, and their relations. Let the *joint* of each object contain the following parts:

- A context-independent pointer to the object's body, for the naming network ability to allow a multi-user selective sharing of the object.
- An owner/user justification structure.
- Resource (and/or server) requirements.
- A ticket check mechanism for the protection scheme.
- A time constraint for an executable object.
- A replica/alternative control mechanism for the fault tolerance scheme.

Using the mechanisms that the above architecture supports, let us consider a possible computation model. In our model, objects that relate to each other are connected via the owner/user justifications in the joint. These relations are compatible with the visibility restrictions and the set of operations to which the justificand is subjected and on which the justifier is operating. Operations in this set can change an object state, evaluate the current state of an object, and allow visiting parts of an object. One can carry out these operations on object bodies as well as on object joints. We can model a system as a graph whose nodes are objects and whose directed arcs go from justifier to justificand representing the owner/user relationship. In order to support one-to-many and many-to-one relations between objects, we can group objects of the same type into a meta-object. The rest of the objects may refer to such a group as a whole entity.

3.1.5   Relations and Operations

Depending on their relations with other objects, we can divide executable objects into three classes [21]:

- *Actor*. An object that is subjected to no operation. It only operates on other objects.

---

[2]Hard real-time systems are characterized by their property of having a nonrecoverable fault when a computation does not complete before its deadline.

- *Server*. An object that is only subjected to operations by other executable objects. It does not operate on other executable objects, but it may operate on non-executable objects.
- *Agent*. An object that operates on (one or more) executable objects on behalf of another executable object. Other executable objects may operate on it.

In addition, there are objects that are only subjected to operations and thus are non-executable.

Figure 3.4 describes an example of such a system. It is important to notice that the owner/user relationship is not necessarily an operation, although when an executable object is involved it is compatible with a set of permissible operations. For example, consider the relations between passive objects. Since a passive object does not operate on other objects, its relations with other objects are mainly of an existential justification nature. Possible examples include the case of using copies for fault tolerance or in distributed databases. The latter type of relationship necessitates the grouping of objects of the same type into a meta-object to which the rest of the objects may refer as a whole entity. We distinguish between the grouping of a set of executable objects (a *troupe* [35]) and the grouping of a set of non-executable objects (a *pack*). The dissimilarity originates in the different requirements of fault tolerance, which are discussed in the next section.

The object type determines the operations suitable for a system object, the ones it carries out as well as the ones carried out on it. For example, a passive object has an empty set of operations it is allowed to carry out on executable objects. One can define three classes of operation types on objects [21]:

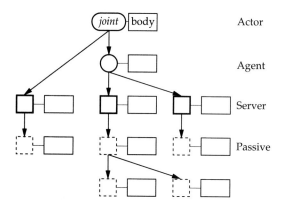

FIGURE 3.4
Relations between different types of objects.

- Operations that change an object state.
- Operations that evaluate the current state of an object.
- Operations that allow visiting parts of an object.

Recall that these operations can be carried out on object bodies as well as on object joints.

3.1.6   Fault Tolerance Relations

Requirements for fault tolerance impose maintenance of redundant objects with relations that adhere to the fault tolerance specifications. In an object-oriented system, a support for maintenance of objects that are copies or versions of other objects is required. It is the operating system that should support this maintenance, according to the application specification, but without the application's continuous control. There might be any whole number of copies, or versions, of an object, according to the requirements of the system to which the original object belongs. We distinguish between copies or versions of an executable object, denoted as *alternatives*, and copies of a non-executable object, denoted as *replicas*. While replicas must be the same, alternatives may differ internally. Both alternatives and replicas raise an additional constraint that we must satisfy, the *consistency* constraint. This constraint adds a new dimension to our model of a system, requiring links between the original object and its alternatives or replicas.

Fault tolerance of executable objects utilizes mechanisms that allow recovery from a fault. The most common mechanisms used to recover a system upon detection of an error are roll-back mechanisms [122]. These mechanisms employ a sequential strategy of execute–acceptance test–recover. Another approach is a strategy of parallel execution of redundant modules followed by selection of outputs by a decision algorithm. Figure 3.5 compares a recovery block scheme, which is a roll-back strategy, with N-version program execution (NVP), which is a modular redundancy strategy. In the recovery block scheme, $prog_1$ is executed first. Then, its state is acceptance-tested by $<AT1>$. Upon a successful test the block terminates, but upon failure execution returns to a recovery point and initialization is carried out for another execution, this time of $prog_2$ (which may be a replication of $prog_1$, or different). This execution is acceptance-tested by $<AT2>$, and so on up to N predefined trials. In the modular redundancy approach all the n modules, $prog_1$ to $prog_n$, execute at the same time.

In real-time systems a simple roll-back strategy leads to a deadline miss, an unrecoverable fault itself. A deadline miss might occur if an error is detected when there is not sufficient time to activate an alternative. Hence, in real-time systems one must activate alternatives soon enough, even before their original executable object (the preferred alternative) begins an acceptance test. Such a roll-forward approach is usually used in a modular redundancy design and in N-Version programming (NVP). Its major drawback is the high degree of *determinism* it requires. A set of alternatives is completely deterministic if each alternative has

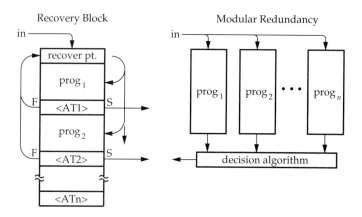

FIGURE 3.5
Recovery block versus modular redundancy.

exactly one possible execution for each of its reachable states. We have introduced above the troupe as a set of alternatives of an original executable object. A troupe may decrease the degree of determinism required (and increase asynchrony) by allowing more application dependency [35] or by forcing all the troupe members to satisfy a set of conditions [100].

Executable objects that apply a roll-forward approach raise the consistency constraint because of contentions. Roll-back mechanisms may solve such contentions by the use of an audit trail. A coordinator object creates the trail for the update of semi-idle cohort objects that serve as backup [19]. This checkpoint mechanism supports the availability of accessible executable objects for a specific job. Checkpointing keeps these objects available while maintaining information on required start-up points for the backup alternatives.

We often solve problems of consistency for objects that execute concurrently by using a very expensive atomic broadcast operation [128, 18, 39, 70]. An atomic broadcast satisfies properties of termination, atomicity, and ordering. In other words, every message eventually reaches its destination, every message is either delivered correctly to all destinations or not delivered to any, and all receivers receive the messages from all senders in the same order. In atomic broadcast operation, a broadcast message is sent as an atomic action. This solution is unsuitable for real-time applications because of the stringent timing constraints to which the communication network is subjected. An atomic broadcast requirement may therefore overload the communication network, or at least reduce its efficiency, to an undesirable level. Hence, the above solution is unacceptable. Another extensively researched area in checkpointing is the determination of the optimal interval for checkpointing [27, 50, 51, 52]. However, an optimal checkpoint interval may conflict with imposed real-time constraints.

Fault tolerance of non-executable objects is often achieved by maintaining replicas of the objects and enforcing a uniform serializability of the operations on all replicas of each object. The property of ensuring that concurrent execution of operations on a passive object and its replicas is equivalent to a serial execution on the passive object is called *one-copy serializability*. A common method for ensuring that replicas are consistent is a weighted voting. For example, consider replicas of a passive object that are subjected only to read and write operations [53]. One may maintain consistency by setting a read quorum and a write quorum ensuring non-null intersection of any read quorum and any write quorum. This method is highly suitable for the roll-forward schemes of the executable objects, although it is serial to a concurrent execution of the alternatives. Its predictability is very high, especially from execution time aspects.

Maintaining consistency is also achievable via atomic actions [6, 94, 123]. Since an atomic action is indivisible, it allows the system to have transitions only from one consistent state to another. Furthermore, if an inconsistent state is detected, the action is not carried out anywhere. For a distributed message-passing system, commit protocols provide the means for implementation of atomic actions [135, 136, 79]. The success of recovery procedures depends on satisfaction of recoverability conditions by the object's internal view, or its implementation [146]. Atomic actions are very expensive for the reasons previously stated; namely, applying this approach in a real-time system consumes an enormous amount of resources.

The use of replicas and alternatives raises issues of partitioning of a pack or a troupe. One particularly important issue is how to ensure a one-copy serializability of replicas across partitions. Both syntactic and semantic strategies can deal with these issues [41]. In cases where a transaction is not allowed to be rolled back for a recovery procedure (thereby preempting execution), we have to adopt a *pessimistic* approach. This approach prevents inconsistency by limiting availability, assuming the worst on the other partitions. On the other extreme, if the availability is more important, or if an access to a part of a pack is sufficient, an *optimistic* approach may be adequate. This approach allows global inconsistency to occur and later (upon connection of the partitions) be recovered by some resolution mechanism, such as undoing, compensating, or correcting. The choice between the two approaches is application-dependent. It seems, however, that the more restricted a system is, the more pessimistic its approach will be.

3.2 REQUIREMENTS FOR EXCEPTIONS

This section discusses the adequacy of object architecture for dealing with computation irregularities. We consider three major properties of computation inconstancy: interrupts, preemptions, and exception handling.

3.2.1 Interrupt Driven Systems

Interrupt driven systems are frequently used in real-time applications, especially in control systems. The system reacts to each interrupt that triggers the system with an interrupt service process, defined by the system designer. This service process is invoked by the operating system through its interrupt handler. The handler identifies the arriving interrupt and passes control to the appropriate service process. The interrupt service definition contains a time constraint. The system designer defines the maximal frequency with which each interrupt is allowed to occur. A deadline for the service of each interrupt is distinctly set, along with computation requirements. The system designer also specifies conditions on start times. Hence, each of the interrupt service processes is expressible with a time constraint, using the quintuple defined in section 2.2. However, an additional mechanism is required to ensure that a particular service process is to be executed if and only if the interrupt it serves has already occurred. In other words, a time constraint of an interrupt service process depends on the occurrence of an *event*, and not only on the start timing condition.

The requirement of guaranteed deadlines in a real-time system implies that the scheduling mechanism must take interrupts into account. Most scheduling mechanisms ignore the effect of services given to interrupts. A simple interrupt handler serves an interrupt the moment it occurs, preempting the object currently being scheduled to execute. In such a preemption, one may cause a deadline miss, which may be an unrecoverable fault. Furthermore, there may be enough time to execute the service process after the currently executing process completes, without any preemption at all. The above reasons justify a selective preemption approach, and the object's architecture we propose is well suited to it. As we have mentioned above (section 3.1.4), an object has a *state* that we can evaluate and change. We may use this property to deal with interrupt driven processes without contradicting a guaranteed deadline.

INTERRUPT DRIVEN OBJECTS. An interrupt-activated executable object may have two states: *idle* and *active*. Let the state of such an object be *idle* as long as the interrupt it serves has not occurred. The off-line scheduler and the process of allocating resources must take the interrupt service requirements into account. This way, the operating system may be able to guarantee meeting the deadline of an interrupt service while maintaining guarantees given to already *active* objects. Therefore, *idle* and *active* objects are all considered executable, regardless of their states. The on-line scheduler applies a *state-evaluation* procedure to the object which is most likely to use the resource next. If it is an *active* object, then this object receives control of the resource. We must postpone the execution of an *idle* object, even though it may be favorable from a timing point of view. However, we can advance an *active* object scheduled for a later time. To do so, we must be able to carry out the execution ahead of time without violating the postponed object's time constraint. In this case, this *active* object receives control of the resource. Figure 3.6 describes such a case, demonstrating that P_1 can execute before serving the interrupt. Note there is no reason to preempt P_1, even if the interrupt occurs during the execution of P_1.

The interrupt handler invokes the proper *state-change* procedure according to the interrupt source. This procedure changes an *idle* object to an *active* one. Both the *state-evaluation* procedure and the *state-change* procedure are very short in their execution times. Each consumes a constant overhead cost for all the

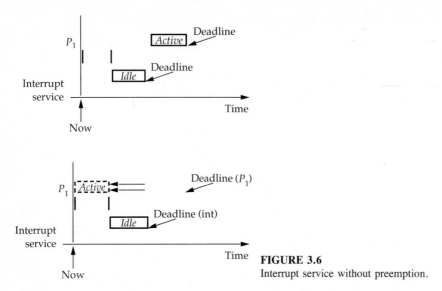

FIGURE 3.6
Interrupt service without preemption.

devices at a specific processing node. This result is due to the direct access to objects through the *joint*'s justification, as described in Section 3.1.2.

It is wasteful, however, to apply a very safe approach. Above, we have allowed advancing execution of active objects only if they can complete without violating the time constraint of the postponed interrupt server. Hence, we want to utilize the slack[3] of an idle object, as long as it is idle and we do not violate its time constraint. Figure 3.7 gives such an example. P_1 executes although the interrupt service deadline is earlier, until there is a conflict with the service time. Upon conflict detection the service preempts P_1. One of the problems with this approach is the overhead cost of the context switching. An additional problem is the depth of nested preemption allowed while guaranteeing satisfaction of all the constraints. One way to solve these problems is to selectively allow such switches at checkpoints, thus allowing preemption only at a finite number of points in the execution trace of an object.

EXAMPLE OF AN INTERRUPT HANDLER. The system's interrupt handler is a hardware-invoked server. An occurrence of an interrupt event triggers this invocation. Such a server needs three service access points (SAPs) to perform the tasks listed below.

1. *Interrupt Definition.* When a hardware device signals that it needs its service, the system must recognize this service identification in order to invoke the proper service. An invocation of this entry of the interrupt handler defines and updates the mapping from device identifiers to the server objects. Often

---

[3] Time slack is defined as $\max(d_{Id} - c_{Id}, 0)$ where d_{Id} is the time to deadline and c_{Id} is the computation time [103].

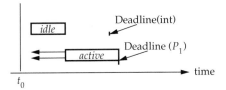

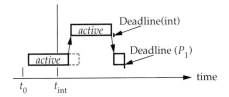

FIGURE 3.7
"First-deadline" scheduling with preemption.

systems manipulate data structures in order to perform the mapping. Other systems use a dedicated memory in the hardware vector interrupt driver. We denote this data structure as the *Interrupt_Map*. The *Interrupt_Map* must support a very efficient mapping mechanism, being a part of the interrupt overhead. This action interrupts the execution of a guaranteed time constraint, even when we do not invoke a particular interrupt server. In cases in which we have a large number of interrupt sources, look-up tables become inefficient. In such cases, one can implement the mapping data structure by an ordered and balanced tree, whose nodes are the tuples

$$< device\_identifier, object\_server >$$

Each node serves as a *user-justification* for its server object.

When one invokes this entry, supplying the proper tuple, we expect the interrupt handler to insert the node to the *Interrupt_Map*. We also expect it to update properly the justification scheme. We give below a description of these expectations in a pseudo-programming language form.

Upon Interrupt_Define(*device,server*) :

    begin

    if ($\exists x : \exists < device,x > \in$ *Interrupt_Map*)

        then

            exception

        else begin

            Interrupt_Map $\leftarrow$ *Interrupt_Map* $\cup < device,server >$

            server.justification $\leftarrow$ *server*.justification

                    $\oplus\& < device,server >$

        end

    end

where $\cup$ is an insertion algorithm (e.g., [75, Section 6.2.3]), $\oplus$ is a union operator, and & *<device,server>* is a backward link from the joint to the node.

2. *Interrupt Removal.* The converse of the above operation is the removal of a service from the recognized ones. When one invokes this entry, indicating which device the handler must remove, we expect the interrupt handler to remove the node from the *Interrupt_Map*. Here too, we must update the proper justifications. An implementation example of these requirements follows.

Upon Interrupt_Remove(*device*) :

> begin
>
> if ($\exists x : \exists < device,x > \in Interrupt\_Map$)
>
>> then begin
>>
>>> *server*.justification $\leftarrow$ *server*.justification
>>>
>>>> $\ominus$ & *<device, server>*
>>>
>>> *Interrupt Map* $\leftarrow$ *Interrupt Map*
>>>
>>>> $(\cup)^{-1}$ *<device, server>*
>>
>> end
>
>> else
>>
>>> exception
>
> end

where $(\cup)^{-1}$ is a deletion algorithm (e.g., [75, Section 6.2.3]), $\ominus$ is a set subtraction operator.

3. *Interrupt Response.* The interrupt service is not within the responsibilities of the interrupt handler. The off-line scheduler and the allocator reserve resources and account for the server's requirements. This server executes after the interrupt occurrence, according to the on-line scheduler decision. Therefore, the only activity required from the interrupt handler as a response to an interrupt occurrence is to record the occurrence. The occurrence recording must reflect an active state of the server to the on-line scheduler. It must also acknowledge the hardware in order to clear the request and allow other requests to arrive. A possible implementation that achieves these goals follows.

Upon interrupt occurrence (*device*) :

> begin
>
> interrupts disable
>
> if ($\exists server : \exists <device,server> \in Interrupt Map$)

```
        then begin

                server.state  ←  active

                I/O clear (device)

                end

            else

                I/O clear (device)

            interrupts enable

        end
```

Assuming maintenance of the *Interrupt_Map* balanced and ordered by the off-line SAPs (the former two), here the response time is negligible with respect to jobs execution time. Two properties of this response allow its on-line employment. First, it is homogeneous, in the sense that all the interrupts receive the same response. Second, its execution load is predictable and deterministic, and can be derived from the implementation of the *Interrupt_Map*.

Let us consider an operating system with a core resident kernel and a boot mechanism that loads it. When the boot mechanism loads the kernel, it loads a basic *Interrupt_Map* with it, containing services for the devices of the system. Users may define new services for existing devices, and expand the system with additional devices. We take care of mutual exclusion in accessing *Interrupt_Map*, making sure that the users cannot access the *Interrupt_Map* directly. Only the handler object manipulates this data structure, on behalf of one user at a time.

Let us now consider some cases that do not agree with our assumptions. These are cases in which the system clock's granularity is extremely fine and the sum of responses to interrupt occurrences is not negligible. In such cases, one should compensate the maximal number of possible interrupt occurrences as a continuous overhead cost of the system. In order to guarantee meeting a job's constraint we have to advance its required deadline accordingly. Let each response require δ time units (assuming homogeneity). Let the maximum number of interrupts in the system be n, and let each interrupt i occur at a frequency f_i. For a time constraint with a frequency f_k, one must advance the deadline by $\sum_{i=1}^{n}(f_i/f_k)\delta$. This way we can guarantee meeting a deadline even though an overhead cost delays it.

3.2.2 Communication Service as an Agent Object

Communication between two distinct processing nodes is one of the following events:

1. Processes that execute on different nodes make a synchronization attempt.

2. A process on one node initiates an object migration to the other.

3. An object requires a remote service.

Real-time systems differ from others in the way they support remote synchronization. A communication synchronization attempt without a timeout bound may introduce a variable delay and unpredictability. Furthermore, an unbounded communication synchronization contradicts a bounded execution-time, and thus prevents by its existence any possibility for a guarantee. However, there are time-bounded solutions to synchronization such as clock synchronization and calendar management for resource allocation and scheduling.

We do not consider object migration an on-line task. The size of an object may be modified at run time, a fact that prevents using a bound on migration execution time. Therefore, we do not consider the above two communication occurrences (synchronization and migration) here.

Remote services are an important feature of distributed systems. A request for a remote service usually originates in the absence of an adequate local *server*. This absence may be due to executive and functional reasons or fault tolerance reasons. The guaranteeing procedure that is used for local computations is not adequate in such a case. Here the equivalent procedure needs access to resources whose control is shared with other mechanisms, some of which may interpret data differently. One needs an *agent* process to interface between the local *actor*[4] and the *remote server*. The agent process must acquire all the knowledge of the execution time parameters of the server. Then, the agent must impose a real-time constraint on the proper server, such that the actor satisfies its own real-time constraint. Figure 3.8 describes the difference between a local and a remote service.

REMOTE SERVICE CONSIDERATIONS. Analysis of the tasks an agent has to perform results in a set of activities that should take place in both the actor's node and the server's node (see Figure 3.9). Let the time required to execute service b at node B be t_0 time units. Agent a (at node A) cannot guarantee that the execution of b at B will take only t_0 time units. Additional time is required because of

1. Communication delays t_{comm}.

2. Clock inaccuracies ϵ_A and ϵ_B.

3. Agent overhead t_{agent}.

Figure 3.10 describes these timing considerations. Server b at B can guarantee an execution interval of $t_0 + 2\epsilon_B$. The communication portion at B extends this

---

[4]An agent may initiate the request for a remote server as well. For simplification, we use an actor in our example.

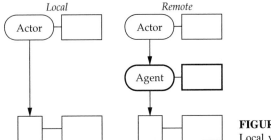

FIGURE 3.8
Local versus remote servers.

interval to $t_0 + t_{comm} + 2\epsilon_B$. This results in an execution interval $t_0 + t_{comm} + t_{agent} + 2\epsilon_A$ at node A.

In this model the communication is a part of the guaranteed execution time. The communication delays t_{comm} include both the access time and the transfer time. Since in this model the communication is a part of the guaranteed execution time, this time must be bounded. This property is effective not only during the execution phase, but also during the allocation and scheduling phases. We do not regard the communication just as a point-to-point message delivery; rather we consider it as a part of an agent that is responsible to satisfy guaranteed deadlines at remote nodes.

3.2.3 Exception Handling

A state-space model of a computation includes a set of states and a set of state transitions. The *standard domain* of a program specification P is the set of initial states s' for which execution terminates in the set of final states s, satisfying *post*(s', s). The *exception domain* is the set of initial states that do not belong to the standard domain [37, 38]. We distinguish two cases in the following discussion on exception handling: exception prevention and reaction to exceptions.

EXCEPTION PREVENTION. A total avoidance of exceptions is not achievable in most cases, especially in concurrent programs. However, a preventive approach may decrease the unpredictability of programs due to exceptions. A smaller exception domain is the goal of our preventive approach. In order to achieve this goal, we must first understand the causes for exceptions. Let us distinguish two groups of such causes: design faults and invocation faults. Avoidance of design

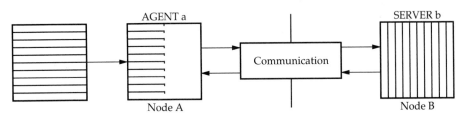

FIGURE 3.9
Objects involved in communication.

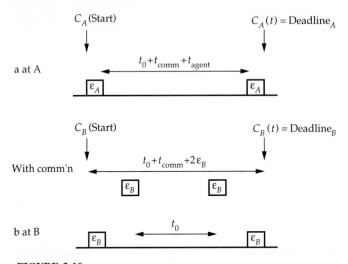

FIGURE 3.10
Timing diagram for local and remote nodes.

faults requires a very complicated proof system, which may become cumbersome in cases of large distributed programs. It is much easier to deal with invocation faults.

Let us start by examining the invocation mechanism. When one object invokes another, it must specify and identify the proper action required. Furthermore, the invoking object must supply a correct parameter block which the invoked object uses.[5] Errors and faults in the parameter block generate states that belong to the exception domain. So do errors in action references. Let us consider a mechanism we call *bounded semantic link* which reduces these fault causes. We base this mechanism on two major properties: a very strong type checking on the parameter block and an a priori agreement on the invocation. The first property tries to minimize generation of states in the exception domain due to errors in the parameters. The latter tries to minimize wrong action invocations.

The a priori agreement serves as a connection protocol to assure invocation of the proper action. It also establishes the frame for the parameter block, assigning type for each parameter. It further assigns a default value to each parameter. We note here that a parameter type can be very restrictive and imposition of bounds on each parameter is desirable. Each time the invoking object changes a parameter value in the bounded semantic link, a strong type check is performed. If the invoking object attempts to insert an erroneous parameter, no value change will take place. Furthermore, as the insertion attempt fails, the link notifies the invoking object. The latter can react immediately and take corrective actions.

---

[5]The same arguments hold for a "procedure call" mechanism as well.

There is no need to postpone a corrective action until the invoked object uses the parameters. Thus, no time is wasted as expected in real-time systems.

Note that this preventive approach allows the proof system to have a better definition of the system behavior. Even parameter-dependent behavior can have bounds, and thus we enhance the predictability of the system. The bounded semantic links have other desirable properties for real-time systems, and we return to them later in this book.

REACTION TO EXCEPTION. The invocation of some mechanisms is postponed when we detect exception. Most of them do not consider the detection of an exception, and deal with the reaction that follows the detection. Among the reactions we find the following:

1. Report and cease execution.
2. Produce a special value or a boolean. An example is the returning of -1 in Pascal. It is not clear how an object can resume execution based on this scheme, supporting a general scheme.
3. Invoke a corrective action.

We denote as *local* a corrective action performed by the object that contains the fault. If, however, a local action is impossible, a *remote* action must follow. Let us assume that when a detection is possible, the detector can *signal* the remote handler that is able to react to that exception. In order to allow remote reactions, the system must define which object handles a signaled exception before its occurrence. In addition, the system must impose a policy on resumption or preemption of execution where exception is detected. We note here that we must specify a default value in order to resume execution. Default values by their nature are application-dependent, and we must treat them as defined above for the bounded semantic links.

Two signal mechanisms may be used:

1. A single-level mechanism, which upon exception detection at the invoked object signals the invoking object. We find examples of these mechanisms in CLU [95], Argus [94], and Ada[6] [1].
2. A multilevel mechanism, as in Mesa.[7] Here, execution can resume at a level higher than the one that transmitted the signal.

The multilevel mechanism is more powerful, but it contains two drawbacks. First, when execution resumes at a higher level, we need a "clean-up" of all the lower-level activities we preempt. In addition, we may contradict here our

---

[6]Ada is a trademark of the U.S. Department of Defense (Ada Joint Project Office).
[7]Mesa is a trademark of Xerox Corporation.

objectives of autonomy and containment. Letting the exception affect a distant activity at a higher level may spread the effects of the exception. For example, in hierarchical systems a higher level affects more objects than a lower one. The second drawback is the degree of unpredictability that results from this approach. Real-time systems cannot allow using loosely controlled activities for clean-up and garbage collection.

Therefore, the object architecture we present here for real-time systems supports exception handling in two ways: the semantic links and the single-level reaction to exceptions.

3.3 GUARANTEES IN HARD REAL-TIME SYSTEMS

When a request for a specific object invocation arrives at a hard real-time reactive operating system, the operating system has to allocate (when it is feasible) all the resources required. Resource allocation must consider the object's time constraint and support methods that guarantee constraint satisfaction.

A real-time reactive operating system uses the time constraint as the key to its decisions on execution initiation and resource scheduling [104]. Before execution initiation, the allocation and context initialization are required to ensure the existence of a feasible schedule for all accepted jobs. In our model of operating system, these tasks are carried out by

- An off-line *allocator/binder* that manages the acceptance of jobs (requests to execute objects), the name binding and the allocation of the resources before loading.
- An on-line *loader* that activates schedulable objects that are invoked.

Before binding and loading, the operating system must verify positively the feasibility of a schedule according to the invoked object time constraint. Allocation of the required resources should support the guarantee that the object is going to meet its deadline. This policy restricts the scheduling and it is necessary for the guarantee, although it is not so for the scheduling.

It is not only processors that the operating system allocates for an object. An object may rely on other server objects in order to perform its functions. These other objects may or may not reside at the same site. Remote services emphasize the needs for agents and for communication; each must be schedulable within the time constraints of the invoked object. One must take into account that time constraints are projected between different sites. Each of these sites may have access to a different clock with a different accuracy and correctness. This projection is discussed in detail in section 4.3.1.

When user-objects share a server object, a selected (and loaded) allocation should avoid conflicts regarding violations of the user-objects' time constraints. When the operating system allocates a server to a new user, it checks the server's future schedule to show feasibility within the new user's time constraints. The feasibility must demonstrate no violation of the services this server has already guaranteed to serve. Once we can verify feasibility of such a schedule, the binder can update the justification links.

In our system model we consider each object autonomous and thus able to maintain its own schedule. Therefore, in order to support the spectrum of scheduling activities described above, we divide the scheduling in our model into two parts.

- An *off-line scheduler* process manages the policy of a scheduling discipline. For example, when a resource is added to the system, in addition to recognizing the availability of that resource, a new discipline may be required. The allocator invokes this process to allow the schedule feasibility verification.
- An *on-line scheduler* applies the current scheduling discipline.

3.4 CONCLUDING REMARKS

This chapter introduced an architecture based on objects. We have defined each object to have a control part (denoted as a joint) and a body. Relations between objects, classification of objects, and manipulation requirements have been introduced as well.

The main objectives achieved by this architecture are the containment and determinism properties. These properties support autonomy characteristics required for fault tolerance along with predictable temporal bounds for execution times. In the following chapter we show how we use these characteristics to allow constructing a deterministic model of object temporal behavior.

CHAPTER

4

ADDING TIME TO OBJECTS

We start this chapter by introducing a mathematical basis and notation that support expression and analysis of temporal properties and relations. This mathematical basis is used in later sections to state and prove temporal conditions and properties.

4.1 TEMPORAL RELATIONS

4.1.1 Time Representation

An appropriate representation of time is essential in a wide variety of applications. The study of the representation of time has varied from reasoning and planning in artificial intelligence to accurate scheduling in real-time systems. Some aspects of these discussions have been introduced in Section 2.1. We summarize below our requirements for the characteristics of a representation of time:

1. It should allow the representation of instantaneous events, expressing *dates* or *time points*.
2. It should allow the representation of events with durations, expressing named periods or *time intervals*.
3. It should support a description of events whose duration may be *convex* (contiguous) or *non-convex* (containing gaps). Particularly, it should support representation of both *periodic* and *sporadic* non-convex event durations.
4. It should allow reasoning about a variety of temporal ordering relations.

5. It should support different granularity levels, allowing the resolution to vary according to the reasoning needs.

6. It should support relative as well as absolute quantification.

4.1.2 Temporal Relations

BASIC DEFINITIONS. The most commonly used time entities are time points and time intervals. The following definitions concern entities with which one can reason about time.

Definition 1. *A* time point *is a real number that represents the occurrence time of an instantaneous event, and is an indivisible entity.*

   The time is always defined with respect to a reference. A time point having zero value defines the reference instance.

   The order of two time points is defined if and only if the two time points are expressed in terms of the same reference frame (i.e., the same origin and scale). Let t_α and t_β be such time points.

Definition 2. *There are two binary relations between time points,*

- $t_\alpha < t_\beta$ *(t_α before t_β) and its inverse* $t_\alpha > t_\beta$ *(t_α after t_β);*
- $t_\alpha = t_\beta$.

Definition 3. *A* convex time interval *is a contiguous period that specifies a range of time points such that*

$$< t_\alpha, t_\beta > \ \equiv \ \{t : t_\alpha \le t \le t_\beta\}$$

The above definition implies that a time point t_α can be associated with the time interval $< t_\alpha, t_\alpha >$.

Definition 4. *The* duration *of a convex time interval* $< t_\alpha, t_\beta >$ *is a measure of the interval such that*

$$\|< t_\alpha, t_\beta >\| = |t_\beta - t_\alpha|$$

Definition 5. *A* non-convex time interval *is a set of sub-intervals expressed as a union of disjoint convex intervals.*

   The last definition means that, unlike the contiguous convex interval, a non-convex interval might contain gaps.

CONVEX INTERVAL RELATIONS. In the following definitions let A and B be convex time intervals, such that

$$A = \ < t_\alpha^A, t_\beta^A >, \ B = \ < t_\alpha^B, t_\beta^B >$$

A set of thirteen binary relations between convex intervals [6] supports descriptions of various ordering relations:

- *equal* $(A = B)$

$$(t_\alpha^A = t_\alpha^B) \wedge (t_\beta^A = t_\beta^B)$$

- *precede* $(A < B)$ and its inverse *succeed* $(B > A)$

$$t_\beta^A < t_\alpha^B$$

- *meet* $(A \Uparrow B)$ and its inverse *met-by* $(B \Downarrow A)$

$$t_\beta^A = t_\alpha^B$$

- *overlap* $(A \varnothing B)$ and its inverse *overlapped-by* $(B \varnothing^u A)$

$$t_\alpha^A < t_\alpha^B < t_\beta^A < t_\beta^B$$

- *start* $(A \uparrow B)$ and its inverse *started-by* $(B \uparrow^u A)$

$$t_\alpha^B = t_\alpha^A < t_\beta^A < t_\beta^B$$

- *during* $(A \ll B)$ and its inverse *contain* $(B \gg A)$

$$t_\alpha^B < t_\alpha^A < t_\beta^A < t_\beta^B$$

- *end* $(A \downarrow B)$ and its inverse *ended-by* $(B \downarrow^u A)$

$$t_\alpha^B < t_\alpha^A < t_\beta^A = t_\beta^B$$

Figure 4.1 provides a summary of these relations.

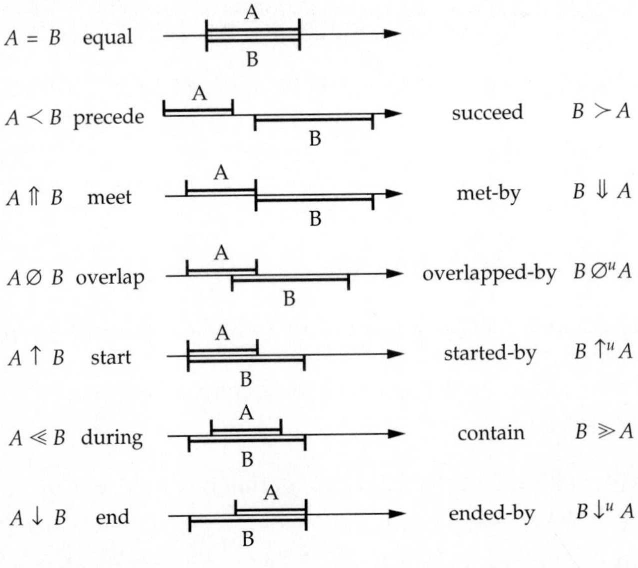

FIGURE 4.1
Convex interval binary relations.

We can express the relation *disjoint* ($\bowtie$) as

$$A \bowtie B \equiv (A < B) \vee (A > B)$$

and all the containment possibilities as

$$(A \uparrow B) \vee (A \lll B) \vee (A \downarrow B)$$

It can be shown [7] that one primitive, *meet*, is sufficient for constructing all the other relations. Using only one relation to describe temporal relations becomes very complicated, and therefore, although expressions that use only one or two primitives to reason about time may be correct, they are impractical. On the other hand, using only relations on event times and intersection and union of intervals is artificial. Events can be instantaneous in one granularity of the knowledge of time, and not so in another. Furthermore, intervals are not necessarily continuous. The variety of relations generated by the presence of gaps makes the oversimplified model of instantaneous events artificial as well.

NON-CONVEX INTERVAL RELATIONS. The definition of a time constraint as given in Section 2.2 shows the need to extend the relations of convex intervals to non-convex intervals. A non-convex interval easily models having a constraint whose frequency is lower than the reciprocal of the computation time. In Definition 5 above, we defined a non-convex time interval by an operator applied to convex time intervals. In the following definitions, let A and B be convex time intervals, such that

$$A = < t_\alpha^A, t_\beta^A >, \ B = < t_\alpha^B, t_\beta^B >$$

We now define the application of some operators on these time intervals.

Definition 6. *The* interval intersection *of convex time intervals A and B is defined for* $\neg (A < B) \wedge \neg (A > B)$ *as*

$$A \sqcap B \equiv < \max(t_\alpha^A, t_\alpha^B), \min(t_\beta^A, t_\beta^B) >$$

and ϕ (null) for $(A < B) \vee (A > B)$.
Note that the intersection of two convex intervals that *meet* each other is a non-null convex interval of duration zero. In other words, it is a time point.

Definition 7. *The* cover *of convex time intervals A and B is a convex interval defined as*

$$A \uplus B \equiv < \min(t_\alpha^A, t_\alpha^B), \max(t_\beta^A, t_\beta^B) >$$

The cover is a symmetric and commutative operation [86], a property that allows defining the operation on a set of more than two intervals

$$\biguplus_{i=1}^{n} \{c_i\} = c_1 \uplus c_2 \uplus c_3 \uplus \ldots \uplus c_n$$

Definition 8. *The set of* maximal convex sub-intervals *of convex time intervals A and B is defined as* $\mathcal{S}(\{A\},\{B\})$, *such that*

- $A \sqcap B = \phi \Rightarrow \mathcal{S} = \{A, B\}$
- $A \sqcap B \neq \phi \Rightarrow \mathcal{S} = \{A \uplus B\}$.

The set of maximal convex sub-intervals of a non-convex time interval D is the set of maximal convex sub-intervals of all its convex members $\{d_i\}$.

Definition 9. *The* set union *of non-convex time intervals C and D is a non-convex interval that consists of the set of members in* $\mathcal{S}(\{C\})$ *and the set of members in* $\mathcal{S}(\{D\})$

$$\{C\} \cup \{D\} \equiv \mathcal{S}(\{C\}) \cup \mathcal{S}(\{D\})$$

Note that the cover of the set union

$$\uplus (\{C\} \cup \{D\}) = < \min(t_\alpha^D, t_\alpha^C), \max(t_\beta^D, t_\beta^C) >$$

The union is a symmetric and commutative operation, a property that allows defining the operation on a set of more than two intervals

$$\bigcup_{i=1}^{n} \{c_i\} = c_1 \cup c_2 \cup c_3 \cup \cdots \cup c_n$$

Definition 10. *The* interval union *of non-convex time intervals C and D is a non-convex interval E, denoted*

$$E = C \sqcup D$$

such that

$$E = \mathcal{S}(\{C\} \cup \{D\})$$

Note that the cover of the interval union equals the cover of the set union, and that the interval union is commutative too. Hence,

$$\bigsqcup_{i=1}^{n} \{c_i\} = c_1 \sqcup c_2 \sqcup c_3 \sqcup \cdots \sqcup c_n$$

Applying generalization to the above convex interval relations results in non-convex interval relations as described below. Let C and D be non-convex intervals, and let $\{c_i\}$ and $\{d_i\}$ be their corresponding sets of maximal convex sub-intervals. Let $\mathcal{R}$ and $\mathcal{Q}$ be convex relations.

- *mostly. C* mostly-$\mathcal{R}$ *D* if

$$\forall d_j \in D : \exists c_i \in C : c_i \mathcal{R} d_j$$

- *always.* C always-$\mathcal{R}$ D if and only if C mostly-$\mathcal{R}$ D and D mostly-$\mathcal{R}^u$ C, where $\mathcal{R}^u$ is the converse relation to $\mathcal{R}$.
- *partially.* C partially-$\mathcal{R}$ D if and only if

$$X = \{x_i\} = \{c_i, d_i : c_i \mathcal{R} d_i\} \neq \phi,$$
$$\{C - X\} \sqcap \{D - X\} = \phi$$

- *sometimes.* C sometimes-$\mathcal{R}$ D if and only if

$$X = \{x_i\} = \{c_i, d_i : c_i \mathcal{R} d_i\} \neq \phi.$$

- *disjunction.* C $\mathcal{R} \vee \cdots \vee \mathcal{Q}$ D if and only if

$$\forall c_i \in C, \forall d_j \in D : c_i \mathcal{R} d_j \vee \cdots \vee c_i \mathcal{Q} d_j \vee c_i \bowtie d_j$$

- *totally.* C totally-$\mathcal{R}$ D if and only if

$$\forall d_j \in D : \forall c_i \in C : c_i \mathcal{R} d_j$$

For example, one can express the non-convex intervals disjoint ($\bowtie$) relation as "totally-$\bowtie$", meaning

$$\forall d_j \in D : \forall c_i \in C : c_i \bowtie d_j$$

Another important set of relations is based on convex relations between the leftmost and rightmost maximal convex sub-intervals of non-convex intervals. Generalization by functors cannot generate all these possible relations, because these relations are based on specialization of particular sub-intervals—the leftmost and the rightmost ones. Let $\lhd C$ denote the leftmost maximal convex sub-interval of non-convex interval C, and let $\rhd C$ denote the rightmost maximal convex sub-interval of non-convex interval C. Some relations based on these sub-intervals can be expressed using functors. For example,

$$C \text{ totally-} < D \text{ if and only if } \rhd C < \lhd D$$

However, a large variety of relations cannot. For example, *meet*: non-convex interval C meets non-convex interval D, denoted $C \Uparrow D$, if and only if $\rhd C \Uparrow \lhd D$.

4.2 CALENDARS

Scheduling real-time computations is an extremely important part of a real-time system because it is the phase in which we assign the actual temporal properties to the computations. Chapter 12 describes work that has been carried out in this field. In this chapter we show how the object architecture is suitable for scheduling objects that have time constraints. The major characteristic we require a real-time scheduler to demonstrate is supporting the guarantee requirement of Section 3.3. Such a support is necessary for a predictable assignment of temporal properties to the system elements, in our case the objects.

In our system model, we describe computations as graphs, where the vertices (nodes) are executable objects and the edges are relations between them. We assume that each of the active objects in the system has an access to a "time-knowledge" resource, usually called a *clock*. Let $C_i(t)$ be the monotonic function that maps real-time (sometimes called global time or universal time) to clock-i time. The clocks in the system are *inaccurate* due to nonzero drift-rates. This inaccuracy results in *incorrect* time readouts, in other words $C_i(t) \neq t$, as described in Chapter 2. We assume that each computation is able to access a clock and acquire the estimate of the current real-time $C_i(t) = t \pm \Delta_i(t)$, through the service of a *time server* or a *time provider*.

Assuming that time servers use a linear clock interpretation, the service for a *get-time* request at computation node p is a construction of T_p, for $t \geq t_p^{(0)}$, by

$$T_p(t) = a_p(t)C_p(t) + b_p(t)$$

where $C_p(t)$ is the local clock which synchronizes periodically at least every J time units with the other clocks in the system. Let us denote the synchronization times by the sequence $t_p^{(i)}$.

Most of the time service algorithms (e.g., [83]) that have been published deal with two major issues. The first issue, synchronization or ordering of events in the system, may be associated with the past, in the sense that its requirements are due to events that have already occurred. The major property required in this aspect is that any two clocks in the system must differ from each other in the lowest possible value. Hence, when reasoning about two events that are related to different local views of the global time, the proper resolution is obtained for event ordering. Local histories, which are based on the sequence of values assigned to local variables and on the sequence of local times at which these assignments took place,[1] provide the means to analyze the past in a formal axiomatic approach.

The second issue, providing the knowledge of the global (universal) time, may be associated with the present. Here one expects the service to answer the question "what is the time *now*?" In that respect, the major property required from each clock in the system is to be as correct as possible. In other words, each clock must be as close as possible to the global (universal) time.

A third issue is the way in which a time service deals with projections onto the future. This issue is of extreme importance in hard real-time systems. In these systems some important decisions are made about events that have not occurred yet, but are known to occur in a known time interval in the future.

Figure 4.2 describes a temporal justification scheme. The same server object is allocated to different users at different times. Hence, it creates a user justification for this object at different time intervals. These intervals are in the future and according to them real-time scheduling decisions are to be made. A very

---

[1]Namely, relating event counters to an occurrence function while satisfying an accuracy axiom ([133, 26]).

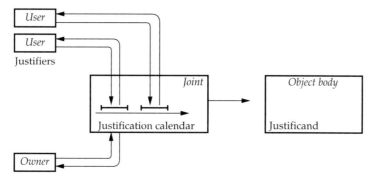

FIGURE 4.2
Object's owner and user temporal justification.

important issue arises in the above justification scheme. The time according to which the decisions are made is a local and imprecise view of the global time. Distributed computations may have the same local view at different nodes at different "real" times. Therefore, future projection of time should avoid ambiguities and conflicts that originate in differences between local views.

The future projection issue is expanded in the following section. In order to have a better understanding of the needs, we must first consider the way in which a guarantee to meet a deadline is examined in a real-time system.

Having defined the conditions for schedulability for incoming time constraints, we have to define mechanisms that provide the ability of verifying these properties. The mechanisms consist of data structures and algorithms. In Section 3.3 we proposed a set of modules that perform the allocation of a resource or an object. Upon a request for allocation, the local *allocator* verifies the schedulability of the request in the local *calendar*. It then passes the request to other resources or objects if they are needed. The knowledge of the resource requirements is taken from the *joint* of the invoked object. If the requests it has passed are confirmed along with a verification of local schedulability, it reserves the local resource. The reservation is for an a priori decided time. The requesting node must acknowledge the reservation within this time by invoking the *loader*.

In the above concept a *calendar* is a set of accepted and reserved time constraints. Figure 4.3 describes an example of an implementation of such a data structure. In this example we assume that the computation is represented by a contiguous time interval. The variable *calendar pointer* points to an ordered list of time constraints. Each constraint in the list includes the user justification and the timing properties for the execution associated with this user. The list is doubly linked to support fast insertion and removal, as will be discussed in later chapters.

```
typedef struct convex_time_interval {
    float start;
    float fin;
```

float *reference_scale*;

float *reference_bias*;

};

typedef struct *time_constraint* {

object **user_justification*;

struct convex_time_interval *occurrence_window*;

float *backward_slack*, *forward_slack*;

struct convex_time_interval *computation_window*;

float *frequency*;

int *state*;

struct time_constraint **successor*;

struct time_constraint **predecessor*;

};

struct time_constraint * *calendar_pointer*;

FIGURE 4.3
A calendar expressed in *C*.

4.3   TIME PROJECTION

The temporal relations defined in the previous section serve as a basis for reasoning about scheduling. Later we propose conditions along with mechanisms for a policy of accepting requests for invocations of objects (or resources). This acceptance policy guarantees that a deadline of an accepted request will be satisfied.

One first must determine the way in which other objects view temporal properties of an executing object. Recall that an invocation of an object contains three phases of scheduling activities. In the first, the incoming time constraint is verified to be schedulable. In the second, the requesting user object chooses the computation localities for execution from those for which schedulability has been confirmed. The third phase carries out an on-line selection and a context switch. These phases are performed at various levels of the computation graph. Although the nodes (objects) are autonomous, they are not necessarily independent; an object may require services that another performs in order to integrate a whole task. The relation between such an object and the required server is expressed as an arc in the computation graph. The arc encounters both the logical and the temporal relationships, representing an *invocation* of the server by the object.

Fault-tolerance redundancy requirements give ground to cooperation among objects that reside in different computation sites. Hence, one must be able to support remote invocations for such cooperation. In other words, there must be a way for objects that have access to different clocks to reason about their temporal relationship. However, this requirement alone is not sufficient. In a real-time system, objects may be constrained in terms of global (universal) time. Thus, objects must also have a way to reason about their global-time (*real-time*) properties.

The following section deals with problems of satisfying time constraints in a distributed execution-environment. We suggest and justify ways in which one can express temporal properties of remote relations.

4.3.1   Constraint Projections

Each time constraint can be considered as a *set of possible occurrences* [126]. This set represents a domain in which the beginning, the end, and the duration are constrained. Let us consider a contiguous execution of a particular invocation as an occurrence. Each particular occurrence is represented by a point in the begin-end plane. The point's begin coordinate corresponds to the start time of the execution associated with the invocation. The end coordinate respectively corresponds to the execution completion. Note that the diagonal represents all the occurrences for which the end time equals the begin time. Thus, the diagonal may be considered as the axis of time points. However, there is a need to extend the representation of an occurrence from a point to a two-dimensional one. We want to emphasize two reasons for this extension: the time-knowledge uncertainty and the duration variance.

Time-knowledge uncertainty, as demonstrated in Figure 4.4, originates in describing a local time point in global-time (real-time) terms. The begin coordinate must reflect the uncertainty due to the local clock correctness bounds, and so must the end coordinate. Thus, one can see that a time point that we express in real-time terms creates an interval in the begin-end plane. Now we need to extend this reasoning to any occurrence description, not necessarily a time point on the diagonal. Each begin coordinate and each end coordinate reflects the uncertainty due to the clock correctness bounds. Therefore, an occurrence is expressed as a two-dimensional region in the begin-end plane.

The second reason for extending the description of an occurrence to a two-dimensional region is the variance of the duration of an occurrence. For each given

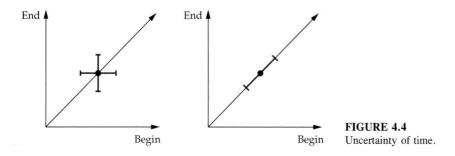

FIGURE 4.4
Uncertainty of time.

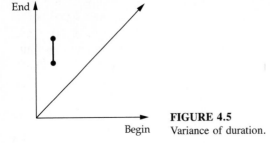

FIGURE 4.5
Variance of duration.

begin coordinate there may exist a set of possible end coordinates, as described in Figure 4.5. The duration of an occurrence may vary due to reasons that are either internal or external to an execution associated with it. Since our model deals with guarantees of temporal properties, this variance must be accounted for.

Let us now consider how the above model represents the specification of temporal behavior of the executable objects. According to the definition of time constraints in Section 2.2, the conditions imposed on the beginning, *Taft(condition$_1$)*, and on the end, *Tbef(condition$_2$)*, create a time window whose duration must be at least c_{Id}. Generally this window is wider and upon execution there are some possibilities that satisfy the constraint. The greater the window size, the more laxity that constraint allows.

Figure 4.6 demonstrates a simple set of possible occurrences, expressing it graphically on begin-end axes. This representation creates a "window" of the constraint laxity. Each point within the window satisfies the given time constraint. It starts after the earliest and before the latest begin times. It ends after the earliest and before the latest end times. In addition, its duration varies from the minimal to the maximal duration time.

Periodic time constraints, which consist of finite convex subintervals yet are not finite non-convex intervals, are fairly difficult to deal with using this method because it does not support any benefit gained by the knowledge of the periodicity of the finite intervals. Therefore, periodic constraints simply appear as infinite constraints if we do not use the periodicity properties.

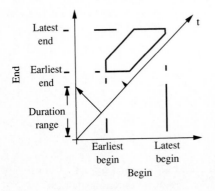

FIGURE 4.6
Time constraint laxity "window."

A simplification commonly used to overcome this disadvantage is the "local" approach. In this approach, analysis is confined to a limited region. Relations are derived and constraints are propagated only within the limited region. This solution solves many problems in which there is no need to reason about constraints that are far apart from each other. It is also applicable to periodic constraints. Let us consider an interval whose duration is the equal to the product of the length of the periods of two periodic objects. Such an interval contains all relations between subintervals of the periodic objects. For example, suppose we have two periodic objects, whose periods are T_1 and T_2 time units, $T_1, T_2 > 1$. Any interval of duration $T_1 \times T_2$ contains all possible relations between the corresponding subintervals of the two computation requirements.

Let us now return to the projection issue of correctly mapping a constraint and its coherent interpretation at different computation nodes. Being served by different clock servers results in different interpretations for an imposed time constraint. We assume that the time servers use a linear interpretation of the following type. The service for a *get-time* request is

$$T_p(t) = a_p(t)C_p(t) + b_p(t), t \ge t_p^{(0)}$$

as defined in Section 4.2. The bounds on the correct knowledge of $a_p(t)$ and $b_p(t)$ set the scale in which a projection of a time constraint is propagated. The projection scale must ensure that no violation of the constraint will occur due to the projection.

Let us define the following four terms for expressing the uncertainty in the local knowledge of a time constraint, expressed in global-time terms. Let the time constraint be TC_i. We define

$$\Delta a_p \equiv \max |1 - a_p(end_{\max}(TC_i))|$$
$$\Delta b_p \equiv \max |b_p(end_{\max}(TC_i))|$$
$$\delta a_p \equiv \max |1 - a_p(begin_{\min}(TC_i))|$$
$$\delta b_p \equiv \max |b_p(begin_{\min}(TC_i))|$$

Let the time constraint imposed in terms of local time be TC_i'. Accordingly, at a computation node p an imposed time constraint TC_i maps to the following local bounds on TC_i':

$$begin_{\min}(TC_i') = begin_{\min}(TC_i) + \delta a_p begin_{\min}(TC_i) + \delta b_p,$$
$$begin_{\max}(TC_i') = begin_{\max}(TC_i) - \delta a_p begin_{\max}(TC_i) - \delta b_p,$$
$$end_{\min}(TC_i') = end_{\min}(TC_i) + \Delta a_p end_{\min}(TC_i) + \Delta b_p,$$
$$end_{\max}(TC_i') = end_{\max}(TC_i) - \Delta a_p end_{\max}(TC_i) - \Delta b_p.$$

We reduce the laxity, but no violation of the constraint can happen due to clock inaccuracies. We denote this projection of a globally defined time constraint to a locally defined time constraint by the mapping

$$TC_i \leftrightarrow TC_i'$$

In the remainder of this book we assume that the above mapping is applied to every incoming time constraint before accepting it.

4.3.2   Assessment

The use of a calendar as a part of each object's joint provides the means for planning the future activities of that object. In addition, a calendar is used to reserve time for an execution in the future and thus support contention prevention and guarantee of deadline satisfaction.

Some operating systems, such as CHAOS [129, 130], merge the second and third phases into one. We find it very expensive to choose computation localities upon each context switching. Our approach uses three phases while minimizing the context switching problems. The first phase is carried out by an off-line *allocator*, the second by an on-line *loader*, and the third by an on-line *scheduler*.

We note, however, that there is a cost involved in this data structure manipulation. The autonomy achieved by attaching a control part to every object justifies that cost, but in many applications this cost may be too heavy. In such cases, a reduced autonomy may be acceptable, and calendars may be used selectively.

4.3.3   Constraint Propagation

Let us now discuss the propagation of time constraints in a distributed time knowledge environment. We have shown above the existence of an uncertainty in describing a global-time point in terms of local clocks. The uncertainty exists also in describing a time point as observed by a remote clock in terms of a local time knowledge. One therefore must account for such uncertainties whenever imposing a temporal relationship between occurrences. We will expand this discussion later regarding the propagation of time constraints.

We may express a temporal relationship between two occurrences in terms of time as observed by one of the occurrences. Therefore, when a remote object imposes a time constraint on a server, we may use time terms as observed by either the invoker or the invokee. However, such constraint propagation requires the node whose terms are used to have the knowledge of the uncertainties of the remote node. Such requirements are impractical in distributed systems, leading to a centrally maintained global knowledge. A better approach must rely only on local knowledge of the uncertainties. In order to allow such an approach, we need a common reference for the invoker and the invokee. We have chosen the global time to be that common reference, as described in Figure 4.7.

Thus, when one node invokes another they both reason in terms of global time. The invokee interprets the imposed constraint, say TC_i, according to its local interpretation by projecting

$$TC_i \mapsto TC_i^{'}$$

As stated above, this projection ensures adherence to the constraint as expressed

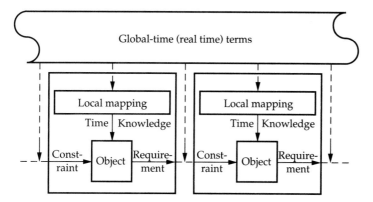

FIGURE 4.7
Constraint propagation using global-time terms.

in global-time terms. Note that if the invokee needs to invoke another object, it also uses terms of global time, as described in Figure 4.7.

Figure 4.8 describes the way in which a time constraint TC_1 is propagated onto another time constraint TC_2. Projecting the latest possible $end(TC_1)$ onto the *begin* axis of TC_2 creates a window of occurrences, denoted $\mathscr{A}$. The points in $\mathscr{A}$ stand for occurrences for which the relation $TC_1 < TC_2$ definitely holds. In $\mathscr{A}$, the value of any begin coordinate of TC_2 is greater than the largest end

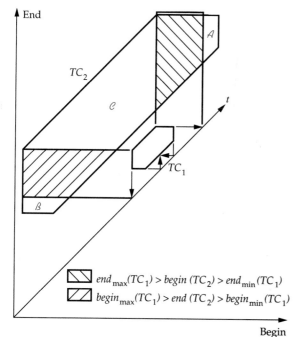

$$end_{max}(TC_1) > begin\ (TC_2) > end_{min}(TC_1)$$
$$begin_{max}(TC_1) > end\ (TC_2) > begin_{min}(TC_1)$$

FIGURE 4.8
Time constraint propagation.

coordinate of TC_1. Projecting the earliest possible *begin(TC_1)* onto the *end* axis of TC_2, creates the region $\mathcal{B}$, for which $TC_2 < TC_1$ holds. The reason for this is that in $\mathcal{B}$ the value of any end coordinate of TC_2 is less than the lowest begin coordinate of TC_1.

In $\mathcal{C}$, the intersection of TC_1 and TC_2 is clearly non-null. In this set of occurrences, the end of TC_2 succeeds the latest begin of TC_1 while the begin of TC_2 precedes the earliest end of TC_1. The two streaked areas in Figure 4.8 show regions in which the temporal relation between the time constraints is not certain. In these regions the relation can be determined only with an accurate knowledge of the actual *(begin, end)* point.

SPECIFYING CONSTRAINT PROPAGATION. Objects in our model are autonomous but not necessarily independent. Therefore, a node in the computation graph may require services of another node. This requirement is defined functionally using logical terms, and is assumed to be triggered by an invocation mechanism. We propose here a way to specify the temporal relationship between the invoker and the invokee in accordance with the constraint imposed on the invoker.

Let the incoming constraint imposed on the invoker be the convex time interval denoted as TC_{in} and let P_{in} be the invoker's computation non-convex time interval associated with this constraint. Let the constraint imposed by this invoker on its invokee be denoted as TC_{out}. As explained above, both TC_{in} and TC_{out} are expressed in global-time terms. Our interest is in a mechanism that allows a derivation of TC_{out} as a function of TC_{in}, constants and interval relations as defined in Section 4.1.2. To constitute this specification, we define the relations based on the following:

- $\mathcal{R}_{in}$ and $\mathcal{R}_{out}$ two convex interval relations,
- a constant duration $\| TC_R \|$ of a convex time interval TC_R, and
- the relation $TC_{in} \mathcal{R}_{in} TC_R \mathcal{R}_{out} TC_{out}$.

EXAMPLES. Consider the constraint TC_{in} defined as $< t_\alpha^{in}, t_\beta^{in} >$. Let the service to be invoked be required to succeed TC_{in} by at least γ time units. This relation can be defined as follows:

- $\mathcal{R}_{in} \equiv\, <$ and $\mathcal{R}_{out} \equiv\, <$,
- a constant interval TC_R with $\| TC_R \| = \gamma$,
- the relation $TC_{in} < TC_R < TC_{out}$.

Using the definitions in Section 4.1.2 entails the following inference. From $TC_{in} < TC_R$ we have

$$t_\beta^{in} < t_\alpha^R$$

From $\| TC_R \| = \gamma$ we have

$$t_\beta^R = t_\alpha^R + \gamma$$

Combining the above results in

$$t_\beta^R > t_\beta^{\text{in}} + \gamma$$

From $TC_R < TC_{\text{out}}$ we have

$$t_\alpha^{\text{out}} > t_\beta^R$$

and thus we can conclude

$$t_\alpha^{\text{out}} > t_\beta^{\text{in}} + \gamma$$

If, on the other hand, the service to be invoked is required to complete execution in less than γ time units after TC_{in} is completed, then the relation can be defined as follows:

- $\mathscr{R}_{\text{in}} \equiv\, <$ and $\mathscr{R}_{\text{out}} \equiv\, > \vee \Downarrow \vee \varnothing^u \vee \downarrow \vee \gg$,
- a constant interval TC_R with $\| TC_R \| = \gamma$,
- the relation $TC_{\text{in}}\mathscr{R}_{\text{in}}TC_R\mathscr{R}_{\text{out}}TC_{\text{out}}$

As in the previous example, from $TC_{\text{in}} < TC_R$ we have

$$t_\beta^{\text{in}} < t_\alpha^R$$

and from $\| TC_R \| = \gamma$ we have

$$t_\beta^R = t_\alpha^R + \gamma$$

that can be combined into

$$t_\beta^R > t_\beta^{\text{in}} + \gamma$$

From $TC_R\mathscr{R}_{\text{out}}TC_{\text{out}}$ we have

$$t_\beta^{\text{out}} < t_\beta^R$$

and thus we can conclude

$$t_\beta^{\text{out}} < t_\beta^{\text{in}} + \gamma$$

4.4 CONCLUDING REMARKS

We have introduced in this chapter a mathematical basis and notation which support expression and analysis of temporal properties and relations. The mathematical basis and notation support both interval-based and point-based time references. Computation models and their relations have been presented to demonstrate both convex and non-convex properties. In later sections, we rely on this chapter to state and prove temporal conditions and properties.

Using the above mathematical basis, we have introduced mechanisms we have called *calendars* that support time-based resource management. We have proposed these mechanisms at the object level, both for application objects and for resources. In addition, the use of calendars supports reservation schemes we employ for guaranteeing temporal behavior and for avoiding ambiguity.

Special attention has been given in this chapter to projection and propagation of time constraints. The significance of these issues grows in distributed environments, in which access to the knowledge of time is of a local nature. Further complications due to the autonomous execution of objects have been considered and dealt with as well.

Equipped with the basis and mechanisms, we will now examine aspects that relate to application and operating system design and implementation.

PART

II

REAL-TIME
APPLICATIONS

CHAPTER
5

THE
REAL-TIME
SYSTEM
LIFE
CYCLE

The life cycle of a real-time system is very complex and rich in multidisciplinary activities. Here we briefly review each of these activities. The preliminary activities establish the conceptual basis for the system. Then the development phase starts, and on its termination the production and deployment phases follow.

Many engineering research efforts have been invested in establishing the life cycle for a system. One of the results is a standard adopted by the United States Department of Defense, DOD–STD–2167. This standard provides a comprehensive description of the steps required to construct a solid life cycle model for a system. We do not review or consider the products and milestones suggested by the DOD–STD–2167 in this book. However, it is important to consider some of the activities mentioned in this standard. In this book we concentrate mainly on the full-scale development phase, as it is very difficult to have any later well-developed phases without a correct beginning. This is not to say that this phase is more important than the others; however, in software products its significance is very high.

The full-scale development phase starts with a requirements specification. Once the specification is complete, the preliminary design starts. The detailed design follows, although sometimes it overlaps parts of the preliminary design. After the design of a configuration item is complete, we can start implementing it. The implementation is followed by the last part of the development phase, the verification. The purpose of verification is to assure that the implementation and the specification are consistent.

Unfortunately, an approach that is too formalistic tends to give ground to a "document driven" design and not necessarily a creative one. Furthermore, serialization of the activities of definition, design and implementation contradicts good engineering practices. These activities have many interacting domains and are never really separated from each other. In our competitive world, playing around with the definitions too long may leave you behind in the long run. Thus, adopting the serialized "specification–implementation–verification–installation–

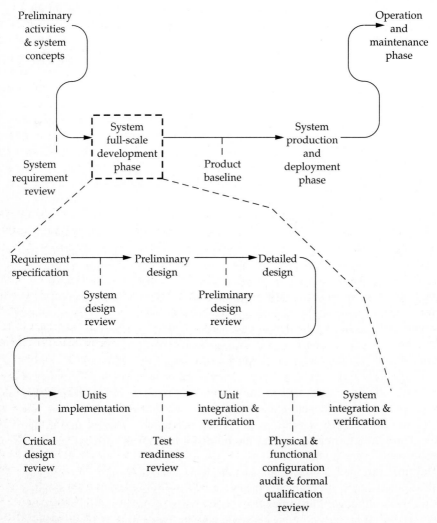

FIGURE 5.1
Life cycle of an ideal real-time system.

maintenance" model calls for a very short specification phase. We note this tendency, even though specification and requirement identification have crucial effects on the rest of the phases, including their cost and schedule.

Our own experience shows clearly that although requirement specification has an enormous significance, implementation must start as early as possible, perhaps even before the requirement specification is complete or matured. Some committees[1] recommend an iterative approach of specifying and building a rapid prototype according to these specifications. The stiffness of the linear ordering of activities in the strict waterfall model can be solved by other methods, as the spiral model [21]. Our own experience teaches us that modern practice favors an incremental development.

We therefore deal with the application domain issues in this chapter without emphasizing a particular order of the activities. Although activities are presented in DOD–STD–2167 classification, the order in which we recommend carrying them out is completely different.

5.1 Requirement Specification

The development of a complete and consistent requirements specification is an activity whose influence spreads throughout the system life cycle. The method of the requirements specification and its products is important to real-time software design, as it is to hardware and system design. Although some methods emphasize only the documentation part of this early phase of design, other methods provide good tools for structure construction and feasibility checks. Let us review two requirements specification methods which were employed in complex real-time systems design. Note that the details of the requirement specification techniques are not presented here as that is not the main focus of this book. We continue with the method employed in the A–7 aircraft project and we then discuss the statecharts technique.

A–7 REQUIREMENTS SPECIFICATION. An important approach for requirements specification has been introduced in the redesign of the avionics software of the A–7 Navy aircraft [62]. The documented flight program is a part of the navigation and weapon-delivery system of the aircraft. The program has high accuracy requirements and stringent real-time constraints. It receives input data from the aircraft sensors and from operational switch panels, and controls many devices (e.g., the inertial measurement system, the head-up display, the doppler, the barometer, etc.). The program's main tasks are to calculate the navigation information and to control the weapon delivery. The A–7 requirements specification document demonstrates methods to deal with a large system in consistent ways. However, it does not deal in particular with the temporal properties. We

---

[1]For example, the Defense Science Board Task Force on Military Software, September 1987.

note that in this particular implementation, the avionics software is a closed and fixed set of programs, with no dynamics at all.

REQUIREMENTS DOCUMENT OBJECTIVES. The objectives of a requirement-specification document, as suggested by D. Parnas in the A–7 project, can be listed as follows:

1. The document must specify external behavior only, without implying a particular implementation.
2. The document must specify constraints on the implementation. It must especially specify the details of hardware interfaces, in cases of computer embedded systems.
3. The document must allow easy changes.
4. The document must demonstrate ability to serve as a reference tool.
5. The document must allow recording forethoughts about the life cycle of the system.
6. The document must characterize acceptable response to undesired events. A possible way to classify these undesired events is also suggested.
   (*a*) Resource failure.
      • Temporary.
      • Permanent.
   (*b*) Incorrect input data.
      • Detected by examining input only.
      • Detected by comparison with internal data.
      • Detected by user realizing he made a mistake.
      • Detected by user from incorrect output.
   (*c*) Incorrect internal data.
      • Detected by internal inconsistency.
      • Detected by comparison with input data.
      • Detected by user from incorrect output.

REQUIREMENTS DOCUMENT DESIGN PRINCIPLES. The design principles that the A–7 requirements specification document reflects allow the designer to separate concerns. The organization of the document is such that any project member could concentrate on a well-defined set of questions. Any requirements specification document must be as formal as possible in order to obtain precision, consistency, and completeness. Let us review now techniques for describing hardware interfaces and software interfaces, as employed in this project.

DESCRIBING HARDWARE INTERFACES.

• Organization of data items. A data item is a unit concerning an input or an output that changes value independently of other inputs or outputs.
• Symbolic names (for data items and values). Data items contain two kinds of

information: arbitrary details and essential characteristics. The A–7 document expresses essential information in a way that allows using it separately from the rest of the document, without referencing the details.

- Templates for value descriptions. Describing each data item in ad hoc fashion produces inconsistencies between the documents. The existence of templates enhances consistency between documents.
- Input data items described as resources. In this project, description of the input data items is as in an inventory of available resources. The description is independent of software use.
- Output data items described as effects. In avionics, and in effect in most computer embedded systems, we can view most of the output data items as effects on external hardware. Describing them as such is therefore natural.

DESCRIBING SOFTWARE FUNCTIONS.

- Organizing by functions. Functional hierarchy is adopted as in MIL–STD–490. Two classes of software functions are distinguished: periodic functions and sporadic (on-demand) functions.
- Output values as functions of conditions and events. A condition is a predicate that describes a system property for a measurable time interval. An event occurs when a condition changes its truth value. Hence, events are associated with time points and conditions with time intervals. Events mark the beginning and end of periodic functions, and they trigger sporadic functions.
- Using modes to organize and simplify. Modes (i.e., classes of system states) help in simplifying and organizing the hierarchical structure. Furthermore, we can employ a transition list which includes entries from one mode to another. Such a discipline allows detection of illegal transitions along with its control functions.
- Special tables for precision and completeness. The A–7 document uses two special tables to express information precisely and completely. A condition table defines an output value upon a specified active mode and a condition that occurs within that mode. An event table shows when a sporadic function should be performed, or when a periodic function should be started or stopped, with respect to the currently active mode.

The A–7 project demonstrates a model of a disciplined approach to requirement specification for complex systems. This project has had a significant influence on enforcement of such approaches in many reliable real-time systems. Various tools for specifying hard real-time properties of an open system are nevertheless still required.

5.2 STATECHARTS

Statecharts is a method that uses a visual formalism in order to specify the behavior of complex reactive systems [60]. A reactive system repeatedly responds to external stimuli, maintaining an ongoing relationship with its environment [61]. Statecharts is a specification language rather then a programming language, in that it emphasizes execution modes and external view rather than internal structure.

Statecharts determines system behavior by means of

- states
- events
- conditions
- transitions

In statecharts, we denote states as labeled boxes and transitions appear as directed arcs. Events and conditions trigger the transitions between states. Thus, we label each arc with its enabling event or condition. Statecharts view system inputs as events. Outputs can be associated with either events, denoted as activities, or states.

Let us consider a statechart example, as described by the planar graph in Figure 5.2. The system in this example comprises three states (A, B, and C) and three events (X, Y, and Z) that trigger transitions between the states. Note that event X causes a transition from state A to state B only if condition C_1 holds. In this case the condition acts as a guard rather than as a transition trigger.

States can be decomposed to lower-level states, in a process called *refinement*, or combined to a higher level state in *clustering*. Figure 5.3 describes how we cluster the states of the above example. In this figure we generate a state D as a higher level state of A and B. Since event Z caused both A and B to change to C, we denote it by a single transition Z from D to C. The single transition refers to two possible transitions, each from one of the "substates." Another issue that Figure 5.3 emphasizes is the default transition, denoted as a directed arc that starts at a dot. Thus, any transition directed to D will obey the default transition and will cause a transition to A. Therefore, event Y has the same effect as in Figure 5.2.

The main objective of statecharts is to solve the problems that characterize finite state automata. Two of the severe problems in finite state automata are the

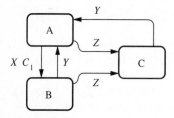

FIGURE 5.2
Statechart example.

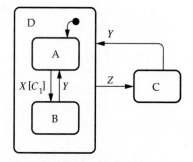

FIGURE 5.3
Clustering states in statecharts.

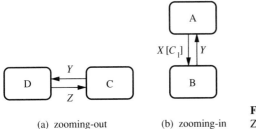

FIGURE 5.4

(a) zooming-out   (b) zooming-in   Zooming in statecharts.

lack of support for modularity and the exponential state explosion. These problems are elegantly solved by the statechart's visual concept of *zooming*. Figure 5.4 demonstrates zooming in both directions, as related to the above example. We can zoom-in and consider only events and substates in superstate D, or zoom-out and disregard these details.

AND and OR clustering relations between different state abstraction levels support these top-down refinement and bottom-up clustering. For example, Figure 5.5 describes a state T that consists of two AND-components, labeled M and N.

States at a given abstraction level are either exclusive or orthogonal. These relations, used by statecharts' mechanisms, allow manipulating these modules separately. Furthermore, orthogonality of states can be shown to support concurrency and independence. In Figure 5.5 we show how states A and B are orthogonal to states G, H and J.

Orthogonality of states on any level of zooming eliminates the need to explicitly consider all the possible states. Thus, the exponential explosion of states does not exist.

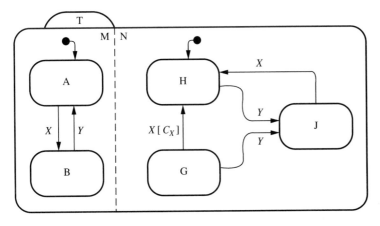

FIGURE 5.5
States orthogonality in AND decomposition.

5.3   CONCLUDING REMARKS

In this chapter we have discussed the very first activities in a real-time system life cycle, namely the requirements specification. The significance of this life segment is reflected in the enormous effort invested in it during the last decade.

We continue describing the life cycle activities in the following chapters. Three chapters deal with the preliminary and detailed design activities. In Chapter 6 we describe a structural approach. Petri nets modeling is discussed in Chapter 7. In Chapter 8 we review axiomatic approaches in real-time system design. We turn to implementation issues in Chapter 9. Finally, an examination of verification and validation of real-time systems is given in Chapter 10.

CHAPTER

6

STRUCTURED DESIGN APPROACHES

A structured design consists of two main components:

1. Two sets of criteria, *cohesion* and *coupling*.

2. *Top down* decomposition of a system into modules.

The objective of the design is to produce a system in which modules have high coherence and low coupling.

In this chapter we examine two major real-time software design methods: a process-based structured design method, and a graph-based design method. One can further divide the methods according to the modeling enforced and the system specification and analysis approaches adopted. However, let us first get acquainted with an event-driven modeling approach, and ways to introduce precedence relations in such a model.

6.1 EVENT-BASED MODEL

An event-based model of a system separates the system's properties into two major categories. The first, the *behavior*, mainly concerns the external view of the system. The second, the *structure*, reflects the internal view of the system. In this point of view, proving the correctness of a system becomes a consistency check between the behavior and the structure. Note that in this approach, independence of properties allows verification of each independently. Thereby, we avoid "exponential state explosion" when deriving the test sets.

6.1.1 Model Description

We construct an event-based model from events and their relations [30].

Definition 11. *An* event *is an* instantaneous *(takes zero time)* atomic *(happens completely or not at all) state transition in the system's computation history.*

In a system design we want to order events according to the time in which they occur. This objective is further emphasized in real-time systems.

We achieve *time ordering* with the partial ordering *precede* ($\rightarrow$) relation.

Definition 12. *Event e_1 precedes* event e_2 $(e_1 \rightarrow e_2)$ *if*

1. *e_1, e_2 are events of the same process, which is executing in an autonomous computation node and has its own local clock, and e_1 comes before e_2, or*
2. *e_1, e_2 are events of different processes, and e_1 is a* send message *event, and e_2 is a* receive *event of the very same message.*

This partial ordering ensures that $e_1 \rightarrow e_2$ implies that e_1 happens before e_2 by any measure of time. Note that it is not a bidirectional relation. The implication holds only for one direction. The ordering is transitive, irreflexive and anti-symmetric.

Our model requires *causality* ordering as well. We can achieve this ordering with an *enable* ($\Rightarrow$) relation, which is also a partial ordering. We can define this ordering as follows.

Definition 13. *Event e_1 enables* event e_2 *($e_1 \Rightarrow e_2$) if and only if the* existence *of event e_1 will* cause occurrence *of event e_2 in the future.*
This ordering is also transitive, irreflexive and anti-symmetric.

6.1.2 Properties of the Event-Based Model

The model allows program verification in a theorem-proving fashion. We use the model's definitions combined with first order predicate calculus. In order to simplify complex proof procedures, we can use our knowledge of relations independence. Further simplification is possible through the use of hierarchical descriptions of the system. We can also enforce abstraction levels to deal with very large systems and therefore reduce the complexity of system description.

One possible solution for describing relations of the system with its environment is to employ special facilities [30]. The system interacts with its environment by exchanging messages through *unidirectional ports*. In the ports we retain locally the local history, and we specify and measure the *behavior* properties.

6.1.3 Examples

Let us consider two examples of the use of an event-based model. In these examples we demonstrate proving relations between events that establish system properties.

- *Concurrency* of events e_1 and e_2 is proven if and only if $\neg(e_1 \rightarrow e_2)$ and $\neg(e_2 \rightarrow e_1)$.

  In other words, concurrency requires the absence of any precedence relation. Note that this property does not hold in a different system in which events are not instantaneous, and may overlap.

- *Liveness* of an event is proven by applying a sequence of "enables" to the initial state.

This type of liveness proof guarantees that each event will *eventually* happen. The method proves starvation freedom or message delivery, but more strict timing requirements cannot be proven by it, because this proof system provides only partial-order relations, which are not sufficient for proving temporal properties.

6.2 PROCESS-BASED STRUCTURED DESIGN

A process-based model for a system uses the schedulable entities of the system, the processes, as the elements of the model. Logical and temporal properties of the processes establish the behavioral patterns in the system. However, it is not only the individual process properties, but also the relations between processes, that establish the whole system behavior model. Therefore, the process-based design considers both process internal properties and interprocess relations.

6.2.1 Description of a Theoretical Model

In order to analyze the system behavior, we can use the following model for describing a system [103]:

- Let M_p be the set of all the periodic processes in the system.
- Let M_s be the set of all the sporadic processes in the system.
- Our system model M is therefore $M = M_p \cup M_s$.
- Each process T_i is a quintuple (i, c_i, b_i, p_i, d_i), where: c_i denotes the computation time of the process, p_i denotes the process period, b_i denotes the begin constraint, and d_i denotes the process deadline.
- The relation between the elements of the above quintuple of each process i is $\forall i : c_i \leq d_i - b_i \leq p_i$.

6.2.2 Structured Design Method Characteristics

Many control systems, including real-time control systems, demonstrate parenthood relations in their control structure. Figure 6.1 depicts the above nature of hierarchy. A higher-level process controls and coordinates the activities performed by its lower-level neighbors [108]. Thus, the top-level process is viewed as the supervisor of the entire system activities. Let us describe the characteristics of structured design methods, which allow designing such control systems.

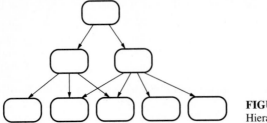

FIGURE 6.1
Hierarchical control structure.

In a structured design method, we decompose the modules hierarchically. When applied to a real-time system, this method provides the characteristics listed below.

1. *Data-flow oriented design*. Let us consider a reactive system in which we want to respond to events by producing output. Let each triggering event be defined through data items that arrive at a process receiver. In such systems, the data-flow characterization of the system provides a powerful way to determine the logical and temporal behavior of the system. Therefore, a data-flow oriented design provides the designer with handles to specify and analyze the system behavior.

We can distinguish two design approaches [54].

- *Transform-centered design*, in which the major streams of data are identified as they flow, transformed from external input to external output.
- *Transaction-centered design*, applicable where the data flow consists mainly of control information. In other words, it is applicable when data passed to a transform initiates an action (or a sequence of actions) based on the incoming data.

2. *Process synchronization*. Two synchronization primitives are the most common in current systems [23, 63, 115]

- Semaphores, used to control concurrent access to a data item shared between processes, while imposing mutual exclusion in critical sections.
- Signals, used in a rendezvous synchronization, where one process awaits a signal from another in order to proceed.

In order to support relations between processes, one must require that the processes have the ability to synchronize with each other.

3. *Process communication*. A distributed system requires a strong communication support due to its scattered architecture. There are three common ways to implement the communication support:

- Using the operating system primitives.

- Using a language run-time support.
- Using a module that provides the services (the module itself uses operating system primitives, as implemented in MASCOT channels).

4. *State dependency.* A structured design method must incorporate state dependency as well as data dependency. Incorporating state dependency allows validation of legality of actions according to the system state. It also allows us to express conditions on executions of such actions.

An important concept in structured design methods is the *information hiding concept* [112, 113]. In cases of data sharing between processes, there is a need to guarantee a consistent use of the data. One way to enforce such consistency is to let only one module know each key, thereby keeping the shared data to a minimum. Modules are therefore more self-contained, and fault tolerance performance and autonomy are enhanced. In addition, the system becomes more modifiable and more maintainable. The cost involved in this approach is the overhead in accessing data via a function rather than directly.

Let us consider the example described in Figure 6.2. Processes P_1, P_2 and P_3 must access modules B and C via a function a that hides them. In this example, a is responsible for the consistency of B and C. Due to this single-key approach, access may involve wait-time in a queue as long as a is busy. For example, consider the case of a simultaneous access by P_1, P_2 and P_3: only one of them can be served at a time, and therefore the other two must wait.

6.2.3 DARTS

DARTS is a design approach for real-time Systems, proposed as an extension of the older structured design methods, to include process structuring as well as process interface definitions [54]. DARTS was developed by General Electric, and was initially applied to two projects, a robot controller and a vision system. The approach has been extended to an Ada-based design [55].

Design activities in DARTS start with requirement specifications. Analysis of data flow through the system provides tools for determining the major functions

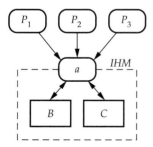

FIGURE 6.2
Information hiding concept.

that are needed. The data flow analysis produced consists of: transforms, data depositories, and data flow between transforms.[1]

PROCESS DECOMPOSITION. Once the data-flow analysis is complete, the designer must decide on a way to decompose the system processes based on the transforms identified. The designer can derive the concurrency properties of each transform from the data-flow analysis. Then one can use the asynchronous nature of the transforms within the system as the main consideration of the decomposition process. The criteria used in DARTS for deciding whether a transform should be a separate process, or grouped with other transforms into one process, are given below. Let us review them as an example of this design approach.

1. I/O dependency. If a slow I/O device dictates the speed of execution of a transform, then a separate process is adequate.
2. Time-critical functions. If a high priority is distinguished for a particular function, then it receives a separate process.
3. Computational requirements. If a function requires intensive computations, then it receives a separate process.
4. Functional cohesion. If functions are closely related to each other, DARTS group them to reduce system overhead. Within this process, one can distinguish modules for functional coherence at the module level.
5. Temporal cohesion. If the same stimulus triggers some transforms, DARTS suggests grouping them into one process. Within the process it is still possible to distinguish between the different modules.
6. Periodic execution: if there is a requirement to execute a transform periodically, then a separate process is adequate for this transform, activated at regular time intervals.

In summary, functional and temporal cohesion justify grouping transforms into a process and distinguishing between them at a module level. Criticality and special requirements justify dedicating a process to a specific transform.

INTERPROCESS COMMUNICATION. The interprocess communication must support data delivery functions along with synchronization. DARTS performs data delivery with two modules, one for message communication and one for shared data. A typical communication module contains a data structure and an access procedure to that structure. The access procedure controls also the mutual exclusion and the synchronization features, which may use operating system primitives.

---

[1]Although a graph description and analysis is performed, the method as a whole is completely process-oriented.

A communication module for data delivery is always linked to the process that invokes it. The two types of communication modules provided by DARTS are

1. Message communication module (MCM) supports both closely coupled and loosely coupled communication. In loosely coupled communication, message queues include binary semaphores for mutual exclusion. In closely coupled communication, DARTS forces the queue size to one.

2. Information hiding module (IHM) is used mainly in cases of shared data. The IHM defines both the data structure it hides and the access procedure to it. For example, in Figure 6.2, the IHM defines both the function a and the module B and C.

Let us now consider the synchronization facilities in DARTS. Typically, a synchronization module has a supervisory nature (it could be the "main" module which has the same nature). If no actual information has to be exchanged during synchronization, one can use special synchronization events. In DARTS, the operating system provides primitives for signaling an event and for awaiting an event.

We have presented the DARTS example in order to demonstrate a structured design approach that is process based. One can see that the main concern of this approach is decomposition and its cost in system performance. This approach is mainly suitable for single application systems that are data flow oriented, and whose functionality can be expressed with transforms, data flow between them, and data depositories.

6.3 GRAPH-BASED THEORETICAL MODEL

A graph-based design method uses techniques taken from graph theory in order to analyze and construct a system. The main difference between this method and the previous structured method is that all data dependencies are explicitly expressed. This method is superior to the structured method in its capability to identify operations on data that are common to many timing constraints.

A graph-based model M is an ordered pair (G, T), where G is the communication graph of the system, and T is a set of time constraints [104]. The set of time constraints satisfy $T = \{T_p\} \cup \{T_a\}$, where the subsets T_p and T_a are the periodic and asynchronous (sporadic) constraints respectively. The communication graph $G = (V, E)$ is a digraph which may contain cycles. In this representation, V is a set of vertices and E is a set of edges (directed arcs).

Let us represent each time constraint in T with a triple (C, p, d). In this representation C is a time-constraint acyclic graph (compatible with G), and p, d represent the periodic and deadline constraints respectively. The time-constraint graph (C) expresses the precedence relations between computational events. Let us denote an execution of a functional element by a node, and data transmitted in the communication graph (G) by directed arcs. Let w_V be a function that assigns a non-negative weight to each node in V, the set of vertices of G. Since C is compatible with G, we can obtain a bound for the computation time of a time constraint (C, p, d) by summing the weights of all the nodes in C.

For example, consider the case illustrated in Figure 6.3. This example describes a communication graph G, which contains vertices v_1 to v_7. Each vertex represents an execution instance that follows data reception and precedes data transmission. The time-constraint graph, C, is compatible with it, and contains vertices v_1 to v_5. These vertices are assigned with weights w_1 to w_5, denoting the execution-time bound of the individual execution instances. Assuming zero-time transmission and recalling the acyclic nature of the graph, we can determine a bound on C by

$$w_C \leq \sum_{\forall i : v_i \in C} w_i$$

In this particular example

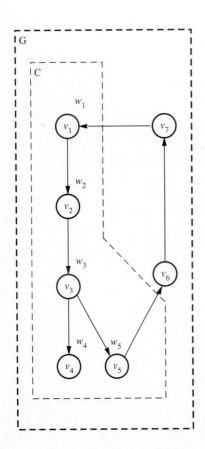

FIGURE 6.3
Computation graph model.

$$w_C \leq max(w_4, w_5) + \sum_{i=1}^{3} w_i$$

$$\leq \sum_{i=1}^{5} w_i$$

$$= \sum_{\forall i : v_i \in C} w_i$$

If (C, p, d) is activated at time t, then C must execute within the time interval $[t, t + d]$. Let S be a subset of the (multi)set of the functional elements of C. We say that C executes in a time interval L, if a subset S executes in L and forms a partial order such that the following properties hold:

1. There exists a bijective mapping between the functional elements in S and C.
2. Under this mapping the partial order of S is consistent with the acyclic graph C.
3. For any pair of distributed functional elements u and v that relate to each other with an edge $u \rightarrow v$, an execution of C must include a transmission of the latest output of u to v, before v executes in L.

The graph-based design approach supports a very general model of a distributed computation. Let us examine some aspects that relate to problems we can solve with static schedules.

- A *static schedule* is a finite list Y of symbols from the set of vertices of G.

Let us start with defining metrics that are needed for analyzing static schedules.

- An *execution trace* of a processor is a mapping from the non-negative numbers (index of time intervals) to the set of all the functional elements in G. This mapping includes the "empty" element for the trivial case of an idle execution.

We can implement this mapping in various ways. For example, one can let $F(i) = u$ if the functional element u in G executes in the time interval $(i, i + 1)$.

- We say that an execution trace has a *latency k* with respect to a time constraint, if this execution trace contains an execution of this time constraint in any time interval of length greater than or equal to k time units.

Mok, in [103], has proven important properties for a graph based model (G, T).

- There exists a feasible static schedule with respect to T in the cases where a latency d exists for every (C, p, d) in T.

- Proving the existence of a feasible static schedule when the above requirement is not satisfied is NP hard even for relatively simple cases. Only the application of additional constraints on relations between computation times and deadlines allows proving the existence of a feasible static schedule.

6.4 CONCLUDING REMARKS

The complexity of both process-based and graph-based design methods is significantly increased when the system is required to be open, allowing continuous acceptance of jobs. However, even in its closed form, the assumptions made regarding the requirements from the operating system are strongly supported by the design methods introduced in this chapter.

The methods discussed in this chapter are characterized as top-down system decomposition according to criteria that decrease coupling and increase coherence. This decomposition takes into account the operating system environment with respect to communication, synchronization and constraints. We have assumed in this chapter that our computations are decomposed as concurrent processes that communicate with each other. Based on this assumption we have considered some process-based design approaches. An example of such a design approach, DARTS, has been described, and important concepts have been highlighted.

In this chapter, we have mentioned some graph-based approaches, to which we return later in the book. These approaches are somewhat complex, but they allow the construction of a better model of the system and its accurate analysis. Furthermore, using more accurate models such as the graph-based ones allows a more formal approach to the verification of the system properties. Unfortunately, it turns out that a general solution to schedule feasibility analysis does not exist, since the problem is NP hard. Particular cases may, however, find this method highly favorable.

CHAPTER
7

PETRI
NET
MODELS

Petri nets are exceptionally suitable for cases that involve designing and modeling systems in which concurrent processing considerations and dynamic sequential dependencies exist. The major characteristics of Petri nets that make them suitable for these cases are

- Petri nets support explicit representation of causal dependencies and independencies. When events are independent of each other, Petri net theory introduces a non-interleaving partial order of concurrency.
- Petri net models allow description of a system at different levels of abstraction, without changing the language used in the modeling.
- Properties of the system are representable by means similar to the system. Hence, we can build correctness proof systems using the same methods used for the system model construction.

We do not consider the general use of Petri nets here. Rather, we review some augmentations made to include temporal properties in the model. However, in order to emphasize the augmentation, let us describe very briefly the classic Petri net models [114, 124]. The classic Petri net model is the 4-tuple

$$PN = (P, T, A, M)$$

where:

- $P = \{p_1, \ldots, p_n\}$, a set of places, often drawn as circles.

- $T = \{t_1, \ldots, t_m\}$, a set of transitions, often drawn as bars.
- $A = \{P \times T\} \cup \{T \times P\}$, input and output arcs.
- $M = \{m_1, \ldots, m_n\}$, the net initial marking, often drawn as dots.
- $M : P \to \mathcal{N}$ (the natural numbers), M of p_i is m_i $i = 1, \ldots, n$.

This model becomes dynamic as the tokens that mark the net "travel" between the places through the transitions. The traveling takes place through a "firing," which is the transformation that changes the marking of the net. Marked places enable a transition to fire with their marking. The input arcs $\{P \times T\}$ connect the enabling places to the transitions they enable. The firing of a net has three major characteristics:

1. It is *voluntary*. A transition that is enabled is not compelled to fire, yet it may fire only if it is enabled.
2. It is *instantaneous*. A firing takes zero time.
3. It is *complete*. If a transition fires, a case of a partial firing in which not all the tokens are removed or not all the tokens are placed, does not occur.

Petri nets allow modeling the system states and the events that change these states. A system state is a particular marking of the places, and it can be changed through the firing of the enabled transitions. In particular, we can model task synchronization with a Petri net, according to the definition of that synchronization. We distinguish two orderings in such synchronizations, partial and total. Figure 7.1 describes these two ordering types. In some cases partial order is sufficient, but when mutual exclusion is involved, total order is a must. Let us examine these two cases.

1. *Total order*. In Figure 7.1, p_1 causes a structural conflict between t_1 and t_2. This conflict is effective in case p_1, p_2, and p_3 are marked by one token each. Let us assume that t_1 and t_2 represent two distinct tasks, and that they execute in two different processors. The properties of the firing prevent the case of simultaneous firing of both t_1 and t_2. Thus we can consider p_1 as a synchronization variable, which we protect by a mutual exclusion mechanism.

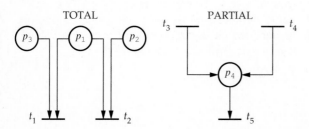

FIGURE 7.1
Total and partial order conflicts.

2. *Partial order.* We can represent a synchronization variable that implements a partial order by a place with a single output-transition and multiple input-transitions. In Figure 7.1 the place p_4 represents such a variable. Both t_3 and t_4 can increase its value by firing tokens into p_4. Yet, only t_5 can decrease its value.

These two ordering types allow modeling both centralized and distributed designs for a large variety of classic problems (e.g., producer-consumer, readers-writer, etc. [36]).

It is important to emphasize in advance some of the drawbacks of Petri net methods in addition to the advantages presented above. The major drawback is the explosion of the reachability set. Additional augmentations demonstrate weakness points that are augmentation related.

In the Petri net classic model, transitions are fired in a nondeterministic way and do not relate in any way to specific times. In order to adjust this modeling method to real-time programs, various modifications have been applied to the classic model. In Section 7.2 we describe an approach that assigns execution time to transitions that are time-annotated [109]. In this approach, the instantaneous nature of the transition is not satisfied unless "inhibit" features are employed. Another approach is to assign stochastic nature to the firing. This approach is very good for average performance analysis, and we describe some methods in Section 7.1 [106, 3, 13]. Nevertheless, the stochastic approach fails to address important temporal properties that are crucial in the design phase of real-time systems (e.g., scheduling, safeness with presence of time, etc.).

7.1 STOCHASTIC PETRI NET (SPN) MODEL ANALYSIS

7.1.1 Definitions

Let us start with a brief summary of the stochastic Petri net (SPN) definitions. We define this net as an extension of the above classic model to a stochastic Petri net

$$SPN = (P, T, A, M, Q)$$

where

- P, T, A, and M are defined as in the classic model.
- $Q = \{q_1, \ldots, q_m\}$, average transition rates, for the exponentially distributed firing times.

Now let us examine the relations between transitions and places.

- Set function $I(t) = \{p : (p, t) \in A\}$, input places for transition t.
- Set function $O(t) = \{p : (t, p) \in A\}$, output places for transition t.

7.1.2 Example of SPN

Let us consider an example of a stochastic Petri net model and the way we solve it. The *SPN* described in Figure 7.2 [106] has the *places* and *transitions* sets

- $T = \{t_1, \ldots, t_5\}$,
- $P = \{p_1, \ldots, p_5\}$.

The places and transitions are connected through the arcs defined in the following set functions:

- $I(t_1) = \{p_1\}, O(t_1) = \{p_2, p_3\}$,
- $I(t_2) = \{p_2\}, O(t_2) = \{p_4\}$,
- $I(t_3) = \{p_3\}, O(t_3) = \{p_5\}$,
- $I(t_4) = \{p_4\}, O(t_4) = \{p_2\}$,
- $I(t_5) = \{p_4, p_5\}, O(t_5) = \{p_1\}$.

The firing probabilities are

$$q_1 = 2, q_2 = 1, q_3 = 1, q_4 = 3, q_5 = 2$$

The initial marking of the net

$$M = \{m_1 = 1; \; m_{i \in 2, \ldots, 5} = 0\}$$

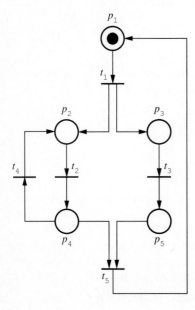

FIGURE 7.2
SPN example.

The net structure shows that we can characterize the transitions in it as

- sequential: (t_5, t_1)
- parallel: (t_2, t_3)
- contention: (t_4, t_5)
- fork: t_1; joint: t_5

Let us now solve the above system using the method suggested in [106]. First, we establish the problem's reachability set. This set describes the possible "token" occupancy in the places set, what we call the net's marking. Each possibility i has a token occupancy

$$M_i = (p_1, p_2, p_3, p_4, p_5)$$

where p_k represents the number of tokens in place k. In our example, there are five members in the reachability set, or in other words, five possible markings of the net.

- $M_1 = (1,0,0,0,0)$
- $M_2 = (0,1,1,0,0)$
- $M_3 = (0,0,1,1,0)$
- $M_4 = (0,1,0,0,1)$
- $M_5 = (0,0,0,1,1)$

The transitions between the five states in the reachability set form an ergodic Markov Chain.[1] We can solve this chain [74] in the following way to obtain the steady state probabilities of the net markings.

- $2Pr[M1] = 2Pr[M5]$
- $2Pr[M2] = 2Pr[M1] + 3Pr[M3]$
- $4Pr[M3] = Pr[M2]$
- $Pr[M4] = 3Pr[M5] + Pr[M2]$
- $5Pr[M5] = Pr[M4] + Pr[M3]$
- $Pr[M1] + Pr[M2] + Pr[M3] + Pr[M4] + Pr[M5] = 1$

The above equations results are the marking steady state probabilities:

- $Pr[M1] = 0.1163$

---

[1]A Markov chain is ergodic if all its states are aperiodic, recurrent, and nonnull [75]. The probability distribution of such a chain always converges to a limiting stationary distribution, independent of the initial state distribution, often denoted as the steady state or equilibrium probabilities.

- $Pr[M2] = 0.1860$
- $Pr[M3] = 0.0465$
- $Pr[M4] = 0.5349$
- $Pr[M5] = 0.1163$

Knowing the probability of each state and the places that are marked in each state allows us to calculate the probabilities of token occupancy

- $Pr[m_1 = 1] = 0.1163 = Pr[M1]$
- $Pr[m_2 = 1] = 0.7209 = Pr[M2] + Pr[M4]$
- $Pr[m_3 = 1] = 0.2325 = Pr[M2] + Pr[M3]$
- $Pr[m_4 = 1] = 0.1628 = Pr[M3] + Pr[M5]$
- $Pr[m_5 = 1] = 0.6512 = Pr[M4] + Pr[M5]$

The probabilities calculated above depend on the reachability set, which in turn depends on the initial marking. If the initial marking was 2 tokens in p_1, the reachability set would consist of 14 states. Furthermore, the case of 3 tokens in p_1 would produce 30 states. These numbers demonstrate the problem of "states explosion" even in a simple net, as in this example.

The ergodicity of the chain allows us to use flow balance technique and Little's law[2] for average performance analysis. In this example, we can calculate the *average* delay time T_{av} as follows. Transition t_1 can be enabled only if p_1 contains a token. Hence, the utilization of t_1 equals 0.1163. Having $q_1 = 2$ implies an average token flow of 0.2326 tokens per time unit in p_1. Since t_1 is a fork, the average token flow in the parallel paths is doubled (0.4652), and reduced again in the joint t_5. Since the system conserves tokens (neither destroy nor produce), we can apply Little's law, knowing the average flow rate in each branch from above

- $T_{av} = N_{av}/q_{av}$
- $N_{av} = \sum_{i=1}^{5} m_i^{(av)} = 1.7674$
- $T_{av} = 1.7674/0.4652 = 3.8$ time units

The above example demonstrates the use of stochastic Petri nets for average performance analysis. We have seen two techniques (based on [107]) with which this model can be used.

---

[2]Little's law states that "the average number of customers in a queueing system is equal to the average arrival rate of customers to that system, times the average time spent in that system [75]." The flow balance technique is based on the equality of flow into and out of a state in an equilibrium case.

7.2   ANNOTATED PETRI NETS

Let us now examine a method of assigning time properties to a Petri net model by extending the classic Petri nets. The extension suggested here [109], is done by *annotations* and *initial considerations*. They provide processing content and external dependencies to the firing of the net. We carry out this extension while obeying the following rules:

1. Assign actions that do not relate to the net itself to *transitions* with a corresponding annotation. Examples of such actions are applying a function to a specific data structure, firing another net, and calling a procedure.
2. Assign boolean expressions that express external dependencies through an appropriate annotation to *output arcs* of a transition.
3. Assign an integer selector to a *transition*. When this transition fires, it marks at most one of its output places. The selector determines which output place to mark.
4. Use two special types of transitions that have only input or output arcs: the *initial* and the *terminal* transitions, respectively.

Figure 7.3 demonstrates an annotated Petri net model built according to the above rules. This example describes the specification

> upon acceptance of an invocation request from a sender, acknowledge the sender and examine the incoming parameter. If the parameter is in the limits, update the link.

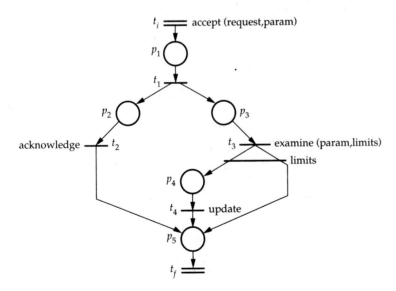

FIGURE 7.3
Annotated Petri net example.

Note that we have assigned transitions t_i, t_2, t_3, and t_4 with annotations expressing external dependencies. We can describe this model in a language called PNL [109], getting the following result:

t_i: *init* (p_1) invokes(accept(request,param))
p_1: place(t_1)
t_1: trans(p_2,p_3)
p_2: place(t_2)
t_2: trans(p_5) invokes(acknowledge)
p_3: place(t_3)
t_3: trans invokes(examine(param,limits))
     output select((limits) p_4,p_5)
p_4: place(t_4)
t_4: trans(p_5) invokes(update(link))
p_5: place(t_f)
t_f: *term*

We note that the annotations of transitions t_i, t_2, and t_4 appear as invocations of the specified functions. The annotation of transition t_3 is a selector according to the value of "limits."

We have discussed above some problems in assigning temporal properties to transitions while maintaining the classic Petri net properties. Let us now consider an important implementation issue that raises similar difficulties. Petri net theory does not force a fireable transition to fire, but if a transition does fire, the firing is complete and consumes zero time. Implementing a transition firing with a program imposes a firing that is not instantaneous. In a multiprocessor system, a mutual exclusion mechanism must protect the firing, since more than one processor can focus on a particular input place at a specific time. Therefore, the implementation must provide a semaphore-like *locking* mechanism, and an *atomic* operation which adjusts (increment or decrement) the number of tokens in places.

A tool that helps overcoming the mutual exclusion problem is the *inhibit* arc. Such an arc is presented in Figure 7.4. When transition t_1 fires before t_3, transition t_4 is inhibited by a token existence in place p_1. As long as transition t_2 does not fire, p_3 accumulates tokens generated by the firing of t_3.

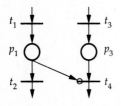

FIGURE 7.4
Transition firing inhibit.

A set of inclusion rules assigns all the places associated with a specific lock to a *lock set*. Each place is assigned to one lock set. The rules take into account the precedence and the inhibit relations between the net places.

7.3 TIME-AUGMENTED PETRI NETS

In this section we review a method that addresses the assignment of temporal properties to a net by an augmentation of the classic Petri net model [34]. The augmented model assigns timing properties to places in the net. The places of the net represent processing (actions), and instantaneous transitions represent start and stop of a process. The non-negative time value assigned to each place depends on the place type. We note that a place may also represent the execution of a condition. In this case, the value assigned to the place is near or equal to zero. If it is a process, then the value equals the bound on execution time of this process. After residing on this place for the assigned time, a token is ready to enable an output transition of the place it occupies. If one transition is enabled when the token becomes ready, this transition fires immediately. If more than one transition is enabled, then a nondeterministic selection takes place. Thus, only one of the transitions fires immediately, while the others become disabled.

7.3.1 Time-Driven System Model

Four *set valued functions* define the relations between the elements of the network. In the graphic representation of a net, directed arcs represent these relations.

- $I_t(t_i)$ Transition input function maps transition t_i to the set of places **from** which there exist arcs **to** t_i
- $O_t(t_i)$ Transition output function maps transition t_i to the set of places **to** which there exist arcs **from** t_i.
- Place input function ($I_p(p_i)$) and place output function ($O_p(p_i)$) are similarly defined.

In the following, let us denote the *cardinality* of a set A by $|A|$.

THE DRIVING CYCLE. The mechanism which activates the marking of the augmented net is called the driving cycle. An example of a driving cycle is shown in the left side of Figure 7.5. The cycle satisfies the following properties:

- The initial marking of p_1 ($m_1 = 1$) reproduces itself with a fix period T_1.
- $I_t(t_1) = p_1$.
- $p_1 \in O_t(t_1)$, and $|O_t(t_1)| > 1$.
- $I_p(p_1) = O_p(p_1) = \{t_1\}$.

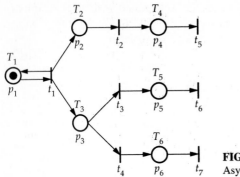

FIGURE 7.5
Asynchronous subsystem.

7.3.2 Concept of Relative Firing Frequency

The augmented Petri net assigns two important properties to places and transitions in the net: MRFF and MTIAT. The Maximum Relative Firing Frequency (*MRFF*) represents the number of times a *transition* fires during each firing interval of the driving cycle. We calculate this number for the case in which all the decisions[1] between the driving cycle and that transition are made "in favor"[2] of the path to that transition. The Minimum Token Inter-Arrival Time (*MTIAT*) represents the shortest possible time interval between two consecutive arrivals of tokens to a *place*.

The above definitions establish an important relation. If t_i is an input transition to a place p_j, and T_1 is the driving cycle period, then

$$MTIAT(p_j) = \frac{T_1}{MRFF(t_i)}$$

7.3.3 Subclasses of Time Driven Systems

We can divide the nets into four subclasses and use them as construction units for any model we build using this augmentation [34]. Let us consider these four subclasses and their properties.

1. Asynchronous systems are constrained by the following two properties:

> **1.** Execution time of any process (i.e., place) cannot exceed the *MTIAT* of this place.

---

[1]Selections of enabled transitions to fire.

[2]If a decision is predetermined, then we know the ratio in which it is taken in favor of a specific path. If a decision is data dependent, then we can only express assumptions or upper and lower bounds.

2. The cumulative execution time of any path cannot exceed any separately stated path execution-time requirement (path latency requirement).

Figure 7.5 demonstrates an asynchronous system of the time-augmented Petri nets.

2. Synchronized systems impose an additional timing constraint on those of the asynchronous systems. To express this constraint, let us define the waiting time tokens spend in the final places of their path while waiting for synchronization. The waiting time at the final place of a specific path is the difference between the greatest total-path-time of the set of paths, and the total-path-time of this specific path. The token at the path with the greatest total-path-time forces tokens at different paths to wait for synchronization. Now, let us phrase the additional constraint due to synchronization.

> For any set of parallel paths, the sum of execution and waiting times that a token spends at the final place of any of the paths must not exceed the *MTIAT* of that place.

3. Independent cycle systems include a cyclic path, as the one described in Figure 7.6. For these systems we impose another timing requirement, in addition to those imposed on synchronized systems.

> For any independent cycle, the cycle execution-time (from t_i back to t_i) must not exceed the *MTIAT* of the entry place.

4. Shared resource systems require imposition of an additional timing constraint for the shared resource constructs. The shared resource is modeled by sharing a place of a cycle. As an example, consider joining two independent cycles as in Figure 7.6, such that the place p_5 is shared by the two. We need to extend the cycle, and to replace p_5 with two places. The first represents the execution of the shared subsystem, and the second (the final place) represents the control part of this subsystem. The initial marking in the shared final place serves as semaphore that controls the mutual exclusion of the resource. The token in that marking can

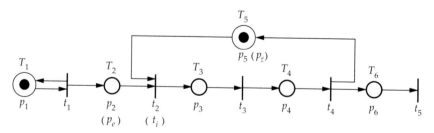

FIGURE 7.6
Independent cycle subsystem.

enable only one of its output transitions at a time. However, its output transitions are also the output transitions of the entry points $(p_{e,j})$ of the different paths that share the resource. The constraint imposed, therefore, has to prevent starvation while accounting for the possible token arrivals and ensuring that only one will take control on the shared resource at any time. If all the entry places receive tokens at a similar rate, let the *MTIAT* of each of the n entry places be T_d. Let us impose the following constraint:

$$T_{e,j} + \sum_{k=1,\neq j}^{n} (T_{c,k}) \leq T_d$$

where

- $T_{e,j}$ is the execution time of entry-place $p_{e,j}$,
- $T_{c,k}$ (or $T_{c,j}$) is the execution time of all places in the cycle, which are activated as a consequence of the input provided by $p_{e,k}$ (or $p_{e,j}$).

The above constraint ensures that $p_{e,j}$ is safe in the presence of time [34].

7.3.4 Proving Safeness in the Presence of Time

Building a network model of a system that is based on construction elements that belong to the above subclasses supports a formal expression of the system temporal behavior. In this model, using the above restrictions based on each subsystem specification, we can show that the overall system requirements are satisfied and safe in the presence of time. The network construction is a process of assembling subsystems and imposing their constraints. One starts with the driving cycle, and iteratively adds arcs, transitions and places according to the real system specification. This method for constructing a complete model allows the proving of some safeness properties in the presence of time [34].

SAFENESS FOR SIMPLE PLACES. A "simple place" is a place p_i with $|I_p(p_i)| = 1$ and $|O_p(p_i)| \geq 1$, such that each transition t_k in its output set satisfies $|I_t(t_k)| = 1$. One can prove that a simple place is safe in the presence of time in the worst case if and only if

$$T_i \leq T_1/F_j$$

where T_i is the execution-time of this place, T_1 is the cycle-time of the driving cycle, and F_j is the *MRFF* of the input-transition to this place.

SAFENESS FOR FINAL PLACES IN A PARALLEL PATH. One can prove that each of the final places, $p_{fi}(i = 1, 2, \ldots, n)$, of a synchronized parallel construct with n parallel paths is safe in the presence of time in the worst case, if and only if

$$\forall j \in 1..n : P_j - P_i \leq (T_1/F_{fi}) - T_{fi}$$

for each of them. In this constraint P_j is the total path time (execution + waiting) of path j, F_{fi} is the *MRFF* of the input transition to p_{fi}, and T_{fi} is the execution time of p_{fi} itself.

SAFENESS FOR ENTRY PLACES OF INDEPENDENT CYCLES. Let us define the cycle-time (T_c) as the time interval from firing of t_i to "token ready" in p_f, as shown in Figure 7.6. Let us denote the execution time of the entry place as T_e, and the *MRFF* of the input transition to the entry place as F_e. An entry place of an independent cycle construct is safe in the presence of time if and only if

$$T_e \leq T_1/F_e \ \wedge \ T_c \leq T_1/F_e$$

An outcome of this result is that if p_e is safe in the presence of time, then the waiting time for *all* the tokens arriving to this place is *zero*.

SAFENESS FOR PLACES IN A SHARED RESOURCE. A shared cycle time $T_{c,k}$, for a cycle containing $t_{i,k}$ in a shared resource construct, is the time that elapses from firing of $t_{i,k}$ until the token arrives at p_f. Given that all the entry places receive marking from identical *MRFF*s, and the *MTIAT* of the entry places is their execution time divided by the *MRFF*, then each entry place $p_{e,j}$ (to a shared resource construct) is safe in the presence of time if and only if

$$T_{e,j} + \sum_{k=1}^{n} T_{c,k} \leq T_{c,j} + T_1/F_e$$

7.4 ASSESSMENT OF PETRI NET METHODS

Let us start with a summary of the weaknesses of the Petri net variations introduced in this chapter.

- The reachability set, which includes all the system states reachable from an initial state, explodes easily.
- The results are very sensitive to changes in process or path execution time.
- The annotated model needs expensive enabling to assign process execution time to an instantaneous action like transition firing.
- The annotated model imposes a heavy overhead in order to assure a consistent instantaneous firing in a distributed environment.
- Absolute timing is needed in the stochastic Petri nets method.
- An alteration construct is needed in the augmented Petri nets method.
- The restriction on a shared resource (limited only to the case of identical firing rates) is too strong.
- The absence of performance analysis tools does not allow the examination of timing problems rather than safeness (e.g., bottle-neck).

- The restrictions imposed in the construction of the augmented Petri net narrows significantly the cases that can be treated.

We find the augmented Petri net method as the most advantageous because of the following reasons:

- No cost is involved in assigning time to firing, which is instantaneous. Time is assigned to places.
- The ability to formally and explicitly express the timing constraints.
- The automatability of the method.
- The ability to verify timing properties in the design phase.

While Petri net models are an effective and versatile tool, useful extensions for hard real-time applications are still required.

CHAPTER
8

AXIOMATIC APPROACHES

Axiomatic approaches (theorem proving techniques) are often preferable in system design and analysis because one can communicate assertions to computers via compilers, and then manipulate them by simplification procedures. Due to this advantage, proof systems for many design and development approaches have been introduced. For example, axiomatic proof systems have been introduced for distributed programs [111] and for CSP programs [10]. However, these proof systems are based on the nondeterministic interleaving model for concurrency. They do not deal with timing properties, and they provide no means for real-time verification. Thus, current proof systems for concurrent programs fail to address temporal properties even in a single processor system. The complexity of verification grows significantly when the required implementation is distributed. It is therefore important to note that there are some major difficulties in using an axiomatic approach, even in systems which do not have timing constraints. Let us highlight some of these difficulties.

- Time dependent properties of concurrent systems (concurrency, mutual exclusion) are difficult to specify.
- Finding invariants for complex systems is extremely difficult.
- Simplification of long expressions is generally tedious.

In this chapter we review some ways to specify and verify the temporal properties of a system using axiomatic approaches. The first approach [59] uses Dijkstra's weakest precondition definitions to derive the latest time to begin execution of a computation. The second approach introduces real-time logic [67, 68] through which we can state and infer temporal properties. The third approach we review here uses time related history variables [26] to reason about temporal properties. Finally, we review a method that combines extended state machines and real-time temporal logic [110].

8.1 WEAKEST PRECONDITION ANALYSIS

8.1.1 Predicate Transformers

The weakest precondition analysis of program temporal properties [59] is based on three major assumptions.

1. The program consists of parts that are sequential and parts that are parallel. The sequential parts are constructed from Dijkstra's *guarded commands* [44], and the parallel constructs, called *PARCs*, are CSP-like [43, 64] parallel interpretation of the guarded commands. Figure 8.1 depicts some characteristics of the multiprocessor configuration used to execute these parallel constructs.

2. The *weakest precondition* predicate, "wp," provides the execution time properties to the program parts in the following way.

   (*a*) Let us consider the case of a *simple statement* (*S*), which is neither iterative nor conditional. We can define the execution time of *S* as the non-interrupted execution time needed for the implementing *processor*. We can interpret the weakest precondition as "the latest starting time" *t* to meet deadline *T* with statement execution time t_s:

   $$wp(S, t \leq T) \equiv t \leq T - t_s$$

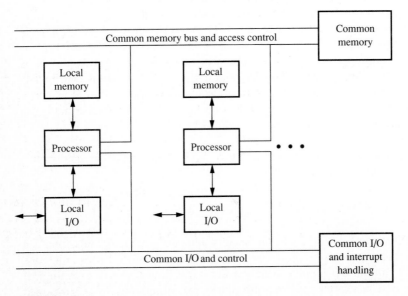

FIGURE 8.1
PARC execution configuration.

(b) Now let us examine an *action*, a non-interrupted sequence of sequential statements ($action = S_1; \ldots ; S_n$). We can examine the weakest precondition of an action in terms of the simple statements in the sequence

$$wp(action, t \leq T) = wp(S_1, wp(S_2, \ldots wp(S_n, R) \ldots))$$

$$= t \leq T - \sum_{i=1}^{n} t_{si}$$

$$= t \leq T - t_{action}$$

3. In addition to being hardware dependent, the execution time is also *input-data dependent*. We can characterize this property (which appears in branching points and in iteration decision) with Dijkstra's *predicate transformer rule*

$$t_{action} = f(d_1, \ldots, d_e)$$

where $d_1, \ldots, d_e$ are input data of *action*.

8.1.2 Program Time Behavior

TIME BEHAVIOR OF SEQUENTIAL PROGRAMS. In order to analyze sequential programs we first have to transform our program into a guarded-command notation. We transform non-iterative and non-branching parts into a sequence of simple statements. As described above, we derive the weakest preconditions appropriately. Now we must analyze the conditional and iterative statements.

Conditional statements are transformed into Dijkstra's IF

IF

$\quad g_1 \rightarrow action_1$

$\quad .$

$\quad .$

$\quad g_n \rightarrow action_n$

FI

Deriving the weakest precondition for this IF yields

$$wp(IF, t \leq T) = (\exists j : g_j) \wedge (\forall i : g_i \rightarrow t \leq T - t_{action_i})$$

Iterative statements are transformed into Dijkstra's DO

DO

$\quad g_1 \rightarrow action_1$

$\quad .$

$\quad .$

$\quad g_n \rightarrow action_n$

OD

Deriving the weakest precondition for this DO yields

$$wp(DO, t \le T) = (\exists k \ge 0 : H_k(t \le T))$$

where

$$H_0(t \le T) = (t \le T) \text{ AND} \neg (\exists j : g_j) \qquad \text{and}$$

$$H_k(t \le T) = wp(IF^+, H_{k-1}(t \le T)) \text{ OR } H_0(t \le T)^1$$

After the program is written in an equivalent guarded commands notation, the *program's weakest precondition* has to be *constructed*, applying the sequential rules introduced above. In order to *evaluate* the program's weakest precondition, we can apply the above approach

$$wp(program, t \le T) = wp(S_1, \ldots wp(DO, \ldots wp(IF, t \le T) \ldots) \ldots)$$

TIME BEHAVIOR OF PARALLEL PROGRAMS. When we consider parallel programs that we want to verify with an approach similar to the above sequential approach, we have to make some restricting assumptions. First, we must be able to assure mutual exclusion of the guards. Then, we have to consider the different behavior of the conditional and iterative constructs.

Let us consider *parallel condition constructs*, denoted IF-PARC

PAR-IF

$$g_1 \to action_1$$

$$\| \ .$$

$$\| \ .$$

$$\| \ g_n \to action_n$$

PAR-FI

The formulas that define its semantics are

$$(R_1) \wedge (R_2) \ldots \wedge (R_n) \to R$$

and

$$wp(IF - PARC, R_1 \ . \ . \ and \ R_n) =$$

$$\forall i \in 1 \ . \ . \ n : (g_i \to wp(action_i, R_i) \wedge \neg (g_i) = R_i) \to wp(IF - PARC, R)$$

Now let us substitute all R_i with $t \le T$, and omit false g_is (which do not contribute to execution time). The latest starting point is therefore

$$wp(IF - PARC, t \le T) = \forall i : g_i \to (t \le T - t_{action_i})$$

---

[1] IF^+ denotes the same guarded-command set with assumed IF/FI brackets.

Now let us consider the *parallel iterative construct*, denoted DO-PARC

PAR-DO

$\quad g_1 \to action_1$

$\quad \| \; .$

$\quad \| \; .$

$\quad \| \; g_n \to action_n$

PAR-OD

Semantics identity between DO and DO-PARC allows using parallel structures as well:

$$wp(DO - PARC, t \leq T) = (\exists k \geq 0 : H_k(t \leq T))$$

However, the *evaluation* is *different*:

$$\text{DO: execution time } = t_{ai} + t_{aj}$$

$$\text{DO-PARC: execution time } = max(t_{ai}, t_{aj}).$$

8.1.3 Method and Example

We can use the above definitions to examine a method for evaluating the latest starting point of a program, an action, or a statement [59].

1. Represent each *action* by a *vector in the state space* of PARCs.

2. Establish the *paths*, the sequences of *actions*, leading from assumed *pre-states* to given *post-states* of the whole activity.

3. Consider the following cases (see Figure 8.2):

Case a. If the path between any two states is *unambiguous*, then take into account the *sum* of the intermediate execution times of the steps.

Case b. If the path is *ambiguous*, *determine* partial sequences that can be *exchanged*, and then take into account the *maximum* execution time of the partial sequences.

Let us consider the example in Figure 8.2. In this example we assign equal execution times to the actions of P_i (every vertical step), denoted by t_v. In addition, let us assign equal execution times to the actions of P_j (every horizontal step), denoted t_h. We can then conclude

- 4 to 3: $action_j \to t_h$
- 3 to 1: $action_j \| action_i \to max(t_h, t_v)$
- 1 to 0: $action_i \to t_v$

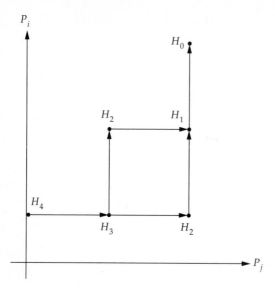

FIGURE 8.2
Paths example of weakest precondition solution.

Therefore, the calculation of the weakest precondition is restricted by

$$t \leq T - t_h - t_v - max(t_h, t_v)$$

8.2 REAL-TIME LOGIC

Real-time logic (RTL [67, 68]) is a reasoning system for real-time properties of computer based systems. RTL's computation model consists of events, actions, causality relations, and timing constraints. The model is expressed in a first order logic, describing the system properties as well as the system's dependency on external events. The Real-Time Logic system introduces time to the first order logic formulas with an event occurrence function denoted @. This function assigns time values to event occurrences. The ith occurrence of event e happens at time $@(e, i)$. The constraints and the scheduling disciplines are represented as restrictions imposed on the function.

RTL uses three types of constants:

1. *Action constants* may be primitive or composite. In a composite constant, precedence is imposed by the event-action model using sequential or parallel relations between actions.

2. *Event constants* are divided into three classes. Start/stop events describe the initiation/termination of an action or subaction. Transition events are those which make a change in state attributes. In other words, a transition event changes an assertion about the state of the real-time system or its environment. The third class, external events, includes those that can impact the system behavior, but cannot be caused by the system.

3. *Integers* assigned by the occurrence function provide time values, and in addition denote the number of an event occurrence in a sequence.

RTL translates assertions about the physical state of the system over time into *algebraic relations*. These relations describe the occurrences of the appropriate transition events, using equality and inequality predicates. RTL uses *state predicates* as a notational device for asserting truth-values to attributes during a time interval.

We can derive a set of axioms from the event-action model of the system, by translating the system specification and characterizing the following properties.

* Relations between actions and their start/stop events.
* The sporadic and periodic event constraints.
* The causal relations which may initiate a transition event.
* We can add artificial constraints to the specification in order to prevent the scheduler from executing particular actions. It is a useful way to prevent execution of actions that are not required.

A timing property of a system (an RTL assertion) is derived and proven by refutation. We do this by showing that there is no occurrence function that is consistent with the system specification, in conjunction with the complement of this particular property. The mechanism to achieve it is the *deductive resolution*.

For example, consider the specification [68]:

> Upon pressing button #1, action SAMPLE is executed within 30 time units. During each execution of this action, the information is sampled and subsequently transmitted to the display panel. The computation time of action SAMPLE is 20 time units.

which we can translate into the following two formulas

$$\forall x: @\ (\Omega button1, x) \le @(\uparrow SAMPLE, x) \land$$

$$@\ (\downarrow SAMPLE, x) \le @(\Omega button1, x) + 30$$

$$\forall y: @(\uparrow SAMPLE, y) + 20 \le @(\downarrow SAMPLE, y)$$

and safety assertions are then derived. Precedence relations can be derived through inequality predicates which use the inequality operator ($\le$).

An important use of RTL is to check legality of a specification or a safety property of the system. Let us consider a way to do it [68]. The first step constructs a graph of the system specification expressed in RTL. The nodes of this graph are action occurrences. They are connected by weighted, directed arcs. Each arc's direction is compatible with the inequality the arc represents. The weight assigned to the arc represents a constant added to the node that the arc leaves. In that way, the second formula in the above example gets the following form:

FIGURE 8.3
RTL constraint graph representation.

- a node @($\uparrow$ *SAMPLE*, y),
- an arc that leaves that node with a weight of 20,
- a node pointed by that arc @($\downarrow$ *SAMPLE*, y).

Figure 8.3 illustrates this representation.

The above specification example can therefore be represented as illustrated by Figure 8.4. This constraint graph can then be clustered into the one described in Figure 8.5(a) while we cluster nodes with the same functions of the same event constants. This clustering combines the relations of the whole specification, providing a tool for analyzing its consistency.

An algorithm that detects positive cycles in the constraint graph [67, 68] supports detecting unsatisfiable specification. This algorithm iteratively removes nodes from the graph while updating the arc weights accordingly. Figure 8.5 demonstrates the way it checks the unsatisfiability of the above example. Part (a) of the figure starts with the clustered constraint graph, which is reduced in part (b) by removing the node @($\uparrow$ *SAMPLE*, x). It is done while updating the arc weight to the sum of weights of the arcs adjacent to the removed node. We can see in part (c) of the figure that the only cycle in the specification is negative. However, if the specification is changed to state

Upon pressing button #1, action SAMPLE is executed within 15 time units . . .

we find a contradiction with the twenty time units needed for computing SAMPLE. This contradiction results in a positive cycle of five time units, demonstrating the unsatisfiability of the specification.

In addition to system consistent specification, we can prove safety assertions using this method. In such an algorithm, we start by negating the required safety assertion and adding it to the specification. The second step scans the graph in order to detect positive cycles. We can do it with the above algorithm that removes nodes from the graph and updates the weights of the arcs. This algorithm has an important property of preserving positive cycles. The third step uses the positive cycles detected in the second to determine the desired unsatisfiability.

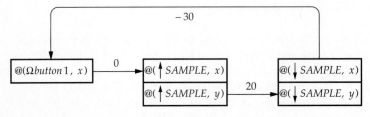

FIGURE 8.4
Constraint graph example.

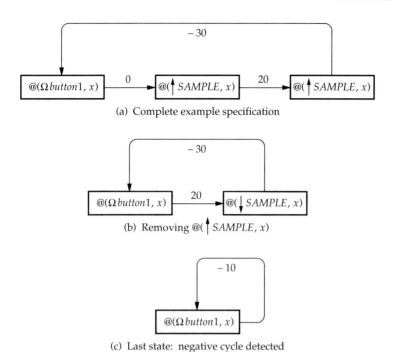

(a) Complete example specification

(b) Removing @($\uparrow$ SAMPLE, x)

(c) Last state: negative cycle detected

FIGURE 8.5
Positive-cycle detection by node removals.

We can also combine the use of RTL with non-temporal concurrency analysis techniques [14]. One way to do this is to state our timing expressions in RTL, and assign a meaning to the timing expressions with a function. Adopting this approach requires the use of two functions that connect timing expressions and operations. A function *tm* maps the timing expressions to boolean values

$$tm : timing\ expression \mapsto boolean$$

An additional auxiliary function *op* maps timing expressions to operations

$$op : timing\ expression \mapsto operation$$

We can assign a time meaning to a predicate of the functional specification via a function *mn* which maps from behavioral specification to boolean values

$$mn : predicate \times timing\ expression \mapsto boolean$$

Note that in this approach we assign the functional specification with a time meaning in terms of first order logic as used in RTL.

8.3   TIME RELATED HISTORY VARIABLES

We use history variables in many proof systems in order to prove correctness of sequences. In order to attach timing properties to a sequence, we can represent the history of a variable by both its assigned values and the times of these assignments [26]. A loosely increasing function, *time(e)*, associates with every natural number *n* the time of the *n*th occurrence of event *e*. Every variable *x* is modelled by

$$< range(x), val(x), asg(x) >$$

In the above model, *range(x)* is the set of all the possible values of *x*. We interpret the event *asg(x)* as: *x* takes the value *val(x)(n)* at the instance *time(asg(x))(n)*.

The use of functions to associate a value with every element in their domain is very useful in this approach too. We denote a composition of two functions *g* and *f* as

$$g \circ f \equiv g(f(x))$$

DELAY OPERATOR. This approach uses a delay operator D^δ expressed as

$$time(D^\delta e) = time(e) + \delta$$

to allow expressing temporal relations.

EVENT COUNTERS. Let us define event counters and express them in the following lambda expressions [26, 29]. The relation

$$time(e)^- = \lambda t \cdot \sup\{n | time(e)(n) \le t\}$$

associates with any time *t* the rank of the last occurrence of *e* that has happened **before** or **at** *t*, denoted *lcount(e)*. The relation

$$^- time(e) = \lambda t \cdot \sup\{n | time(e)(n) \ge t\}$$

associates with any time *t* the rank of the occurrence of *e* that has happened **after** or **at** *t*, denoted *count(e)*. In other words

$$count(e) \equiv (\mathcal{I} - 1) \circ^- time(e)$$

where $(\mathcal{I} - 1) = \lambda n \cdot \max(0, n - 1)$. Hence,

$$count(e) \le lcount(e)$$

LOOSE PRECEDENCE. We are now at a point where we have enough tools to describe some precedence properties. We can express the property of loose precedence $e \le f$ in three equivalent ways:

$$e \le f \Leftrightarrow time(e) \ge time(f)$$

$$e \le f \Leftrightarrow count(e) \le count(f)$$

$$e \le f \Leftrightarrow lcount(e) \le lcount(f)$$

SUM OF EVENTS. Counting event occurrences requires a way to combine the counts of some events together. Let us define the sum of events *e* and *f* as an event $e + f$ such that

$$lcount(e + f) = lcount(e) + lcount(f)$$
$$\wedge$$
$$count(e + f) = count(e) + count(f)$$

The above definition means that $e + f$ occurs each time either e or f occurs, and twice when both occur.

CURRENT VALUE. In order to retrieve the value of a variable just before (or just after) its assignment, let us consider the following operators

$$current(x) = val(x) \circ count(asg(x))$$

and similarly

$$lcurrent(x) = val(x) \circ lcount(asg(x))$$

We can use these definitions in any statement that requires the value of a variable immediately after or immediately before its assignment.

LAST, NEXT, ACTUAL OCCURRENCE. We need additional definitions in order to support strict precedence relations. Let us define the *last* and *next* occurrence functions as follows.

$$last(e) = time(e) \circ count(e)$$
$$next(e) = time(e) \circ lcount(e + 1)$$

Similarly, we define *llast(x)* and *lnext(x)* with

$$llast(e) = time(e) \circ lcount(e)$$
$$lnext(e) = time(e) \circ count(e + 1)$$

From these definitions, we can obtain the relation

$$last(e) \le llast(e) \le \mathcal{I} \le lnext(e) \le next(e)$$

Now, let us define

$$actual(e) \equiv \inf(\mathcal{I}, count(e)(+\infty)$$

to denote the event between the last and the next.

STRICT PRECEDENCE. Using the above definitions we can derive strict precedence ($<$) relation from

$$e < f \Leftrightarrow actual(e) \circ lcount(e) \le count(f)$$

EXAMPLES. Let us consider three examples that demonstrate clearly this method in proving three properties [26].

1. $e < f \Rightarrow e \leq f$

The definition of *actual*( ) let us write

$$count(e) = actual(e) \circ count(e)$$

which always satisfies

$$count(e) = actual(e) \circ count(e) \leq actual(e) \circ lcount(e).$$

However, the given strict precedence yields

$$actual(e) \circ lcount(e) \leq count(f),$$

from which we can conclude

$$count(e) \leq count(f)$$

which is equivalent (see above) to $e \leq f$.

2. $e \leq f < g \leq h \Rightarrow e < h$

The left loose precedence relation yields

$$actual(e) \circ lcount(e) \leq actual(e) \circ lcount(f)$$
$$\leq actual(f) \circ lcount(f).$$

From $f < g$ and the strict precedence implication

$$actual(f) \circ lcount(f) \leq count(g)$$

and from the right loose precedence relation

$$count(g) \leq count(h).$$

Therefore,

$$actual(e) \circ lcount(e) \leq count(h) \Rightarrow e < h$$

due to the strict precedence rule.

3. $e < f \Rightarrow count(e) \leq count(f) \circ last(e)$

From the definition of strict precedence we have

$$e < f \Rightarrow actual(e) \circ lcount(e) \leq count(f).$$

Hence,

$$actual(e) \leq actual(e) \circ lcount(e) \circ time(e)$$
$$\leq count(f) \circ time(e).$$

However, since

$$count(e) = actual(e) \circ count(e),$$

we have

$$count(e) \le count(f) \circ time(e) \circ count(e),$$

and we can substitute the proper definition of *last(e)*.

A detailed application example is given in [26] containing the specification, the description, and the proof of a distributed bus arbiter.

8.4   STATE MACHINES AND REAL-TIME TEMPORAL LOGIC

The last axiomatic approach we present in this chapter is a method that combines state machines and logic [110]. The combination of these two disciplines gives this approach the power to support specification and verification of computer embedded systems. Extended state machines (ESMs) with time bounded events are employed to describe both the controlled processes (the *plant*) and the *controller*. This approach represents a plant/controller ESM model M as

$$M = M_0 \| M_1 \| \ldots \| M_k \| M_{k+1} \| \ldots \| M_{k+n}$$

In this representation, M_0 is the global clock, $M_1 \ldots M_k$ are plant processes, and $M_{k+1} \ldots M_{k+n}$ are controller processes.[2]

8.4.1   ESM Components

Each ESM contains the following elements:

* An activity variable with a specified type.
* Data variables, each with a specified type.
* A set of communication channels.
* A set of event labels.

Each *event* in this model is represented by an exit activity A_e, a source activity A_s, an operation, and a boolean-valued expression in the data variables *guard*

$$(A_e, guard, operation, A_s)$$

Each ESM *operation* is one of the following three: assignment, send, or receive. Operations of these types construct events in this model.

Recall our system model, which is a parallel execution of control processes and plant processes M_m ($m = 1, 2, \ldots, k + n$). Consider now distinct events that occur in different processes. Let E_i be an event in M_i and let E_j be an event in M_j. These two events may cooperate in an action in which their respective assignment statements participate. Furthermore, these two events can be a corresponding pair

---

[2]A detailed analysis is given in [110] for $M = global\ clock \| train \| gate \| controller$.

of send and receive operations. Let a *transition set* $\mathscr{E}_i$ be associated with E_i to represent its cooperation or communication with the rest of E_j's. Let us express each transition τ in this set as

$$\tau = (\alpha, e, h, l, u)$$

where

- α is the event label of E_i[3];
- e is an enabling condition;
- h is a transformation function whose domain is the state assignment space of M_i; and
- u and l are upper and lower time bounds, respectively. The bounds are relative to the time τ is first enabled, and they delimit the state assignment.

Note that l and u introduce the real-time properties to the transition τ, and their reference is the time in which the enabling condition becomes true.

   A path in the state space of the system M, called a *trajectory*, consists of a sequence of states and events. The paths that M is constrained to follow are called *legal trajectories*. They provide formal operational semantics along with semantics for real-time temporal logic (RTTL). Let us now consider how real-time temporal logic allows expressing and deducing properties of M.

8.4.2   Real-Time Temporal Logic

The real-time temporal logic is an extension of an older linear-time temporal logic. It uses two basic operators: *until* ($\sqcap$) and *next* ($\odot$) to construct many other useful temporal operators:

- *eventually* ($\Diamond$), where $\Diamond w$ is an abbreviation for (*true* $\sqcap$ *w*), to say: eventually w will hold true in some state;
- *henceforth* ($\Box$), where $\Box w$ is an abbreviation for $\neg (\Diamond (\neg w))$, to say: henceforth w holds true for all states;
- *unless* (U);
- *precedes* ($\mathscr{P}$), where $w_1 \mathscr{P} w_2$ is an abbreviation for $\neg ((\neg w_1) \sqcap w_2)$, to say: if w_2 eventually occurs, then w_1 must precede w_2;
- *previous*;
- *since*, and others.

RTTL uses local variables that may change their value when the system changes from one state to another. We may define locally a set of activity variables,

---

[3] In case E_i cooperates with E_j, they share the same label.

data variables, and the next-event variable **n**. RTTL describes system states with *state formulas*, that are first order logic formulas. These formulas may include variables, but not temporal operators. The *succession axiom* of RTTL connects the ESM transitions to the logic. Let τ be defined as above, with enabling condition e and transformation function h. The axiom states that for any state-formula φ not containing any occurrence of **n**

$$(\mathbf{n} = \tau \wedge \varphi_h^v) \to (e \wedge \odot \varphi)$$

RTTL introduces three important proof rules that conclude in temporal formulas:

- RI, the invariant rule;
- RD, the delay rule; and
- RL, real-time liveness rule;

RTTL introduces these rules such that we can obtain a proof diagram of our system that expresses directly the scheduling constraints that the controller processes must satisfy. If there is no need to constrain individual activities, the rules produce constraints that the sequences must satisfy in order to meet the deadline.

EXAMPLES OF RTTL FORMULAS. Three examples from [110] demonstrate RTTL formulas.

1. $w_1 \wedge (t = T) \to \Diamond (w_2 \wedge (t \leq T + 5))$. If w_1 is true now and the clock reads T ticks (T is a global variable), then within $T + 5$ ticks w_2 must become true.
2. $w_1 \to w_2 \mathcal{P} w_3$. If w_1 is true now, then should w_3 occur at some future state, w_2 must precede w_3.
3. $\Box \Diamond (n = tick)$. The clock ticks infinitely often.

8.5   CONCLUDING REMARKS

We specify a real-time system behavior with logical and temporal properties. The logical properties can be expressed by *liveness* and *safety* assertions. Each liveness property states that an assertion on the system state will *eventually* hold. Each safety property states that an assertion on the system state will *always* hold. These assertions can describe states of subsystems or relations between them. We can see that this description is insufficient for describing temporal properties.

Therefore, we have reviewed in this chapter some ways of asserting real-time properties. A *real-time* property states that an assertion on the system state holds within specified time bounds. We have seen in this chapter four methods that specify real-time properties of a system. Two methods add time variables to the computation model and verify safety and liveness assertions. The two we have described are the weakest-precondition approach [59] and the time-related history-variables [26]. The other two methods involve logics specified for real-time properties: the real-time logic (RTL) [67, 68] and the extended state-machines (ESM) and real-time temporal logic (RTTL) [110].

The strength of the axiomatic approaches is in their ability to verify properties formally. We describe later in this book other verification methods, such as testing, with which we associate an enormous cost of verifying with high confidence levels. A formal (axiomatic) verification provides a *guarantee*, which we can regard as an assertion on the behavior of the system. The confidence level associated with this guarantee is complete.

However, the reader can see from our review of the four methods that it is not very simple to verify real-time properties of complex computation models. Nevertheless, the feasibility exists and we will refer to it later in this book.

CHAPTER
9

LANGUAGE SUPPORT AND RESTRICTIONS

Many real-time programming languages have been introduced during recent years. Although most of them provide time-service support, they totally disregard timing constraints and do not provide support for a predictable temporal behavior of programs. While many of the real-time programs in use today have been written in languages such as FORTRAN or assembly, only a very few really support the needs of real-time programming.

We start this chapter with a programming discipline suggested by N. Wirth. Although this discipline was published more than ten years ago, we can identify its real-time programming applications when we review it today. The next section examines two programming approaches for real-time applications, synchronous and asynchronous. The following section discusses the issue of schedulability analysis, and its effect on a real-time programming language. The chapter ends with some concluding remarks.

9.1 REAL-TIME PROGRAMMING DISCIPLINE

The complexity of programming increases when we move from sequential to multiprogramming, and it increases further when we move to real-time programming. A set of *concepts* (for reasoning) and a set of *facilities* (for description) are added in each step. Adding synchronization signals and mutual exclusion techniques to sequential programming allows us to use multiprogramming. The addition of execution-time properties to it allows dealing with real-time programming. In this section, let us review and examine the needs for real-time programming discipline as suggested in [154].

9.1.1 Language Requirements

The form and structure of a real-time programming language are as important as in conventional distributed programming. A real-time programming language needs no structural concepts in addition to those of conventional languages, which are

1. a notational unit for describing processes (themselves sequentially executed) that can be executed concurrently, and uninterruptably;
2. a collection of shared variables and their operators;
3. an object to trigger communication after waiting (signals).

A real-time programming language, however, does need one additional feature: A facility that provides accurate *execution-time bounds*, as an additional part of an existing compiler. If the compilation is straightforward (i.e., no optimization is performed), we may use a simple execution-time table of the statements which yields reasonably accurate estimates. But with optimizing compilers more complex approach to time estimation is required.

9.1.2 Discipline for Real-Time Programming

N. Wirth has suggested the following recipe for a real-time programming discipline [154]:

1. Restrict time dependent program parts that execute externally (by a device process) to an uninterruptable execution mode.
2. Determine the execution time of these time dependent program parts statically.
3. Assume that each "doio" (which represents waiting time for a device) has a hidden delay, derived from the execution performances and the resource-sharing strategy employed.

The above approach may lead to highly time-consuming *delays*. To prevent such delays, Wirth has proposed a solution based on a *priority interrupt system* [154] requiring adherence to the following constraints:

1. Every device process P_i is *cyclic*, consisting of a sequence of statements S_i, and the "doio" represents the waiting for device completion.
2. Let t_i be the cycle time of P_i, such that $t_i = T(S_i) + T(doio_i)$. At any priority level, t_i is considerably greater than that of all other processes at higher priority.
3. The ratio

$$r_i = \frac{T(S_i)}{T(S_i) + T(doio_i)}$$

over any cycle is very small ($\ll 1$).

4. Each signal emitted by a device must be awaited by single (regular) process only.

5. A device process must never *itself* invalidate the condition associated with the signal it emitted.

The discipline is definitely sufficient for systems that can satisfy the above restrictions and assumptions. However, these assumptions, including the one that all time-dependent program parts will execute in an uninterruptable mode, do not provide for schedulability, determinism, or predictability. A time-dependent program part may wait in vain for its uninterruptable execution, and higher priority processes may postpone it indefinitely. In a multiapplication environment another question arises: what determines (and with what criteria) which process has a higher priority?

This discipline highlights a major need of real-time programs: There is no way to satisfy time constraints if we do not have knowledge of our system execution-time bounds. A facility that determines execution-time bounds at compile time excludes statements with unbounded execution time from the language. Furthermore, it bans the use of dynamically created structures and of an unbounded recursion.

9.2 REAL-TIME PROGRAMMING LANGUAGES

Let us consider two types of languages used for programming real-time systems: asynchronous and synchronous. Although each of these types represents a large set of very different languages, we discuss here only one of each and restrict the discussion to only some of the characteristics that dominate the system behavior.

9.2.1 Asynchronous Real-Time Language

Ada[1] [1] is currently recognized in the United States as a mandatory government standard for programming real-time systems. Let us therefore examine its support for the language requirements.

The Ada programming language supports modularity, parallelism, and dynamic behavior. Regarding the above three structural concepts, Ada supports tasking, shares variables, communicates, and synchronizes in a rendezvous style. This synchronization style reduces the concurrency, imposing execution-time constraints. Figure 9.1 demonstrates this execution constraint, due to which process $\mathcal{P}$ must wait for the execution of process $\mathcal{Q}$. In addition, it does not provide any execution-time bounds, as demonstrated by the *wait* for synchronization in Figure 9.1. Furthermore, its alteration statement, the *select* statement, is defined

---

[1]Ada is a trademark of the U. S. Department of Defense (Ada Joint Project Office).

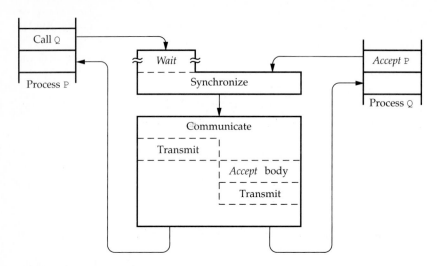

FIGURE 9.1
Rendezvous in Ada typical remote call.

as nondeterministic. Its *loop* and *while* statements are unbounded. All its subprograms can be called recursively and are re-entrant.

Some work has been done in order to allow implementations of Ada programs to be more suitable for real-time embedded systems. Let us review some of the features required to achieve such a goal, as proposed in the Corset and Lace interfaces [12].

The Ada run-time support environment (RSE) is defined for the general case of Ada programming environment. In order to adhere to the above language objectives, we need to define a specialized version of the run-time support environment. Two interfaces are used in this specialized version: Corset, which hides some RSE from the compiler, and Lace, which hides resource allocation from Ada RSE. Thus, we may generate an Ada subset that is simpler than the superset and may demonstrate a predictable program behavior. Examples of Ada features whose elimination may increase program predictability are

• Dynamic task creation and termination.
• Task priorities.
• Unbounded loops.
• Abortion.
• Nested accepts.
• Unbounded recursive subprograms, and others.

Other interfaces must allow modifications due to other real-time issues. For example, the CALENDAR predefined package, whose DURATION type is in seconds, and TIME type range is with a 32-bit accuracy, may be added for handling time.

In summary, a modified subset of an asynchronous language such as Ada can generate programs which satisfy the above language requirements.

9.2.2   Synchronous Real-Time Language

ESTREL [16, 17] is a synchronous imperative programming language in which temporal properties deal with events and not directly with histories. In order to emphasize some of the differences between this programming language and an asynchronous language, let us enumerate some of its properties.

1. A program reacts instantaneously to external stimuli, producing an instantaneous output. In the absence of stimuli the program is idle.
2. The only statements that take time are those that are explicitly required to do so (e.g., a "delay" statement).
3. Control takes no time at all, and therefore the sequencing operator (;) is immediate.
4. ESTREL modules communicate via *signals*, which are transferred in an instantaneous broadcast network.
5. Time is a multiform entity, and it is treated as a signal. In that sense, any signal can be treated as time.
6. An *event* is viewed as an instantaneously broadcast flash of information, formed by simultaneous signals that convey values. No memory is associated with events in that the information is lost in the absence of receivers.

The language supports a basic set of imperative statements which includes assignment, condition, loop, parallel, and others. Let us expand a little on its temporal statements and its signal handling. ESTREL introduces a *watching* statement that defines a time limit to the execution of its body through an event occurrence. Using this statement, we can build many other useful statements, such as *await* to halt an event occurrence, *upto*, and *uptonext*. A *during* construct allows defining a temporal extent of its body. Recall that time is viewed as any other signal, therefore

$$\textbf{during expression do statement end},$$

is really

$$\textbf{do statement uptonext expression end}.$$

The major drawback of synchronous languages is the strong impractical assumptions they make regarding the handling of time and events. They are, therefore, suitable only for applications in which the instantaneous execution assumptions can be justified. On the other hand, synchronous languages provide a deterministic programming environment and significantly simplify language semantics, in particular time manipulation semantics. ESTREL supports three layers of semantics analysis, which use transition systems that are based on *structural conditional rewrite rules*, to construct a proof system for the language.

1. A *static* semantics to check that a program does not raise any temporal paradoxes. In synchronous program these paradoxes may happen in any first instance of its executions. In asynchronous systems such a static test is similar to the one supported by RTL's positive cycles check (see Section 8.2 and [68]).

2. A *behavioral* semantics to define the temporal behavior of a program. It defines the history semantics associated with the program on an individual event basis. This analysis provides a comparison tool to study program equivalence.

3. A *computational* semantics is more complex then the behavioral semantics but allows us to compute what the program does.

9.3 SCHEDULABILITY ANALYSIS

Neither the synchronous nor the asynchronous languages are in themselves sufficient to uniquely determine or prove the temporal behavior of a system that contains more than one program. Current and future real-time systems cannot assume programs' temporal independence, unless programs do not share any resource. To say the least, it seems impractical to assume that each program in a distributed system will use its own, fully dedicated communication subsystem, for example. In this section, we will examine the requirements of combining a real-time language and a real-time operating system to produce a consistent real-time system.

We recognize five major participants in the determination of the execution timing properties of a compiled high-level program.

1. The language compiler.
2. The language run-time support environment.
3. The operating system.
4. Other executing programs with which the program shares data or resources.
5. The resources allocated for the execution.

We can divide these timing contributors into two groups. The first two are known at compile time. The last two are selected near execution time. It seems unreasonable to postpone the processing of timing properties known at compile time to a point of time near the execution. In order to make this processing in advance and in a meaningful way, we have to make some assumptions about the knowledge we have at compile time.

• We assume that the language compiler and its run-time support environment are well characterized and understood. They produce object codes whose execution without preemption and interruption is predictable, if not deterministic. Let us assume that we have a limited number of alternative allocations of resources for executions. Hence, we can "parameterize" the execution timing properties for these alternatives, without preemption and interruption.

- We assume that we have a consistent operating system. By this we mean that if each of the above alternative allocations is selected, the predicted timing properties will hold without preemption and interruption.
- We assume that the operating system can manage resources in such a way that different programs that share resources do not override the decisions of the operating system.

The assumptions we make here about the operating system seem difficult and ambitious. We will come back to support these assumptions later in the book, describing both a design that achieves them and an implementation of the design. However, we will first deal with the first two contributors, using a particular real-time programming language and a schedulability analyzer that has been developed for it.

REAL-TIME EUCLID.   Real-time Euclid [144] is a structured programming language whose compilation produces concurrent processes as schedulable entities for run-time. These processes are activated by a signal or an associated time "frame" defined at compile time. Once activated, a process will complete the execution of its task, and the scheduler must support it within its associated frame. The processes synchronize via signal and wait primitives using monitors. The wait primitive times-out if the waiting period exceeds a predefined bound.

Although Real-time Euclid is a Pascal descendant, it does not have constructs whose executed time is not bounded.

- Recursion is not allowed.
- Unbounded iteration is not allowed. In its first version, Real-time Euclid used a time-out to abort an iteration. Such a mechanism makes the loop post condition and the invariant condition meaningless. Thus, currently only a constant-count loop is supported.
- Dynamic data structures are not allowed.

Real-time Euclid has a run-time support environment that includes the scheduler, the allocator, and the interprocess communication. As in the ESTREL language, Real-time Euclid tries to solve the absence of an appropriate operating system in the "do it yourself" fashion. Thus, all the five timing contributors are under the language control, either through the compiler or through the run-time support environment.

The schedulability analyzer developed for Real-time Euclid [142, 143] makes use of the language control. The analyzer front-end is implemented within the compiler. While assembly code is generated, the analyzer front-end records the associated timing information and the program segment trees. The analyzer back-end resolves external calls by substituting the calls according to the proper segment subtrees. Then, the trees are converted to process trees. The analyzer computes the worst case time bounds for these trees based on the full implementation dependent information it has available. It uses frame superimposition for resolving contentions in monitors, in uninterruptable segments, and in communication.

9.4   CONCLUDING REMARKS

A real-time language by itself cannot produce a predictable temporal behavior of a system. However, the language we choose strongly affects the activities of the development phase of a system. Models and analysis techniques play a major role in these activities as well.

The issue of producing a predictable temporal behavior of the system we design and implement is still an open one. In order to develop a solution to this issue, we still have to show that we can design an operating system that supports the requirements. We need to show that other executing programs with which our program shares data or resources do not violate our constraints. Finally, we need to show that the resources allocated for the execution of our program do not impose unpredictable behavior on our program. All these issues are raised and answered in the following part of this book, in which we discuss the properties of real-time operating systems.

CHAPTER
10

VERIFICATION AND VALIDATION OF REAL-TIME SOFTWARE

The goal of program verification is to prove that a program meets its specification. Program verification is usually done in one of three major ways:

- Using an *axiomatic approach* to infer mathematical and logical assertions that describe the control and data states.
- Using *graph theoretic* properties to obtain the required proof.
- *Testing* the program for the input sequences it may meet when executed in its target plant.

There are applications which employ a combined use of these methods. We can use five combined methodologies to evaluate system performance properties [9]

1. Characterization of the work load of the proposed system.
2. Creation of an approximate queueing model for the system, and evaluating average performance properties.
3. Identification and preparation of hardware tools to allow measurements in the real system.
4. Development of a load-simulator to allow testing under a controlled load.
5. Modeling the system with a detailed simulator, which allows bottleneck identification and answers to "what if" questions.

131

Most of current verification tools are able to guarantee correctness of very simple systems at most, with a narrow interpretation of the term "correctness." Furthermore, many of the commonly used methodologies require us to make assumptions based on previous experience, which is always needed but rarely found.

In this chapter we examine current approaches in real-time program verification. We start with a description of testing methods, and then we examine simulation as a verification tool. Finally, we describe some aspects of the use of proof systems in verification. The chapter concludes with an assessment of the needs and the implications these needs create for "next generation" system architecture and approach.

10.1 TESTING REAL-TIME PROPERTIES

10.1.1 Systematic Testing Methods

Testing issues must be examined in the context of testing goals: (1) proving that the system under test is free of errors; and (2) obtaining some figures about the system reliability [120].

TESTING COVERAGE. Testing a system thoroughly means exercising and testing it with all possible combinations of its inputs. In exercising input sequences of a distributed system, relative changes within an input sequence are very important as well (e.g., synchronization problems). This property may lead to an enormous sequence of inputs for such a test. In order to reduce significantly the size of the input sequence, early approaches have suggested design criteria of asynchronous reproducibility of output.[1] Although this is a desired goal, sometimes it is not achievable. It is especially difficult when we deal with real-time systems that must meet deadline constraints. However, adopting this approach in the design, even partially, significantly reduces the required input sequences.

It is quite clear that testing a system thoroughly is an expensive solution for verifying a large and distributed real-time system. Many attempts have therefore been made to permit the reduction of the size of the input sequence. In the next section, we consider some of the issues involved in attempting to test only a sample of the complete input sequence. However, let us first mention other attempts that have considered performing various types of tests, each of which covers only a part of the whole system. Each type of test method demonstrates applicability for a different coverage of the test. Let us consider two opposite approaches.

"GLASS BOX" TESTING METHODS. "Glass box" testing methods are especially applicable in module-testing levels. A glass box test method starts with an analysis of the module's reachable paths. Then, the calculated path predicates are

---

[1] For a set of inputs, the same output will be produced, regardless of the speed differences or time intervals at which the inputs are delivered.

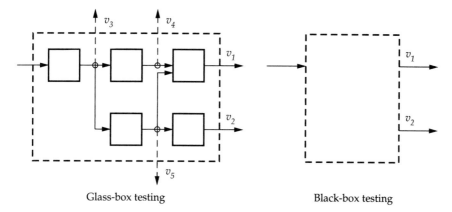

Glass-box testing

Black-box testing

FIGURE 10.1
Glass box and black box testing.

compared with the specification, and a symbolic execution of the tested module follows. The major disadvantage of this method is that it ignores dependencies between modules. Additional weaknesses are its inability to deal with run time changes of control logic, and its inability to pinpoint a missing path. Note that extending this method to a whole system is very hard, since it requires high observability of all the system elements.

"BLACK BOX" TESTING METHODS. In these test methods the system is treated as a "black box" with none of its internal details considered available. A test must be performed both positively—a functional test with inputs chosen according to the specification, and negatively—reaction to abnormal and unspecified events.

Figure 10.1 compares the glass box and the black box testing methods. Both methods have validation points v_1 and v_2, which are the external behavior of the module. However, the glass box testing demonstrates additional reachability to internal details of the module, denoted v_3, v_4 and v_5.

PROBE EFFECTS. The availability of "probing points" in the real-time system is usually limited. In order to trace control flow or data values, we must insert additional probing statements into the program, thereby introducing changes in the environment that the program will meet in a real operating mode. Probe effects are extremely important when dealing with a hard real-time environment, and in many cases they disqualify these testing methods.

10.1.2 Statistical Testing

The temptation to use a "sampled" test set originates in the amount of different inputs required to test a program systematically, which may become enormous. But the smaller the sample size, the lower the reliability, and therefore a decision upon the sample size must be calculated carefully. Typical results of statistical testing methods are an expected value, a risk, a probability, the confidence limits/ levels of significance, and the variance. In real-time software testing a particular emphasis is put on:

- Deadlock occurrence.
- Correctness of a sequence of outputs.
- Occurrence of final / intermediate results in the right time interval.

RISK CALCULATION.   We reduce the cost of the testing by using a statistical approach. Unfortunately, this decreases the testing of the system to less than 100%. We can also view this decrease in confidence as an increase in the risk of deploying the system. A comparison between the cost reduction and the risk involved is therefore necessary. We need a measure for the risk caused by events that we do not cover in our test. It is logical to define such a measure as a weighted sum of the risks involved in each of the events we do not cover in our test. The weights must reflect the probabilities of occurrence of their corresponding damaging events. One way of defining the *risk cost* is [120]

$$r = \sum_a H(a)X(a)$$

where

- $X(a)$ is the loss caused by event a.
- $H(a)$ is the frequency of "loss causing event" a, during the period of time in concern. We can weigh this frequency as

$$H(a) = \sum_i H(i)P(a|i)P(a|a_i)$$

- $H(i)$ is the frequency of "initiating event" i which may cause a.
- $P(a|i)$ is the probability that the system under test will fail to react correctly on i.
- $P(a|a_i)$ is the probability that any alternative action (installed previously) fails simultaneously.

SIMPLE CASES.   Let us analyze the probability of detecting error occurrences [120]. We must first examine the probabilities of encountering an error.

- Let us begin with the probability of encountering one error, with no additional conditions imposed. In such a case, the probability of encountering one error associated with time interval D, in the program run-time T, may be estimated as

$$P_{w_1} = \frac{D}{T}$$

Hence, for N test runs

$$P_{w_N} = 1 - (1 - \frac{D}{T})^N$$

- Now let us examine the probability of encountering one error in one test run, but this time with one binary condition. In such a case, the probability of encountering one error associated with time interval D, in the program run-time T is

$$P_{b1} = \frac{1}{2} \cdot \frac{D}{T}$$

For N test runs and k binary conditions:

$$P_{bN} = 1 - (1 - (\frac{1}{2})^k \cdot \frac{D}{T})^N$$

Let us next consider the case of a sequence of tasks. When M tasks access one resource, there are $M!$ possible access sequences. If we assume equal probability of failure for all accesses, then the probability of detecting one failing access, in N runs, is

$$P = 1 - (1 - \frac{1}{M!})^N$$

If the M tasks access n resources, the number of possible access sequences becomes

$$K = \sum_{j=1}^{n} \sum_{i=1}^{M} (N_i \times m_{i,\,j})$$

where

- N_i the number of runs of task i.
- $m_{i,\,j}$ the number of accesses to resource j during one run of task i.

If we want to consider all possible accesses, then the number of sequences becomes $K!$. We can use the above result to obtain the probability of detecting an error.

When we verify a real-time system that supports interrupts, we have a very similar problem of possible sequences. The occurrences of several possible priority interrupts in a time interval may trigger several task sequences, or require queue rearrangements. These cases are combinatorially treated in the same way as the access problem above.

TESTING LARGE SYSTEMS. The model described above for simple cases does not describe the complicated behavior of large systems. Let us define p_0 to be the probability of one distinct arbitrary property. What we need to obtain is a number of properties, N_t, for which we have to test. We choose N_t that ensures $p_0 < P_0$, within a confidence level $CL\%$, for a desired probability bound P_0. Assuming binomial distribution of properties' error detection probability, the number of properties we have to test for [120]

$$N_t = \frac{4.6}{P_0} \; for \; CL = 99\%$$

$$N_t = \frac{3.0}{P_0} \; for \; CL = 95\%$$

Note that if P_0 is between 10^{-7} and 10^{-4}, N_t becomes enormous. We can reduce this number only if we base our test coverage on system analysis, performed analytically rather than empirically.

PROBLEMS WITH LARGE TESTS.   As shown above, one requires a very large number of runs to obtain a reasonable confidence level. This fact emphasizes some requirements of testing large systems, in addition to those found in the simple cases. Let us examine some of these requirements.

- Testing real-time properties is implementation (and hardware) dependent by nature. Hence, we must test the system as a whole. Since we require many runs, we must employ computerized test equipment that activates the tested computer.
- The test equipment provides the test inputs, controls the timing, and monitors the outputs. Hence the reliability required from the test equipment has to be very high.
- If the test equipment includes a random number generator, the generator's repetition period has to be sufficiently long.
- Let us consider systems under test for which we have to maintain high confidence levels. The statistical analysis shows clearly that in these cases we achieve reduction of test sequences mostly due to formal analysis of the system under test. It is not the statistical approach itself that achieves the major reduction.

10.2   SIMULATION AS VERIFICATION TOOL

10.2.1   Classes and Aims

Let us distinguish between two major classes of simulations that are used to verify properties of a real-time program:

1. Simulation of the system under test itself.
2. Simulation of a plant/load that the system meets as its "real world."

There are various reasons to *simulate the program itself*:

- During the first phases of the design, it helps investigating basic properties of the model used. Thus we can examine the approach chosen to solve the given problem in an early stage of the development phase.

- Using an approximate simulation, we may predict approximate performance of the system, within a certain confidence level.
- Early results, even approximate ones, may help us to check and analyze design tradeoffs.
- After the system completes its development cycle, we may use a detailed simulator to verify achievement of design goals. A simulator supports this goal by allowing a comparison of its outputs to the real system's outputs.
- A simulator may serve as a good tool for providing answers to hypotheses testing, especially when deciding whether to upgrade the system.

A detailed simulator of a system is very expensive to develop [120], and the effort invested in it may lead to having it completed only after the real system is ready [9].

A more common simulation is a *plant/load simulator*, which is very useful in the following cases:

- When we need measurements of the system under a controlled load, the simulator makes it possible to isolate specific properties in a specific environment.
- A plant/load simulator allows proving properties of the system under test, when there is a danger in testing it with the real plant (e.g., control program of a nuclear power plant or a weapon). Note that the risk calculations must justify the effort of developing such a tool.
- A plant simulator is a good debugging tool in trying to reconstruct a pattern that lead to a crash or a deadlock, when only partial information exists for the analysis.

The basic idea in using simulation as a verification tool is to gain an advantage that no test provides. We construct a test according to the system's specification. The simulation provides a *verification of the specification* as well as of the system under test.

10.2.2 Problems in Simulation for Verification

After examining the benefits we can gain from a simulation, we have to consider its weak points. We note four points here:

1. Common mode errors in system and simulation design;
2. the complexity of large simulators;
3. verification of a simulator as a verifier; and
4. the distinction between a faulty system and a faulty simulator.

The first issue we raise here originates in the development philosophy. If the design model and the simulator are derived from the same basic assumptions, a special kind of error may arise, called *common mode errors*. The simulator and the system under test are both mistaken, and we therefore fail to detect the errors.

Simulation of a large system is rarely used, especially due to the cost involved in developing it. A good simulator of a system requires an effort investment that is in the same order of magnitude as the development of the system itself. One of the most difficult problems in simulating a large real-time system is the dependency of its performance on the sequence of inputs data. Since the simulator is required to perform as the real system should, including real-time properties, the complexity required from it is of the same level, and sometimes even higher.

The third issue concerns the simulation reliability and qualification for being a verification tool. When the risks of operating the system are high, the simulator used as a test tool must be highly reliable. To an extent, the simulator must be even more reliable than the system under test. This means that in addition to the development cost, the simulator has to be extensively used per se, before being qualified as a verifying tool.

Finally, when comparing simulator results and system results, we may find discrepancies. The problem of deciding which is "wrong" may be very difficult to solve.

10.3 TESTING CONTROL AND DATA FLOW

Program flow analyses have become important verification tools in computer programming [42]. We distinguish between two major flow analysis approaches. The first concentrates on the flow of control in the program, as emphasized in the transaction-centered design approach discussed in Section 6.2. The second approach concentrates on streams of data and their flow in the system. This verification approach is suitable for the transform-centered design methods described above in Chapter 6.

10.3.1 Control-Flow Verification

Let us examine the principles of control-flow verification techniques through an example, SADAT [151]. SADAT is an automated test tool that supports testing of a single FORTRAN module. SADAT performs a set of test procedures, some of which are listed below.

- *Static analysis* is a procedure that generates the program control graph. In this graph, sequential parts are represented as nodes and the arcs are an interpretation of decision-to-decision (*d–d*) paths. This analysis is capable of detecting unreachable statements and errors in control-flow that the compiler failed to detect.
- *Test case generation* produces a minimal subset that ensures at least one execution of each d–d path.

- *Path predicate calculation* is a procedure that produces the path predicate for every path in the module. In addition, this procedure runs the module's symbolic execution.
- *Dynamic analysis* procedure is provided in the following way. This procedure inserts a control statement, implemented as a subroutine call, in each d–d path. These control statements allow accumulation of the number of executions of each node. The output can be used to track a dynamically "dead" code, to optimize the most frequently executed parts, and to identify additional test cases that are required.

SADAT's major disadvantage is its lack of support for testing distributed and real-time properties. Dealing with a single module does not allow concurrency and parallelism. Furthermore, since no deadline analysis is performed, no critical timing problems can be identified.

Ferranti Computer Systems, Ltd. has developed a complete environment used in their facilities for software development and validation of real-time software [45]. This environment uses MASCOT (Modular Approach to Software Construction, Operation and Testing) and CORAL (block structured language, based on ALGOL60). This environment provides another example of control-flow verification support, consisting of the following tools, called TAS (Test Aid Suite)

- A *unit driver* is a package which is independent of the software under test. This package provides the test harness and allows initialization of set up values, specification of a unit (or a part of a unit) to be executed, and comparison of results obtained to those expected.
- A *path analyzer* partitions the source code into sub-path modules (SPM's). An SPM is a basic block containing no branch points. A sequence of SPM's forms a sub-path.
- An *instrumenter* adds the necessary "calls" to the source code, providing "execution history," debug facilities, test coverage analysis, and static analysis concerning the source structure.

Conceptually, this approach is very similar to SADAT (although testing a structured language) and suffers the same disadvantages.

10.3.2   Data-Flow Verification

When we model a system, we may use two bi-digraphs[1] to describe it. A *control-flow graph*, as we have discussed above, describes the structural behavior of the program and the control-flow during execution. On the other hand, a *data-flow*

---

[1]A bi-digraph is a graph whose arcs are directed and may be bidirectional.

graph (corresponding to each execution sequence) describes the data behavior during this execution [76]. In the control graph, the *vertices* represent *control points*, and the directed *arcs* represent *actions* or control transitions. In the data-flow graph, we find two types of vertices, *data items* and *operations*. The vertices are connected by directed *arcs* describing the data flow.

A data-flow graph corresponds to an execution sequence $S = (a_1, \ldots, a_n)$ in the control-flow graph, by attaching to each arc a_i a mapping of input variables $(X_1, \ldots, X_k)$ into output variables $(Y_1, \ldots, Y_m)$. This functional relation is the vertex of type "operation" that appears in the graph. The graph, which may be very large in the case of a complex program, may be reduced by means of abstraction levels, merging data items to vectors, and sequential actions into control segments. This graph may be used to demonstrate structural properties and to verify some performance ones.

Figure 10.2 describes a data-flow diagram (DFD) that illustrates an inertial navigation computation. We note that in this description the directed arcs represent the data and its flow, while the boxes are nodes of processing these data items.

Data-flow graph analysis demonstrates some important characteristics that support program verification. Independent data items may be detected, and thereby point to the distributed implementation that requires less communication traffic. This optimization problem becomes a partitioning problem, in which we require that the number of arc-cuts be minimized. We also note that each execution sequence, with its corresponding data-flow graph, encounters all the information needed for numerical error-bound analysis.

Many data-flow graph approaches and more advanced tools based on similar principles, such as SPECK [120], share the same deficiencies. Program correctness verification is very difficult to implement, and more difficult to understand. Timing properties are either ignored altogether or receive a simple and fruitless analysis. The statistical nature of inputs is not considered, and average and peak performance evaluation is not provided.

Let us consider a methodology based on data-flow analysis, called SREM [4]. SREM is a requirement engineering methodology that TRW has developed for the Ballistic Missile Defense Advanced Technology Center. The methodology adopts the functional hierarchy requirements of MIL–STD–490, in which each

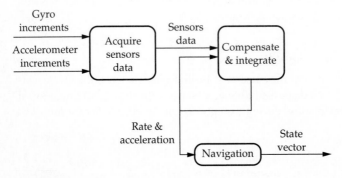

FIGURE 10.2
Data-flow diagram example.

process is divided into functions, each of these is further divided to sub-functions, and so on. The hierarchy imposes validation difficulties, especially in trying to exercise sub-sub-function through input sequences.

SREM has seven key concepts. First, we must specify a testable requirement in terms of data input and output because we test real-time software according to the transform-centered approach. In this approach, we input a MESSAGE and extract the results of its processing (an output MESSAGE) and the content of memory.

Another concept is the use of processing PATHs, which are sequences which contain no loops. SREM defines them in terms of input MESSAGEs, output MESSAGEs, processing steps, and the data utilized and produced.

The third concept is the use of VALIDATION POINTS. These are places in the module where we may perform a test in terms of variables measured on the PATH. We must clearly define the testable variables on validation points such that they assure testability and unambiguity of the requirements.

The following concepts are three tools that allow the construction of the model specification. The first tool, called R-Net, supports net description of the computation. It is an integration of all the PATHs that process a given type of stimulus, into a Requirement NETwork. This is a graph model of the computation and the flow. Five types of nodes are used in the graph: processing step nodes (ALPHA), input/output interface nodes, AND/OR flow nodes, selector nodes, and validation-point nodes. The unidirectional arcs represent the data-flow between the nodes.

Figure 10.3 gives an R-Net example. In this example, we describe the specification:

> Upon acceptance of an invocation request from a sender, acknowledge the sender and examine the incoming parameter. If the parameter is within the limits, update the link.

The example has four validation-point nodes, v_1 to v_4, four ALPHAs denoted as boxes, and input and output interface nodes. In addition, it has an AND flow node and a selector node whose condition is "limits."

The second tool in SREM is RSL, a formal language for specification of requirements. The third tool is REVS. This is an automated tool that speeds up and validates the requirements' completeness and consistency.

The final concept of SREM consists of methodology STEPS that produce intermediate products obeying evaluation criteria for each step. Let us review these methodological steps and their products. The first step is *translation*. This step addresses the following issues:

- Adequacy of subsystem performance requirements (DPSPR) for generating processing requirements.
- An early baseline of the functional requirements.
- Budgeting and scheduling the activities.

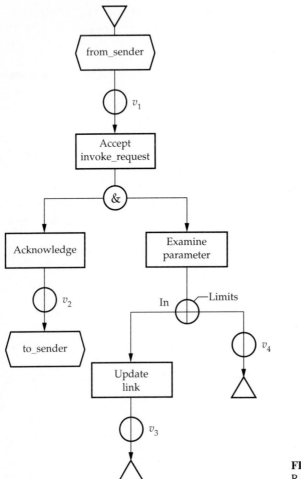

FIGURE 10.3
R-net example.

Some activities are carried out in this step. The RSL originating requirements are entered into REVS database. According to this database, we generate R-Nets, DATA and ALPHAs, with traceability back to DPSPRs. Then, we analyze the consistency and completeness of the requirements. We generate a DPSPR problems report, and we budget and schedule further activities.

The products of the first step include: a DPSPR problem report, R-Nets, ALPHAs, DATA, functional traceability, and plans.

The second step is *decomposition*. This step addresses the following issues:

- Preliminary definition of the performance requirements.
- The incorporation of the processing to satisfy the subsystems constraints into the processing requirements.

The activities carried out in this step start with an identification of the form of the performance requirements to be considered. Then we specify the data collected at validation points (which are software variables). We record the decisions made, to relate accuracy and timing requirements back to DPSPRs.

The products of the second step include refined RSL, performance traceability, and validation points.

The third step is *allocation*. This step addresses the following issues:

• Determining the sensitivity of PATH performance to DPSPRs.
• Establishing the tradeoffs between accuracy and timing of the different PATHs, then selecting an allocation whose restrictions allow it.

After establishing the requirements of each of the PATHs, the requirement and its test are written in RSL. In complicated systems, at this point we develop a functional simulator.

The products of this step include performance sensitivity, performance statement, process performance requirements (PPR), and functional simulation.

The fourth and final step in this methodology is the *analytical feasibility demo*. This step addresses the following issues:

• Example algorithms are implemented to demonstrate that critical processing requirements can be satisfied. This is done before attempting the design of an algorithm for the real-time software.
• A direct check is provided by the above, the algorithms that satisfy the PPR in fact meet the originating requirements—the DPSPR.

The products of this step include example algorithms and a simulator.

CONCLUSION. The SREM methodology allows specifying complete and consistent requirements of a system and its subsystems. The R-Net graph model resembles more advanced models of finite state automata, and provides a good visibility of relations and testability properties. Yet, most of the performance decisions and the structure built up are manual, and depend highly on the designer's skills. The use of a functional simulator to verify performance must be carefully examined to avoid common mode errors, especially considering the high cost involved in developing the simulator.

10.4 PROOF SYSTEMS

We may consider the verification of real-time systems as an extended version of the conventional concurrent systems. In addition to the logical correctness expressed in *safety properties* and *liveness properties*, real-time systems must also show correctness of *temporal properties*. While a liveness property states that a certain relationship eventually holds, a temporal property imposes time bounds on this relationship. In this sense, verification of the correctness of a real-time concurrent system is much more complicated than that of a conventional one.

In Chapter 8 we reviewed the use of axiomatic approaches to proving properties of the system. In order to examine these approaches as verification tools, let us consider the verification as viewed by one of these approaches: the combined ESM and RTTL proof system [110]. Let us recall some features of this proof system as described in Section 8.4. RTTL uses temporal operators for temporal reasoning, as *until* ($\sqcap$), *next* ($\odot$), *eventually* ($\diamond$), *henceforth* ($\square$), *unless* (*U*), *precedes* ($\mathcal{P}$), and others.

A system M is modelled as a set of controller processes and plant processes that execute concurrently. A path in the state space of M, called a *trajectory*, consists of a sequence of states and events. The paths that M is constrained to follow are called *legal trajectories*. A trajectory σ which consists of $s_0s_1\ldots$ which is k-shifted to $s_ks_{k+1}\ldots$ is denoted σ^k.

In order to understand the way RTTL verifies that M meets its specification $\mathcal{S}$, let us first consider the way it defines *satisfaction* and *validity*. Let us denote that a temporal formula w is satisfied in σ, by $\models^\sigma w$. RTTL defines the satisfaction relation for w in σ as follows: $\models^\sigma w$ if and only if w evaluates to *true* at the initial state s_0 of σ. w will be true in the *next* state, or in other words, $\models^\sigma \odot w$ if and only if $\models^{\sigma^1} w$.

Now, let S be a temporal formula that specifies a required property of the plant. Let Σ_M be the set of legal trajectories in the state space of M. RTTL defines temporal specification S Σ_M-valid if it satisfies all the trajectories in Σ_M.

Using the above relations, the problem of verifying that the control processes satisfy the system specification $\mathcal{S}$, becomes the problem of proving that $\mathcal{S}$ is Σ_M-valid.

10.5 Operational Approach

After proving that the system model satisfies the specification, we still cannot state anything about the implementation. We are still left with the problem of verifying that the implementation demonstrates the exact behavior of the model.

An operational approach has been introduced in the PAISLey project trying to bridge the above gap [155]. The main idea is that the external behavior and internal structure of a system may interleave. In order to maintain generality, the operational approach separates the problem-oriented structure of the operational specifications from pure implementation considerations. The operational specifications themselves are written in an operational specification language, which is *executable* and prevents ambiguities. The executability feature of the specification provides a tool for early examination of the results, and can be regarded as a functional simulator that corresponds to the specification constraints. Automated translation (from specification statement to an implementation code) is highly feasible, since problem-oriented internal constraints are taken into account. This transformational implementation would therefore guarantee correctness of the produced code.

Note that the transformational implementation contains all the realization constraints and therefore is not unique but rather implementation dependent. Each individual transformation should therefore be carefully proved, prior to relying on it as assurance of the realization correctness.

10.6 CONCLUDING REMARKS

In this chapter we reviewed methods of verifying real-time systems. The verification activity is viewed throughout the methods discussed here as a test for consistency between the specification and the implementation. We list below features that still do not exist in these current systems but that we find to be extremely important for future systems. These needs are important for multiapplication, adaptive, and fault-tolerant systems. They concern changes in execution environment, and emphasize the role of the operating system in the correctness of each of the applications.

- A system may contain a number of applications executing concurrently.
- Real-time operating systems must allow verifiability of applications independently.
- Systems must support the adaptive nature of the applications in that adding an independent module to the system does not require testing of the whole system.

These needs imply the following properties in an architecture of "next generation" real-time systems:

- Application and operating system relations must support a consistent view, such that assertions in both domains do not contradict each other.
- System modules must be autonomous and thus reduce dependency and allow meaningful testing of parts of the system.
- An application that a system "accepts" for execution must be guaranteed to execute while satisfying its constraints, regardless of other applications that share resources with it.

PART

III

REAL-TIME
OPERATING
SYSTEMS

CHAPTER
11

PROPERTIES OF REAL-TIME OPERATING SYSTEMS

We start our discussion of real-time operating systems with a review of the approaches demonstrated by the principles of current real-time operating systems. We conclude this review with a short comparison of the features supported currently and the requirements of future systems as we foresee them. Since the set of properties of a real-time operating system is rich and colorful, we dedicate the rest of this chapter to a detailed discussion of these properties.

11.1 CURRENT OPERATING SYSTEMS

Real-time operating systems have been in use for a long time and in a variety of environments. Most of them form a centralized computing environment and usually do not guarantee the satisfaction of timing constraints. The management approach adopted by a large portion of current real-time operating systems is the use of scheduling schemes that employ fixed priorities. Some of these real-time operating systems provide limited "time services" to support local knowledge of time.

In this section we present brief descriptions of a few typical real-time operating systems. These examples are chosen to represent major classes of the operating systems that have been in practice.

11.1.1   Priority Driven Systems

Most of the operating systems that have been employed for real-time applications are basically centralized and priority driven operating systems. One widely used operating system that we have chosen as an example is used with Data General and Miltope computers, called RTOS.[1]

Like other operating systems of this type, RTOS executive contains five major functional parts:

- Device drivers.
- System call handlers.
- Interrupt handlers.
- Task call handlers.
- A rescheduling mechanism.

During operation, the system can be in one of the following states:

- Executing an application job.
- Handling interrupt.
- Executing a task call or performing rescheduling.

The tasks are assigned priorities which remain fixed during the system operation. Two queues are used to organize the tasks; the *ready task* queue and the *suspended task* queue. The task with the highest priority in the ready task queue gets control. Control is returned either by a task call performed by the executing task, or by an invocation of the rescheduling upon an interrupt exit. The interrupt exit has to pass through the rescheduling step, since priorities could have been changed through an allowed interrupt nesting sequence.

The major disadvantage of this type of system is the absence of explicit time notions in the control and management structures. It is a hard priority system, and any user task can impose priorities that may affect the behavior of the whole system.

11.1.2   Priority Driven with Enhanced Time Services

In 1987, Intel introduced its iRMK and iRMX[2] operating systems [66] which support the systems built with their 80286 and 80386 microprocessors. These operating systems are good examples of a class of real-time operating systems

---

[1]RTOS is a trademark of Data General Corporation.

[2]iRMK real-time kernel and iRMX–286 are trademarks of Intel Corporation.

that support a rich set of time services, as well as modern approaches for task management, interrupt handling, synchronization, and communication. Some characteristics of these systems are

- The system supports preemptive priority scheduling combined with a round robin mechanism. Periodic reactivation of tasks is supported as well.
- The system interrupt handler is fast and predictable; however, user service for an interrupt is activated upon interrupt occurrence after priority status verification.
- Message communication employs mailbox structures. Combining it with semaphores allows rich intertask communication.
- Time management is local, in the sense that the local clock dictates the knowledge of time. Alarm services (periodic and aperiodic) as well as awakening services are provided.

Although various distribution issues along with fault tolerance issues are not addressed by these systems, let us concentrate on their timing predictability. From the above characteristics one can see that the explicit notion of time in the resource allocation and execution decisions is still absent. In this class of operating systems we find a standardization effort by Motorola, the Real-Time Executive Interface Definition (RTEID [149]).

These systems support a case in which one user interrupt service can cause another task to miss a deadline. Therefore, in these systems the possibility of guaranteeing meeting a deadline cannot exist. User programs in RTEID have "sufficient latitude to change the real-time characteristics of an entire system [149]" using *t_setpri* and *t_mode* functions. This problem can be prevented in operating systems that assume a closed set of tasks and a closed set of action scenarios. Examples of such cases are some applications of the Hawk operating system which has been introduced by Sandia National Laboratories [65]. However, closed systems are special cases and tend to be a limited solution in the long run.

11.1.3 Time Driven Scheduling

Two major issues have been the motivation for research on time driven scheduling, denoted TDS (e.g., [69,147]). The first issue is the possibility of missing deadlines in priority driven operating systems. The need to explicitly decide on allocation and scheduling with respect to time is the second issue. The TDS model uses a time varying *value function* as a measure of the criticality of a task.

The assumptions made in the TDS model, introduce a task whose computation time's stochastic distribution parameters are known. In addition, the TDS model assumes that task completion time can be analyzed in terms of criticality. The model divides each value function into three domain sections. Over each section, an expression of the form

$$V(t) = K_1 + K_2t + K_3t^2 + K_4e^{-K_5t}$$

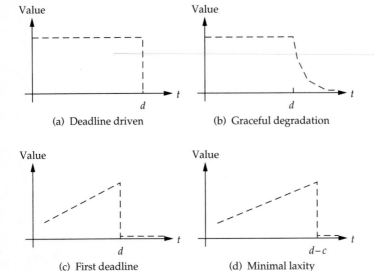

FIGURE 11.1
Time driven scheduling examples.

defines the function. Hence, TDS uses 15 coefficients for the definition of each value function.

Figure 11.1 illustrates some examples of value functions, reflecting some commonly employed scheduling disciplines. Part (*a*) of the figure emphasizes the hard deadline principle, due to which the value function demonstrates a sharp drop to zero value. Once the deadline elapses, passing time *d*, there is no reason to schedule this object; it is already a failure anyway. Thus, the third section of this function is a constant zero. In part (*b*) of the figure we demonstrate a soft deadline approach. Here, the value function drops exponentially to zero. Hence, passing the deadline *d* is not a total failure, and there is still some use in scheduling the object. Therefore, the following value function is adequate for that case:

$$V(t) = \begin{cases} 0 & 0 \le t \\ K_1 & 0 < t \le d \\ K_4 e^{-K_5(t-d)} & t > d \end{cases}$$

Parts (*c*) and (*d*) of Figure 11.1 show value functions that adhere to the first-deadline and the minimal-laxity policies. Thus, for the first-deadline scheduling policy we have the following value function:

$$V(t) = \begin{cases} 0 & 0 \le t \\ K_1 + K_2 t & 0 < t \le d \\ 0 & t > d \end{cases}$$

The reader can derive the value function for the *minimal laxity* scheduling discipline in the same way.

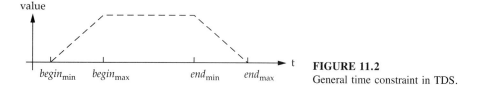

FIGURE 11.2
General time constraint in TDS.

Let us now recall our general model for a time constraint. In that model, we restrict the computation occurrence in a window delimited from the left and from the right by $begin_{min}$ and end_{max}, respectively. Outside that interval the value function gives a negative value. When time passes $begin_{min}$, the value function increases, reaching its highest value at $begin_{max}$. This value holds until end_{min}, and it starts dropping until it reaches the deadline end_{max}. Figure 11.2 describes this value function, formally expressed as follows:

$$V(t) = \begin{cases} K_{1,1} + K_{2,1}t & begin_{max} \leq t(K_{1,1} + K_{2,1}begin_{min} = 0) \\ K_{1,2} & begin_{max} < t \leq end_{min} \\ K_{1,3} - K_{2,3}t & t > end_{min}(K_{1,3} - K_{2,3}end_{max} = 0) \end{cases}$$

This value function based model is used with a best-effort scheduling algorithm. The goal of this algorithm is to maximize the total value of all completed tasks over workloads and given value functions. An *overload estimation* heuristic is computed at each scheduling point, to obtain a probability of overload. When an overload occurs, the tasks cannot meet their deadlines. If this probability exceeds a threshold, a *load shedding* heuristic is invoked. This heuristic selects tasks whose abortion would decrease the probability of overload below the threshold. Then these tasks are aborted in an order that adheres to an expected *value density*. The above heuristics are quite expensive computationally. Thus, time driven scheduling approaches employ some simplification and approximation schemes.

TDS design separates the scheduling policy and the scheduling mechanism. Abstract data types are used to achieve this separation (in object oriented languages, type inheritance facilities are adequate). The policy modules are placed in the operating system kernel, and function calls carry out communication between them and the mechanisms. The primitives for linking a policy module to the system and for specifying a required attribute to a policy are

Set_Policy(schedule, policy_module_name),
Set_Attribute(schedule, $K_1, \ldots, K_{15}$).

The placement of policy modules in the kernel reduces the system overhead of accessing the policy module. Kernel placement results in high maintainability overhead and difficult modifications. However, performance improves from this tradeoff.

Although this system is time-driven, it is not a hard real-time system in that it does not guarantee the meeting of the deadlines. This system is built on top of a general-purpose operating system, in which the values of one user's tasks can cause the abortion of others. In order to prevent undesired abortions, we must have consistent comparison criteria. This requires "global" setting of a value function in order to obtain correct priorities.

11.1.4 Deadline-Guaranteeing Operating Systems

Let us now conclude our review with an advanced real-time kernel that can serve hard real-time application. The Spring kernel, currently in development at the University of Massachusetts [140], is an example of an approach in which time constraints are the motivation for scheduling.

ARCHITECTURE SUPPORT. The environment for which the Spring operating system has been designed is physically distributed and consists of a network of multiprocessors. Each multiprocessor includes one or more application-dedicated processors, one or more system processors, and an I/O subsystem. Each of the above processors has a local memory, and they are all connected to allow the formation of a global memory bank. Speed and temporal determinism of application behavior in this system depend on the offloading of overhead activities from application processes. Thus, management activities such as scheduling and allocation are executed by the system processor and the I/O subsystem. Even interrupts do not disturb the application processor, and they are processed in the I/O subsystem. This subsystem also handles the slow I/O devices and the noncritical activities.

The tasks, which are the scheduling entities of this system, reside in a local memory during execution. The architectural support simplifies the solution to the problem of real-time allocation and scheduling while guaranteeing constraint satisfaction. However, the extra hardware is an additional cost we must pay in this solution.

ALLOCATION AND SCHEDULING. The Spring operating system maintains an ordered table of guaranteed tasks. Allocation of resources and scheduling for execution are implemented in four modules:

1. *Dispatcher*, initiates tasks from a system table of already ordered guaranteed tasks.
2. *Local scheduler*, verifies locally the deadline satisfaction and orders the accepted tasks properly in the above table.
3. *Global scheduler*, allocates remote multiprocessor nodes for execution of tasks that cannot be guaranteed locally.
4. *Meta level controller* (MLC), is an environment change detector and supports user interfaces.

SEGMENTATION. "The Spring kernel is based on the principles of segmentation, as applied to hard real-time systems" [140]. According to the applications and the resources they require, the operating system derives metrics and sizes of resource segments. Decisions on assignments of resource segments are taken with respect to the derived metrics. In this approach, time is treated as a very important resource whose segments should be allocated to computations. Data and memory have to be allocated as well, and their segmentation is derived with respect to functionality and size. The segmentation principle, as applied in the Spring kernel, sets and prepares elements for allocation manipulations that are managed later by the scheduling algorithms.

TASK MANAGEMENT. The Spring kernel provides task management primitives to support the manipulation of the scheduling entities. The creation primitive generates a new task, including the memory and the TCB (task control block) that are required. An allocation primitive assigns a slot for the task and loads its data segments. Deletion and deallocate primitives are also available. Criticality of a task can be set and can be queried. A delay primitive allows a task to switch itself to a time-bounded dormant state, and a special primitive allows imposing a time constraint on a task. Off-line tasks are queued, and their execution is allowed to be suspended and resumed by special primitives.

MEMORY MANAGEMENT. The Spring kernel rejects the use of virtual memory policies, such as page fault and page replacement, for hard real-time systems. These policies are unsuitable because of the large and unpredictable delays they introduce. Instead, according to the segmentation principle, each task requires its a priori known maximal memory requirement. Memory is preallocated, imposing restrictions on the dynamic behavior of uncertain elements. Hence, stacks are size bounded and so are the number of I/O pointers, the number of data segments, and message buffers for each TCB.

INTER-PROCESS COMMUNICATION. Spring tasks communicate with each other via messages, and no memory sharing is supported. Messages are sent and received using task mailboxes as communication buffers. Primitives are provided to send and receive with and without waiting, as well as for mailbox creation. The scheduling mechanism inherently avoids the need for semaphores by the full mutual exclusion it generates in the verification of guarantees.

11.1.5   Assessment of Current Approaches

Considering the evolution discussed above, from simple priority systems to time-deterministic and time-motivated systems, we find that several of the problems of hard real-time systems still need addressing. We believe that any approach taken to designing hard real-time systems should be more general and less implementation specific in order to allow a wider class of solutions. The approach should adhere to the deadline constraints, but in addition it should handle cases in which execution may be started only after a begin-time constraint. Thus, constraining the execution time from both sides enhances predictability significantly.

The fault tolerance goals of the computation should be an integral part of the tightly linked allocation and scheduling activities. The architecture should provide basic elements and mechanisms that support hard real-time, fault tolerance, and distribution. It should also support openness for repeatedly changing user requests along with additions and removals of resources. These elements and mechanisms must demonstrate coherence and uniformity with respect to locality. They should also support the temporal determinism along with the damage containment as required in such systems. The needs listed above are the motivation for the solutions that are proposed later in this book. Fulfillment of these requirements allows development of a class of hard real-time operating systems that are suited for "next-generation" real-time systems.

In order to provide a suitable facility for meeting the real-time requirements, a number of properties of the operating system components may be inferred. In the following sections we define the different parts of the operating system and present our view of the requirements for these parts. In this discussion we consider the requirements of distributed fault-tolerant real-time operating systems. Various aspects in these operating systems are analyzed to emphasize the importance of developing such operating systems separately rather than modifying or adding to conventional systems. The discussion concludes with a summary of these aspects in Section 11.9.

11.2   RESOURCE MANAGEMENT/ALLOCATION

In real-time operating systems the resource management and allocation mechanism should adhere to application timing requirements. In conventional operating systems this mechanism is entirely application independent, and is maintained as an internal issue of the operating system. Chapters 12, 13, and 14 expand on this issue. We highlight here the motivation for the approach as adopted in these later chapters.

11.2.1   Scheduling

Processes in our computation model share servers. These servers need some type of queues manipulated by schedulers to set the order in which they give service. In conventional operating systems we find schedules for processing, for I/O services, for network services, and so on. Many scheduling disciplines are possible, and each discipline may be suitable for scheduling a specific type of service. A particular scheduling policy for a particular type of service should adhere to the requirements of the jobs it serves. However, each scheduling discipline influences the implementation of the applications very strongly. The strong interaction between a real-time operating system and the application programs presents difficulties in meeting our goal of a predictable environment. One result is that when a real-time application job is running, the system may not have much flexibility in scheduling and accepting many additional processing requests. Nevertheless, there are scheduling disciplines that a real-time system can never support. One example is a round robin discipline, in which the overhead of switching control between processes does not conform to the timing requirements. The most general scheduling mechanism is divided into two parts:

- *Scheduling manager*, (also called off-line scheduler) a process in which the management of the policy of a discipline of a service scheduling is dynamically updated. For example, when a resource is added to the system, in addition to recognizing the availability of that resource, a new discipline may be adequate.
- *Run-time scheduler*, (also called on-line scheduler) actual application of current discipline.

In order to describe the relationship between the scheduling and the real-time constraints, we have to define a model that describes it. Elements of this model consist of both the scheduling process and the items we want to schedule—the computation processes. We note that in a real-time operating system the order in which grants for service are given has to assure meeting the timing requirements. The "hard" scheduling *priority* levels are not fit for this task; they serve better as measures of emergency rather than as measures of urgency of execution due to real-time constraints.

We can consider scheduling as maintaining ordered lists (queues), whose items are members of a given set. In these lists the items are sorted according to a specified key. In our model, the given set is the set of active processes. From a real-time point of view, the set of active processes can be partitioned into two disjoint subsets:

1. Synchronous processes which we have to activate regularly at a given frequency (also called *periodic* processes).
2. Asynchronous processes, each of which appears irregularly, but within a bounded frequency (also called *aperiodic* or *sporadic processes*).

Let us recall our definition of time constraints.[3] Each of the above processes, say P_i, is characterized by a *real-time constraint* expressed as a quintuple

$$< P_i, b_i, c_i, f_i, d_i >$$

where c_i is the computation time of P_i, b_i is its begin-time constraint, d_i is its deadline, and f_i is its frequency (for the asynchronous case it is the bound). Two important properties of the above model hold when a working solution exists:

1. $\forall i$ in the model: $c_i < d_i - b_i < \frac{1}{f_i}$.
2. $\sum_i c_i f_i \leq$ the number of available resources.

---

[3]See Section 2.2.

The first property must hold continuously and is a consideration of the "on-line" scheduler. The latter is a condition for the "off-line" scheduler. Note that the latter requirement is stronger than what is really needed: it considers the maximal demand rate the system can handle due to asynchronous processes.

From the above model we can derive the property that distinguishes a real-time operating system from others:

> In a real-time operating system the scheduling decisions are based on the real-time constraints (the above quintuples) of the active processes in the system.

The following scheduling examples illustrate the meaning of the above statement [103].

> Various algorithms may be applicable for an architecture that has a local queue for a specific resource. The most obvious scheduling algorithm is the "earliest deadline" algorithm. The scheduler chooses to execute the process whose deadline is earliest.
>
> A second approach is to use a scheduling policy that chooses the process whose maximal delaying possibility is the lowest. This approach is called the "least slack" algorithm. The slack of a process at time t is defined as the maximum time that a run time scheduler can delay it, without violating the constraints. In other words
>
> $$slack(P_i, t) = \max_{t > b_i}(d_i(t) - t - c_i(t), 0)$$
>
> A third example of real-time scheduling is "latency" scheduling, in which we perform the following steps. First, we consider the whole global state of the system constraints as a graph. Then, we calculate the latency of the constraints. Finally, we allocate the "next time-slice" to the system constraint with the appropriate latency.

Process requests and time servers activate the on-line scheduler. The on-line scheduler implementation must be very efficient. It resides at the "kernel" level allowing the overhead of management to be minimal. We can implement the off-line scheduler at a user process level and not necessarily at the kernel level. User processes are also allowed to be off-line (their deadline can be ∞), such as for log-in, compile, link, and so on. As such, we can schedule them for service in any time-independent discipline (LIFO, FIFO, etc.), a policy used for ordering processes that have the same non-critical "latency."

11.2.2   Processor Allocation

Special processing constraints of a computation may govern the allocation of a processor as a resource by the allocation algorithm. In such cases, the allocation may be in conflict with the architecture—timing optimization imposed by the real-time scheduling. For example, we can find cases in which we must allocate a job to a specific processor because it has an additional coprocessor. Such a case may force us to reject other jobs that are better candidates for this processor simply because no other allocation can support the need for the coprocessor. Let us review a basic method for modelling and resolving such situations.

We may divide software tasks in time-critical real-time systems into several threads, and arrange each of the threads to satisfy an execution-time constraint. For example, in the Ballistic Missile Defense application (BMD), 23 tasks were divided into 7 threads [98]. This application denotes the time constraints on the port-to-port processing time of the thread. A model of the total execution time of a thread consists of four components [99]:

1. Execution time of the task on the processor (E_i), which depends on the task size and the processor speed;
2. the communication network and operating system overhead accumulated cost (Ov);
3. inter-processor communication (IPC); and
4. waiting time (WT) wasted when the task waits in the processor ready queue.

In this model, we can summarize the above contributors to the total execution time of the thread as

$$E_T = \sum_i (E_i) + Ov + IPC + WT$$

Minimizing E_T enhances the system's performance along with increasing the system's ability to satisfy the demands. For a given network, especially for closed systems, Ov is nearly constant. Hence, in order to reduce E_T the following steps may be adopted:

- Reduce WT: assign large tasks to different processors.
- Reduce IPC: assign tasks that have high IPC requirement among them to the same processor.
- Reduce E_i: assign large tasks to processors with higher speed.

We will return to this allocation approach later in this book.

The above considerations refer only to some average-load performance issues. But our resource allocation scheme must also consider the possible effects of peak load occurrences. Moreover, it must consider fault consequences and allocate replicas and alternatives in a way that achieves the fault tolerance objectives. The redundancy issue, among others, implies *exclusion* relations between tasks. If we allocate a task to one processor, another must be allocated elsewhere to assure that at least one of them will survive a local failure.

11.2.3 Architecture Dependency

The architecture of resources should be a significant consideration when allocating them to processes. Physical distances between required resources may imply a different execution time, and thereby shrink the set of possible allocations within given timing constraints. In the BMD application example discussed earlier, minimizing the IPC to meet time constraints can consider a cost function of the IPC which depends on the following parameters:

- task coupling factors: the number of data units transferred from one task to another,
- inter-processor distance: the cost of a transfer of one data unit from one task to another.

The IPC cost function depends strongly on the system architecture. Another architecture dependent parameter in the allocation is the task *preference*. A computation that requires special resources restricts its possible allocation alternatives significantly. Therefore, an algorithm to derive a proper resource allocation must use information about the task preference and the task exclusion. Then, in order to minimize the IPC cost, it must consider both the task coupling factors and the interprocessor distances. Note that many allocation approaches demonstrate dependence on the system architecture. If we do not analyze the architecture properly, we may produce allocations that are highly sensitive. Small changes in the architecture may require large changes in the allocation.

11.3   TIME SERVICES

In addition to simple time services which we find also in conventional operating systems (e.g., get time, get date, time stamp), we find special needs in a real-time operating system. One example is the clock-reset service, an important interprocess service for physical synchronization as well as an important internal service for a process.

A time service in a distributed system uses an algorithm that keeps a collection of locally monotonic clocks synchronized. The algorithm also keeps the clocks adequately accurate with respect to some time standard. Keeping the clocks locally monotonic is simple, and we can achieve it with logical clocks [80]. Yet, this solution allows both anomalous behavior and a large drift between different clocks. In order to examine the adequacy of a service, let us recall a model that describes it.[4]

- Let $C_i(t)$ denote a function that maps real time to clock i time.
- A *standard* clock i is one with $\forall t : C_i(t) = t$.
- A clock i is *correct* at time t_0 if $C_i(t_0) = t_0$.
- A clock i is *accurate* at time t_0 if the first derivative of $C_i(t)$ is 1 *sec/sec* at t_0.

---

[4]We repeat the model definition for reader convenience. The detailed model is presented in Section 2.3.

The use of a set of physical clocks $\{C_i(t)\}$ improves the system's performance (with respect to drift) up to a limit. However, it may be improved further using a synchronization procedure. We regard this procedure as

$$C_i(t_i) \leftarrow F(C_{i1}(t_{i1}), C_{i2}(t_{i2}), \dots, C_{ik}(t_{ik}))$$

where the function calculates its result from distributed data.

In Chapter 2 we introduced the three classes of time servers a real-time operating system can employ. Central clock systems emphasize a hardware oriented solution, usually with expensive equipment and accurate results. Centrally controlled clock systems demonstrate an economic solution with a relatively low communication cost. They often produce good results in reducing differences between clocks. Distributed clock systems emphasize the tolerance of faults achieved mainly with an increased communication overhead.

All these classes support objectives of real-time operating systems, yet they differ in performance and cost. Each set of applications that shares a time-service of an operating system must adopt the service best suited to its own objectives.

In order to adhere to stringent time constraints in a multiple application environment, let us examine an important issue; the service concept. There is a variety of server models we can employ. One possibility is to use a server that is always active, and polls for service requests. Let us say that in case more than one request arrives, the requests are queued. On the other side of the spectrum, there is the dormant server which we activate for execution upon request arrival. Note that in the time service case there is a special requirement on timing. When a process invokes the service commonly called GET_TIME, it queries about the time *now*. Furthermore, if it is a hard real-time process, the time server must not queue its request for an unpredictably long wait period.

We propose the use of a time provider rather than a time server. The time provider can broadcast its clock value. It can update a shared variable, known to all local users, which they, in turn, can read according to their needs. Readers can access the clock value concurrently with no delay at all. Since no request for service is required, even fault tolerant algorithms become easier to implement.

11.4 COMMUNICATION

Two key properties characterize the different nature of a real-time operating system with respect to a traditional one:

1. *Bounded time.* Each job must complete execution within a bounded time. Furthermore, the relative progress of a set of tasks should be controllable and predictable.
2. *Application dependence.* Each temporal property of the real-time operating system may hide extreme consequences for particular applications. Therefore, a real-time operating system should give (within limits) control of the use of time resources to an application designer.

Functional requirements of communication, as supported by any operating system, are also important in real-time operating systems. The additional characteristics of bounded time for jobs and application dependence should also be supported by the communication subsystem of a real-time operating system.

11.4.1 Message Passing

The *type of model* used (e.g., master/slave, balanced, centrally controlled, post-office like, etc.) influences strongly both fault tolerance issues and real-time constraint issues. In cases where communication is synchronous, processes must poll and wait for their turn to send messages. For example, let us consider a centrally controlled communication network, in which one process dictates to all others when each is allowed to transmit. We find such systems in restricted networks (e.g., the Mux-Bus). This approach reduces significantly the system performance, unless we add some dedicated hardware (buffers and communication control) to each processor. Furthermore, the existence of a dictating process makes the system vulnerable to a single failure. Even though there are possible election recovery schemes in case this process fails, the time loss involved in an election may be unacceptable.

Parameter passing in remote procedure-calls emphasizes the interaction between the real-time properties of the communication network and the implemented distributed solution. Let us consider and compare reference versus value parameter passing. Using reference parameters assures a better concurrency control in cases of data sharing, but it complicates the execution, thereby imposing longer access times. On the other hand, using value parameters to transfer shared variables requires additional control and treating the block of shared data as a resource, i.e., enforcing mutual exclusion on access to this block. Nevertheless, execution time is well defined when we use value parameters. Furthermore, let us note that in case the shared object is a program, "value" transfer allows concurrent execution of the replica.

The above considerations suggest that in real-time systems, parameter passing for remote procedural calls must use value parameter-transfer and employ a mutual exclusion control. In addition, we must exclude various formats of information in order to avoid an irregular addition of "translation time" to the execution time of a job. The above considerations influence the storage and access management, and even the issue of file structures.

Fault tolerance of communication has a tremendous effect on time bounds for message delivery. However, the communication network must adhere to the *correctness* of timing requirements of the application, in addition to supporting failure modes. For example, consider the error model we introduced for synchronization of a distributed physical clock system. In order to have a reasonable estimate for $E_i(t)$, the bound on the maximal error of the clock i, one has to have a reasonable bound for the communication duration. Otherwise, the time from the moment a readout has been sampled to the moment it is used to reset a clock is not well defined. These aspects are expanded in the next section.

11.4.2 Error Handling

The ability of the communication subsystem to handle errors and failures is an important measure of a system's robustness. Let us consider two possible error types: errors that originate in hardware failure (either a site failure or a communication network failure), and errors due to design. While the former type can be treated via redundancy and checks, the latter must be treated with special techniques to allow detection and diagnosis of the problem. Some of the potential error detection and recovery procedures in a real-time system are affected by the communication architecture and activities. In both detection and recovery, we must emphasize the special considerations due to real-time constraints.

In some communication subsystems of conventional operating systems, we use a timeout mechanism in order to detect that a remote site has *crashed*. When we deal with a real-time environment, we must note that late delivery of a message may violate time constraints of execution, and thereby lead to a system crash. Therefore, in a real-time operating system, when the computation time is considered prior to scheduling, we must account for possible timeout retrials.

Acknowledgments are commonly used to obtain a safer communication protocol; however, they increase the communication delays along with the network load. The application designer should be the one who decides on the trade-off between high fault tolerance and execution times. Availability of resources may strongly influence designer decisions on choosing between the real-time performance and the degree of fault tolerance.

Idempotency is a problem we find in any distributed construction; it is the requirement to allow transmission repetitions. The requirement rises due to communication recovery procedures. However, these repetitions can affect other desired system properties. For example, consider the use of a shared counter. Suppose a process has sent an increment command to this counter, but has failed to receive an acknowledgment from the counter. If the recovery procedure sends another increment command, the result may be an increment by two. On the other hand, using some kind of "commit" protocol may overload the network and naturally increase the execution time of jobs.

Channel properties affect many other system properties and architecture issues. Some examples are reordering of messages, message loss probability, and bounded delivery time.

11.4.3 Issues of Efficiency in Implementation

Some implementation issues may affect the fault tolerance and efficiency of the system. Let us examine three of them.

1. The effects of reducing the *overhead* of the communication system to a minimum may enhance efficiency, whereas fault tolerance may be decreased.
2. The usage of *special purpose* short messages (e.g., for remote synchronization) may complicate the communication software and hardware, but on the other

hand time consumption can be reduced. It is especially emphasized when we compare the use of these messages for sending empty packets.

3. The question whether or not to have *end-to-end acknowledgement* can be considered as a trade-off between robustness of intermediate nodes versus end-to-end acknowledgement of delivery.

11.5 NAME SERVERS

Name service provides the mapping between three name spaces, keeping it unique for all three [116]:

1. Character *string* names, used in the file system and in user programs.
2. Segment *numbers*, used by a running process to refer to an active segment.
3. A known segment table (of a user), which provides physical *addresses* for the page table of a corresponding segment.

Each name is interpreted with respect to a particular *context* [127]. The context is a set of bindings of names to objects. The context initializing procedure is also called binding, or linking, or loading. It serves as the bridge between the high-level human oriented names to the low-level machine oriented addressing world. A context initializing procedure usually consists of resolving and installing actions. The resolution of a name involves searching an existing object that is identified by a given name in a given context. The unknowns in such a search disqualify it as a possible run time procedure in a real-time system. In a real-time system the context initializer must be allowed only as an off-line task, executed before running a real-time job.

A file system (a high-level context) in a distributed real-time operating system should support

- human oriented names;
- multiple users;
- selectively shared contexts;
- the ability to distinguish user's intent from the programmer's;
- and the ability to adhere to a given timing constraint.

The result of these requirements is a naming service that includes the following [127]:

- A multiple directory system.
- A naming network, in which directories appear as named objects in other directories.
- Usage of a mechanism (closures) that connects an object that refers to other objects by name with the context in which those names are bound. The simplest

implementation of such a mechanism is through the usage of a directory as such.

In addition, in order to adhere to time constraints, the response time of a name service should always be reasonably bounded.

In order to reduce search time, name servers may be limited to small-size, unique names. Such a restriction gives rise to issues of reusability of names, recalling the need to maintain the uniqueness of names in a given context. It is especially emphasized regarding the selectively shared contexts objective. Implementing such a service correctly allows any user to disconnect himself from external objects. However, it requires some additional tools for deletion of objects because other users may be linked to them.

The search rules in a name service of a real-time operating system should be efficient from the real-time point of view. As such, a direct entry in a directory should point to an object. An indirect entry should specify the whole access path of the shared context to the closure. Applying such an approach allows limiting the number of directories we must search during each access (e.g., the user's working directory, a language library, and a system library). The language and system libraries can be kept ordered and balanced, thereby reducing search time to a minimal bounded time.

11.6   DATA ACCESS STRATEGY

11.6.1   Protection

Although real-time computer embedded systems usually neglect protection mechanisms, a real-time operating system cannot. The real-time requirements, as the dominant requirements, necessitate keeping protection timing costs as low as possible. For example, let us consider what happens if we give users direct access to required resources on remote sites. The access time is reduced along with increasing the availability of potentially restricted information.

We divide protection systems into two categories, list oriented systems, and ticket oriented systems (as capabilities). Access control lists imply a search procedure that is not appropriate for real-time systems. Capability systems, in which authorization is verified prior to run time, provide better real-time properties.

11.6.2   Remote Storage and Directory Services

In a distributed system an application program does not have explicit knowledge about the storage locations it uses. Therefore, the operating system must support a service that maintains a link to remote sites. Furthermore, timing properties of different allocation instances may differ significantly. Therefore, the predictability and efficiency of such a service are crucial properties.

11.7   FAULT TOLERANCE

It is not just desirable, but often essential, to support both safety (guarantee of not happening) properties and reliability (guarantee of happening) properties. Since system elements may fail, it is important to support the tolerance of such failures in both safety and reliability objectives. One way to support this tolerance is through *operation modes*. Different modes of operation may be applicable in case of a system element failure. During a recovery procedure that follows the failure, we may maintain a backup mode as long as the recovery is not complete. The whole system may be reconfigured for such a procedure. Once recovery is complete, the system mode of operation may be set back to the normal mode. Reconfiguration is often used in *communication* recovery. Communication failure may require reconfiguration of the system to increase link robustness.

An alternative approach to support safety and reliability in the presence of faults is through *redundancy*. Here we support a resilient computation by data and process replication. A redundant execution of a process consumes resources, and thereby slows down the system's real-time performance. A solution that is less time consuming maintains the backup program in a standby mode, and activates it only upon failure. This solution requires that a failure will be detected early enough to provide recovery procedure time even in a degraded performance mode. It also requires a continuous check-point update to provide a starting point for the backup process. In any case, we can only use it while deadline constraints are still satisfied. Note that reconfiguration schemes must still be devised when switching to any backup mode.

As parts of the system fail it may become unable to satisfy all the requirements of the application. Techniques for *graceful degradation* may be very useful to ensure that critical activities do not fail. We note here that although we require the operating system to support it, it is the responsibility of the internal application to define element's criticality. In most cases different applications cannot share criticality measures unless they are somehow related to each other.

One of the most important architectural issues in a distributed system is *fault containment*. In many research projects, the control of damage containment has been the reason for implementing atomic actions and for controlling nested atomic actions. Architecture aspects should be addressed in that issue in order to provide the required means to inherently prevent damage from spreading when a failure occurs.

11.8   OTHER SERVICES

In addition to those described above, several other services the operating system offers to application programs are significant as well.

11.8.1   Service Architecture

Determining the way in which application programs use the system calls/services has an enormous effect on its real-time performance. There are many architectures that implement such services. For example, a service may poll continuously, waiting for a request to appear, or it may be awakened as a classic procedure. Another example is to have a service treated as a resource, and in case more than one user requests it, to maintain a queue for it. The latter approach is not adequate for real-time applications because it forces an uncertain execution time for a job. Recall that when we discussed the time service we related it to the provider architecture. This architecture is suitable for other servers with stringent time constraints as well. The provider supports a better availability of its service, at the cost of providing it even when not needed.

11.8.2   Reconfiguration Services

Reconfiguration services are very important in a dynamic system. Computation sites that are turned on should boot themselves, sites that fail must reboot themselves, and sites that are turned off should be detected by the resource management and allocation tasks. Moreover, in case of fault detection and recovery procedure, the reconfiguration is of extreme importance.

11.8.3   I/O Device Services

I/O services are used in real-time as well as in conventional operating systems. However, device speeds may significantly influence application performance, especially during jobs in which such services are critical to meeting the timing constraints. Assuring the predictability of device response times is one of the most important issues in real-time operating systems.

11.9   CONCLUDING REMARKS

We may summarize our discussion in this chapter by listing the properties we want to find in a hard, real-time, fault-tolerant, distributed operating system:

1. The operating system must carry out allocation of resources and scheduling of jobs according to the bounded time given to execute the job. Furthermore, the relative progress of a set of tasks must be controllable and predictable. Scheduling and resource management have to be carried out consistently to satisfy the timing constraints.
2. An application designer should have the necessary control over the resource allocation and scheduling of jobs. For example, in cases where timing efficiency and protection are in conflict, the application designer should be able to decide what trade-off to make.
3. Time services with specified accuracy and correctness must be available. We note that the handling of time has to be the central theme in the design of such systems.
4. Communication must support a reliable data transfer, while satisfying the real-time constraints.

5. Remote procedure calls should avoid executable code migrations and pass value parameters along with maintaining a mutual exclusion support for shared objects.

6. Communication acknowledgment should rely on a node-to-node robustness instead of waiting for an end-to-end acknowledgment.

7. The operating system must support a distributed naming network, based on a multiple directory system, using closures for shared objects.

8. The operating system can allow context initialization (binding) only in an off-line discipline.

9. Protection mechanism should be "ticket" oriented.

10. Redundant backup jobs should use check points and be activated when a failure occurs. Data replicas should be updated via check points and migrated upon failure as an off-line recovery procedure. In case there is no time for recovery, parallel execution of alternatives is inevitable.

11. A reconfiguration service should be available both upon user request (failure, login, boot, etc.) and as an automatic service (power-off, etc.).

In general, all "unknown" parameters in the execution time of a job should be avoided, allowing them to occur only under an off-line discipline.

CHAPTER

12

ALLOCATION AND SCHEDULING

Scheduling real-time computations is an extremely important activity in real-time systems, since it is the phase in which we assign the final temporal properties of the computations. In a way, it is a bridge between the future (the execution plan) and the past (the history trace of execution). Its significance in the timing correctness of a computation originates in its task as such a bridge.

A closely related problem is that of allocating the execution of computation elements to computation resources. We note that each computation we want to schedule needs resources in order to execute. These resources can be of the hardware type (e.g., processors, memory segments, communication, I/O devices, etc.) or the software type (e.g., a shared data base). The problem of allocating these resources in real-time systems creates an additional dimension within the conventional allocation problem, that of time constraints. Resource requirements are meaningful only within a specified time interval, resulting in a combined schedulability and allocation problem. This consequence, however, has not always been agreed upon.

Real-time scheduling theory and algorithms have taken the same evolutionary path as have other computer science fields: single processor systems, priority in multi-programming, centrally controlled systems, and finally (today) concurrent and distributed systems. In the next sections, we review some of the important steps in this evolution. Apart from the interesting ideas presented in these steps, we use this review to justify our propositions for the "next generation" systems. Since we deal with hard real-time systems, algorithms and theories that serve either soft real-time systems or graceful degradation in deadline miss are not included here.

Let us first define the scheduling and allocation problems formally, so that we can find a common expression tool for the rest of this book. Then, let us do some "window shopping" in order to find a solution to these problems that will be adequate for both fault tolerant and hard real-time systems. In seeking these solutions, let us review the alternatives step by step, and examine the evolution of a proper solution.

12.1   PROBLEM DEFINITION

There have been many studies about many dimensions of the resource allocation problem. In a large fraction of these studies, the goal of the allocation has been an optimization of some metric of the execution performance, generally one of the stochastic parameters that describes the performance. The model most often used in the above cases reflects an allocation of processes to processors. In this model, both the set of processes and the set of processors have been subjected to some inter-set relations and intra-set optimality constraints. In addition, the nature of each of the processors has been homogeneous, indivisible, and self-contained.

Formally, we define the sets of processes and processors as follows. A set of processes $\mathcal{V}_p = \{p_1, \ldots, p_n\}$ are related to each other through a set of logical links $\mathcal{E}_p$, to form a graph

$$\mathcal{G}_p = (\mathcal{V}_p, \mathcal{E}_p)$$

A set of processors $\mathcal{V}_P = \{P_1, \ldots, P_m\}$ are related to each other through a set of physical links $\mathcal{E}_P$, to form a graph

$$\mathcal{G}_P = (\mathcal{V}_P, \mathcal{E}_P)$$

Allocating processes to processors is a function whose domain is the set $\mathcal{V}_p$ and whose range is $\mathcal{V}_P$. We can consider the allocation optimization problem as selecting the function that minimizes a particular metric. As we show in the following sections, most of the metrics relate in some way to $\mathcal{G}_p$ and $\mathcal{G}_P$ through cost functions that are affected by $\mathcal{E}_p$ and $\mathcal{E}_P$.

The scheduling problem has been extensively examined in the literature. The model that has been most often used reflects scheduling n processes on m identical processors. We can consider the scheduling problem as the combination of the above allocation problem with the generation of m ordered lists of execution that satisfy a set of constraint. According to these common approaches, the allocation problem is viewed either as a partitioning or a clustering problem, whereas the scheduling enforces a partial order on each partition or cluster.

To define it more formally, let us associate each list $\mathcal{L}_i$ with a processor P_i, $(i = 1, \ldots, m)$. $\mathcal{L}_i$ and $\mathcal{L}_j$ are distinct for $i \neq j$. The list $\mathcal{L}_i$ is an ordering of a subset of $\mathcal{V}_p$. The partial ordering, which we denote as $<$, expresses the order of execution in the following way. Let $l_i \in \mathcal{L}_k$ and $l_j \in \mathcal{L}_k$ be such that $i < j$. Then, $l_i = p_{i'} \in \mathcal{V}_p$ and $l_j = p_{j'} \in \mathcal{V}_p$ relate such that $p_{i'} < p_{j'}$. Therefore, $p_{i'}$ executes before $p_{j'}$ on processor k. The rules that generate these lists assure that no more than m processes execute simultaneously, and that the precedence relations obey the constraints [49]. Each of these lists is a valid schedule, but optimization of valid schedules is an NP-hard problem [49, 73, 103, 103], even for simple cases.

12.2 RATE MONOTONIC PRIORITY SCHEDULING ALGORITHMS

Priority driven scheduling algorithms have been widely used in uniprocessor and multi-processor computing systems. A priority scheme is *static* if a priority is assigned to a computation only once (probably before this computation starts executing), while a *dynamic* scheme allows changing the priority with time. An example of a scheme that can be either static or dynamic is the rate-monotonic priority scheme. In this scheme, each task is assigned with a priority that reflects its required frequency (or request rate). The higher the request rate the higher is the priority assigned to the processing request. It has been shown that as long as the processor utilization remains below a certain level the scheduling algorithm will assure the meeting of the deadlines of the tasks. Note that burst tasks are far from being well defined in this priority scheme. If this assignment is static, then for a feasible schedule of n tasks on a single processor [96]

$$\sum_{i=1}^{n} c_i \cdot f_i \leq 1$$

where c_i is the computation time of task i and f_i is its frequency. Another property of the static rate-monotonic priority scheduler is that the least upper bound of the utilization of a single processor on which we schedule n tasks is [96]

$$u = \sum_{i=1}^{n} c_i \cdot f_i \leq n(2^{\frac{1}{n}} - 1)$$

In other words, while the above holds, a feasible static rate monotonic priority schedule exists.

We have to note that rate-monotonic priority scheduling guarantees only average performance. It does not guarantee meeting each individual deadline. A noncritical task with a high frequency may postpone a critical task with a low frequency. This phenomenon has often been called *priority inversion*. Note that this phenomenon is present even under a utilization that conforms with the above bound. We note that the bound itself is an average measure, the utilization, and thus transient peak overloads are still likely to occur.

An alternative solution is to detect peak overloads and to "adjust" the priorities of the most frequent and the least frequent tasks [131] This adjustment, called *period transformation*, requires an artificial change in task periodicity while assigning priorities. With these modified priorities, the critical set of tasks becomes schedulable and postponing noncritical tasks does not violate their deadlines.

Not all real-time tasks are periodic, however, and a combination of periodic and aperiodic tasks in a system is common. The need to further relate to the specific deadline of each occurrence is therefore required. Algorithms like *earliest deadline* and *least slack* (sometimes called also *minimal laxity*) introduce new approaches whose properties differ from those of the static schedulers. The *earliest deadline* scheme selects the task with the earliest deadline to execute, while the *least slack* selects the task whose slack[1] is the lowest. Although the least-slack algorithm has proven to be optimal in single processor environments, this property has not been established for a multiple processor case [104].

The need to meet deadlines of periodic and aperiodic tasks along with the goal of increasing the utilization above the low bound of static priorities requires dynamic changes in priorities. Note that even in the case of a system with only periodic jobs, each job's priority is not a constant when we use the earliest deadline or least slack algorithm. Let us consider what happens when we carry out a dynamic update of task priorities. A good example is the *earliest deadline* algorithm, which revises the deadlines (d_i) dynamically [104].

1. Sort task instances that require execution in time interval [0,L] in reverse topological order.
2. Initialize the deadline of the kth instance of task $T_{i,j}$ to $(k-1)\frac{1}{f_i} + d_i$.
3. Revise the deadlines in reverse topological order by

$$d_k = \min(d_k, (d_{k'} - c_{k'}: k \rightarrow k'))$$

where k and k' are scheduling blocks.

We note that the dynamics acquired by this algorithm are reflected in the cost of sorting, revising, and then scheduling. The former artificial period transformation also introduces a significant change in the cost of the rate-monotonic priority scheduler. Dynamic schedulers are not as bounded as static ones; however, the above examples emphasize the increase in the algorithm complexity.

12.3   NEXT-FIT-M PARTITIONING FOR RATE-MONOTONIC SCHEDULERS

Separation of allocation and scheduling allows simplifying the scheduler to a local one, and in some constraint environments, even to a static one. Let us examine a solution in which the allocation is centralistic, while the scheduling is distributed [40]. The objective is to partition a set of tasks such that each partition will be scheduled later for execution at a distinct locality by a rate-monotonic priority

---

[1]The slack of task P_i at time t is $slack(P_i, t) = \max(d_i - c_i - t, 0)$.

scheduling algorithm. A subgoal of the algorithm is to use as few processors as possible.

In this model, tasks have the following characteristics:

- Each task has a constant frequency.
- Each task has a deadline constraint, and no begin-time constraint is imposed.
- Tasks are independent of each other, without precedence constraints.
- All the tasks require the same computation time-interval.

The algorithm partitions the tasks according to their *duty cycles*. This parameter is the ratio between the identical computation interval and the task's period. They are then assigned to processors such that the processors will schedule them in a rate-monotonic priority scheduling algorithm. Each of the rate monotonic algorithms is known to be bounded by a utility constraint, as defined in the previous section. Therefore, the allocation algorithm maintains the load allocated to each processor such that its utility does not exceed that bound.

Let us now describe the allocation algorithm. The tasks are divided into M classes, such that

- task $T_i \in class\_k$ if $2^{\frac{1}{k+1}} < u_i \leq 2^{\frac{1}{k}}$ for $1 \leq k < M$.
- task $T_i \in class\_M$ if $o \leq u_i \leq 2^{\frac{1}{M}}$.

The algorithm assigns k class-k tasks to each class-k processor, keeping the utilization factor of the class-M processor less than $\ln(2)$. The variables in the algorithm are

- T_i Task, $1 \leq i \leq n$.
- u_i Utilization factor (duty cycle) of T_i.
- $P_{i,j}$ Set of tasks assigned to a processor.
- N_k Number of class-k processors used so far.

The algorithm is attractive because both of its performance and the simple scheduler it allows to work locally. The algorithm allows an on-line allocation discipline, demonstrating time complexity of $O(n)$ and space complexity of $O(1)$.

       Algorithm Next-Fit-M;

begin

    for $k := 1$ **to** M **step** 1 **do**

        $N_k := 1$;

    od;

    for $i := 1$ **to** n **step** 1 **do**

$k := \text{classify}(T_i);$

/* returns k for $2^{\frac{1}{k+1}} - 1 < u_i \leq 2^{\frac{1}{k}} - 1, \text{ for } 1 \leq k < M$ */

/* returns M for $0 \leq u_i \leq 2^{\frac{1}{M}} - 1.$ */

if $(1 \leq k < M)$ **then**

$P_{k,N_k} := P_{k,N_k} \cup \{T_i\};$

if $|P_{k,N_k}| = k$ **then**

$N_k := N_k + 1;$

fi;

else /* $(k = M)$ */

if $\sum_{T_j \in P_{M,N_M}} u_j > (\ln 2 - U_i)$**then**;

$N_M := N_M + 1;$

fi;

$P_{M,N_M} := P_{M,N_M} \cup \{T_i\};$

odfi;

for $k := 1$ **to** M **step** 1 **do**

if $P_{k,N_k} = \phi$ **then**

$N_k := N_k - 1;$

odfi;

end;

The partitioning mechanism of this allocation algorithm is based on the use of local rate-monotonic priority schedulers, and it is therefore totally scheduler dependent. Even so, the model of the above scheduler is too simple to support "next generation" real-time applications. The absence of begin-time constraints, the lack of support for a variety of computation requirements, the absence of important relations between tasks (precedence and others) and the disregarding of loads on processors due to other computations are features that this approach fails to demonstrate. Furthermore, it fails to support any fault tolerance goals and thus does not give a comprehensive solution. However, we find the relationship demonstrated in this algorithm between an allocator and local schedulers important and useful.

12.4   ALLOCATION WITH MINIMIZATION OF IPC

Let us return to an allocation approach we introduced earlier—the centrally controlled allocation scheme used in the Ballistic Missile Defense (BMD) project

[98,99]. This scheme is centralized and it uses a nominated computation node with knowledge of the global status of the system. Each request for task execution is routed through the nominated node to be properly allocated to the resources. The model recognizes only tasks and processors as the participants in the allocation. We can use matrices to describe the relations between tasks and processors as well as between the tasks themselves, and we carry out the allocation according to these matrices.

- Task preference matrix P, where $p[i, j] = 0$ means that task i is not allowed to execute on processor j.
- Task exclusion matrix X, where $x[i, j] \neq 0$ means that task i and task j cannot be assigned to the same processor.
- Task coupling matrix C, where $c[i, j]$ is the coupling factor that represents the amount of data transferred from task i to task j.
- Task distance matrix D, where $d[i, j]$ represents the cost of transferring one data unit from task i to task j.

This approach divides the tasks of a time-critical real-time system into several threads, and each of the threads must satisfy an execution-time constraint, denoted "port-to-port" execution time. The allocation is considered a search tree in which each vertex is a task to be allocated and each arc that leaves the vertex is a possible allocation of a processor to that task. The search algorithm is based on the branch and bound method and is constructed in setting and backtracking phases. The search goal is an allocation that minimizes the execution time of a "port-to-port" thread of executing tasks. The execution cost function consists of the following [98]:

1. Execution time of the task on the processor, which depends on the task size and the processor speed

$$E_i = \frac{size(task\ i)}{processor\ speed}$$

2. The network and operating system overhead (Ov), which is used for concurrency control, integrity checking, recovery check-point update, and so forth.
3. Inter-processor communication (IPC), which is higher if communicating processes reside on different processors.
4. Waiting time (WT) which is consumed when the task waits in the processor enablement queue. This figure depends highly on the sizes and number of tasks, the processor load, and the number of enablements (especially if large tasks are assigned to the same processor).

Combining these contributors to the total thread execution time

$$E_T = \sum_i (E_i) + Ov + IPC + WT$$

while minimizing the contributors is the motivation of this allocation scheme.

The following sequence of activities forms the desired allocation scheme:

- A set of constraints is determined to reduce the waiting time and the task execution time. It may be performed using the following method:

  1. Information about the tasks (sizes, execution frequency of each task, number of data units exchanged between each pair of tasks) and the network (interprocessor distance, constraints) is entered to the model.
  2. Constraints are imposed on the model, using matrices P, X, C, and D.

- A cost function that measures the *IPC* cost is formulated.
- An algorithm that searches for the allocation with the minimum total cost is determined. This search algorithm [99] eliminates search in improper subtrees while branching to a new subtree according to matrix P, matrix X, and the maximal capacity of each assigned processor. Preference is imposed with dominance relations, Ov, and WT. The *IPC* cost is computed for each subtree through matrices C and D, in $\sum c[i, j] \cdot d[i, j]$. The lowest cost solution is chosen out of the set of possible solutions.

THE ALGORITHM. Using the above matrices, the allocation obeys the following rules in order to minimize inter-task communication cost.

B. Generate the "children" vertices, to which there are *arcs* from this vertex. Select a processor (arc) for this task (vertex).

S. Select the next vertex to expand from this one.

F. Check task preference matrix P to eliminate no-solution for a feasible schedule due to improper task—processor assignment.

D. Define the dominance relation that allows eliminating vertices before expanding them.

L. Calculate lower bound to the cost of each partial feasible schedule ($\sum c[i, j] \cdot d[i, j]$ on this search path so far).

U. Calculate upper bound to the complete schedule, as known to be imposed.

E. Use rule D and task exclusion matrix X to eliminate improper branch, and compare local rule L to rule U to eliminate the branches that are "too expensive."

RB. Check resource bound to verify that resource "capacity" is not exceeded. If violated, eliminate this branch.

BR. If no feasible schedule exists, terminate algorithm with rejection. Otherwise, select one of the acceptable schedules with the lowest cost and terminate successfully.

The major disadvantages of this algorithm are its centralistic nature and the requirement of global knowledge. In addition, no time constraints are taken into account at a task level and no fault tolerance goals are set. The above disadvantages indicate that this allocation scheme is not suitable for "next-generation" real-time operating systems. The algorithm nevertheless establishes a nice model for IPC cost and highlights important metrics we need to consider in an efficient solution.

12.5 ALLOCATION WITH BOTTLENECK PROCESSOR LOAD MINIMIZATION

Let us now consider an allocation approach which does not consider directly a global balancing constraint, but rather tries to minimize unbalancing through its extremes. A candidate objective function is one whose optimization constraint is the minimization of the load on the bottleneck processor, or the most heavily loaded processor [33]. We can construct a computation model assuming that the load on a processor is a function of three ingredients. The inter-module communication (*IMC*) is the first, the second is the accumulative execution time (*AET*) of the modules, and the third is the precedence relations (*PR*) between executing modules.

The problem is defined on a set of n modules $(p_1, \ldots, p_n)$ and a set of m processors. Let us assume we can derive the *AET* of module p_j during a particular time interval from the number of times p_j executes during this interval and the average execution time of p_j over peak load periods. We denote the *AET*s of the modules as $\{T_j : 1 \leq j \leq n\}$. In this approach *IMC* incurs the inter-process communication cost (*IPC*) and the processing overhead. We can significantly reduce *IPC* if the allocation assigns pairs of heavily communicating processes to the same processor. The workload on a given processor (P_r), under a given assignment of the n modules to the m processors, is defined as

$$\mathcal{L}(P_r; \mathcal{A}) = AET(P_r; \mathcal{A}) + IMC(P_r; \mathcal{A})$$

where $\mathcal{A}$ is an assignment matrix $[a_{i,j}]$, for which $a_{i,j} = 1$ if p_i is assigned to processor j.

To model *IPC*, this method represents the communication cost as a sum of the cost of outgoing messages and the cost of incoming messages. The costs of module activations and control messages are ignored, thus narrowing the applications that can use this method.

$$IMC_{i,j}(\mathcal{A}) = IPC(i, j; \mathcal{A}) + IPC(j, i; \mathcal{A})$$

We can calculate the average inter-module communication cost at peak load periods, $\{IMC_{i,j} : 1 \leq i, j \leq n\}$ from the volume of the communication between the modules. From the average cost we can derive the *IMC index*

$$\gamma_{IMC}(i, j) = \frac{IMC_{i,j}}{A\overline{E}T}$$

which we use in the algorithm for allocation decision. Thus, the load at processor P_r can be expressed as

$$\mathcal{L}(P_r; \mathcal{A}) = \sum_{j=1}^{n} x_{j,r} T_j + \sum_{s=1 \neq r}^{m} IPC(r, s; \mathcal{A}) + \sum_{s=1 \neq r}^{m} IPC(s, r; \mathcal{A})$$

The bottleneck processor is the processor with the maximal load

$$bottleneck(\mathcal{A}) = \max_{1 \leq r \leq m} \{\mathcal{L}(P_r; \mathcal{A})\}$$

Minimizing this load is a selection between all possible assignments

$$\min_{\mathcal{A}} \{bottleneck(\mathcal{A})\}$$

or in other words,

$$\min_{\mathcal{A}} \{\max_{1 \leq r \leq m} \{AET(P_r; \mathcal{X}) + IMC(P_r; \mathcal{A})\}\}$$

Precedence relations (*PR*) affect the response time of the system and we must include this aspect in the algorithm. We can construct a model of wait-time behavior based on the observed relation between size ratio of modules, $\rho_{i,j}$, and wait-time ratio, $R(\rho_{i,j})$. While $\rho_{i,j}$ is simply the ratio of the sizes of the modules, the wait-time ratio $R(\rho_{i,j})$ depends on the queueing wait time and thus on the scheduling discipline. The algorithm then uses the *PR index*

$$\gamma_{PR}(i, j) = 1 - R(\rho_{i,j})$$

combined with the *IMC index* for the allocation decisions. Let us now present the algorithm.

Algorithm PR–IMC–AET [33]

begin /* Init */

$$\overline{AET} \leftarrow \frac{1}{n} \sum_{j:=1}^{n} T_j; \text{ /* Av } AET \text{ */}$$

$$\overline{PL} \leftarrow \frac{1}{m} \sum_{j:=1}^{n} T_j; \text{ /* Av Processor load */}$$

$$\gamma_{IMC}(i, j) \leftarrow \frac{1}{\overline{AET}} IMC_{i,j}, 1 \leq i, j \leq n; \text{ /* IMC index */}$$

$$\gamma_{PR}(i, j) \leftarrow 1 - R(\rho_{i,j}), 1 \leq i, j \leq n; \text{ /* PR index */}$$

/* Iterate */

for $\alpha \leftarrow \alpha_1$ **to** α_2 **step** $\Delta\alpha$ **do**

  for $\beta \leftarrow \beta_1$ **to** β_2 **step** $\Delta\beta$ **do**

    /* PHASE I: combine modules with high *IMC* */

    /* in groups to reduce sum of processor loads */

    List $\leftarrow$ *Sort* (p_i, p_j) *pairs in descending IMC order;*

    $G_j \leftarrow \{p_j\}, 1 \leq j \leq n;$

    while *List* $\neq \phi$ **do**

pop (p_i, p_j) from top of *List*;

List ← *List* − $\{(p_i, p_j)\}$;

if $\alpha \times \gamma_{IMC}(i,j) + \gamma_{PR}(i,j) > 0$ **then**

  search (s: $p_i \in G_s$, t: $p_j \in G_t$);

  if $(s \neq t) \wedge (T_s + T_t \leq \overline{PL} \times \beta)$ **then** /*combine */

    $G_s \leftarrow G_s \cup G_t$; $G_t \leftarrow \phi$;

    $T_s \leftarrow T_s + T_t$; $T_t \leftarrow 0$;

  fi   fi;

od;

  /* PHASE II: assign module groups to processors */

  /* and exhaustively search for smallest BOTTLENECK */

  $\mathcal{A} \leftarrow \{G_j: 1 \leq j \leq n\}$;

  $\mathcal{L}\{\mathcal{A}\} \leftarrow \min_{\mathcal{A}}\{\max_{1 \leq r \leq m}\{AET(P_r; \mathcal{A}) + IMC(P_r; \mathcal{A})\}\}$;

  record $\mathcal{L}\{\mathcal{A}\}$;

odod ;

end

The above algorithm presents an iterative heuristic approach in which the workload $\mathcal{L}(P_{\text{bottleneck}}; \mathcal{A})$ is recorded for different tuning scale factors α and β. The term α represents the scale factor of combining γ_{IMC} with γ_{PR} and β is a scale factor for the threshold of processor load up to which the algorithm combines heavily communicating processes on the same processor.

The *PR−IMC−AET* algorithm disregards loads on processors due to other computations, rather than $p_1, \ldots, p_n$, and therefore allowing independent computations requires extra knowledge. Because it is centralistic, the global knowledge must also be either centralistic or static. Two major properties of hard real-time systems are not dealt with here: no time constraints are imposed on module execution and no fault tolerance objectives are defined.

12.6   ALLOCATION WITH LOAD BALANCE OPTIMALITY CONSTRAINT

Let us now examine an allocation scheme and its support for recovery from failures. This allocation scheme assigns processes to processors with a distributed load-balancing optimality constraint [72,47]. When one or more processes fail, groups of processes must be relocated. The relocation goal is to maintain the objectives as set by the allocation scheme.

Let us recall our graph of processes

$$\mathcal{G}_p = (\mathcal{V}_p, \mathcal{E}_p)$$

where the set of processes $\mathcal{V}_p$ are related to each other through a set of logical links $\mathcal{E}_p$, and our graph of processors

$$\mathcal{G}_P = (\mathcal{V}_P, \mathcal{E}_P)$$

where the set of processors $\mathcal{V}_P$ are related to each other through a set of physical links $\mathcal{E}_P$. Each node in the above two graphs can be measured according to its incoming and outgoing links, applying some weights to the links to express communication costs. We can use these measures as similarity (clustering) measures, according to which a cluster tree represents each of the graphs, τ_p and τ_P, respectively. An allocation algorithm that maps the nodes in τ_p to the nodes of τ_P, assigns heavily communicating processes to closely connected processors [72].

In this approach, we assume that all the processes load their assigned processors equally with a unit load. We denote the current assigned load on processor P_i as c_i. The current load is bounded by the processor capacity C_i and is required to satisfy an optimality workload constraint

$$\left| \frac{c_i}{C_i} - \lambda \right| \leq \varepsilon$$

where λ is the optimal load and ε is a tolerance. The relation

$$m_i \leq c_i \leq M_i$$

is another way to express the optimality constraint, where

$$m_i = C_i \cdot (\lambda - \varepsilon), M_i = C_i \cdot (\lambda + \varepsilon)$$

When a cluster of processors is observed, the sum of its processors' capacities expresses the cluster capacity. On the other hand, the sum of the currently assigned processor loads is the current cluster load. We can express a metric that represents the *violation* of optimality in cluster j, as

$$V_j = \left| \frac{c_i}{C_i} - \lambda \right| - \varepsilon$$

An allocation scheme that optimizes the load balance may then use the violation values in order to select a candidate cluster of processors for assigning processes. More precisely, it can use the values of the children of a node in the processor cluster tree. The highest violation is selected first.

In order to support fault tolerance objectives, the occurrence of a fault must first be detected. We call a cluster of processors that monitor each other's status and participate in the detection algorithm a *detection unit*. The set of m processors is therefore divided to detection units $D_1, \ldots, D_K$, and each detection unit D_i is assigned with N_i processes. The workload bounds on a detection unit are derived from

$$M(D_i) = \sum_{\forall k: P_k \in D_i} M_k, m(D_i) = \sum_{\forall k: P_k \in D_i} m_k$$

Each detection unit is ordered and has a *leader*, second in command, and so on. It is the leader's responsibility to take action when a member of its detection unit is found to be faulty. If we assume that no failure occurs while recovering from a previous failure, we can replace a failed leader by using a simple protocol. The leader's action regarding a faulty member is to generate a relocation for the processes assigned to the faulty member. A local relocation is of course preferable, because it saves parts of the migration cost and maintains the balance constraint. An external relocation is also possible in the absence of a local solution. Each leader maintains the following items in order to answer the questions of other leaders that cannot relocate in their own detection unit.

- $M(D_i)$,
- $m(D_i)$,
- N_i.

Each leader maintains the following items both for relocating locally (within the detection unit) and for relocating externally (moving processes to another detection unit):

- $D_i = \{P_i, \ldots, P_m\}$,
- R_i the root of the subtree of τ_P corresponding to processors in D_i,
- r_i the root of the subtree of τ_p corresponding to processes assigned to processors in D_i.

When a processor P_j is detected to have failed in detection unit D_i, the leader removes its capacity from the total capacity of the detection unit. The leader of D_i checks whether the fault can be dealt with locally, by a local reconfiguration of the allocation within D_i. If this is the case, then

$$m(D_i) - m_j \leq N_i \leq M(D_i) - M_j$$

and the leader can take the actions described below.

Algorithm Relocate within D_i on P_j Fault;
begin   /* $m(D_i) - m_j \leq N_i \leq M(D_i) - M_j$ */
   do
     1. Update R_i to reflect P_j fault:
       1) delete node P_j from tree R_j;
       2) update parent-node capacities in processor cluster tree;
     2. Update optimality bounds:
       1) $M(D_i) := M(D_i) - M_j$;
       2) $m(D_i) := m(D_i) - m_j$;
     3. Invoke ALLOCATE(r_i, R_i);
   od;
end.

We note that the relocation is really a new allocation of the same cluster-subtree of processes (r_i) in the updated cluster-subtree of processors (R_i). The benefits of a local relocation are the isolation of failures from other detection units and the minimization of the enforcement of departing from optimality.

However, if the relocation cannot be treated locally, the leader must generate a candidate set of (v, k) pairs, to select both the node v to be migrated and the destination detection unit D_k. For each node v to be migrated to detection unit D_k, three cost issues are raised:

1. *migration* cost, $M(v, k)$, which mainly consists of a fix overhead and a cost that is proportional to the number of leaf nodes that are descendants of v;
2. *affinity* cost, $A(v)$, which originates in the increased logical communication between D_i and the migration destination and therefore depends on the links of the migrated node; and
3. *utilization* cost, $B(v, k)$, which is a measure of the unbalanced load and the violation of the optimality measure in D_i and in the destination detection unit.

Combining the above three costs into a *ranking* measure yields

$$R(v, k) = C_1 \cdot A(v) + C_2 \cdot B(v, k) + C_3 \cdot M(v, k)$$

An algorithm that is motivated by the above ranking is described below.

Algorithm Relocate Externally to D_i on P_j Fault ;

begin   /* $N_i > M(D_i) - M_j$ */

LEADER(D_i) **do**

1. Notify $\forall P_n \in D_i$ on P_j fault ;

2. Update R_i to reflect P_j fault:

    1) delete node P_j from tree R_j ;

    2) update parent-nodes' capacities in processor cluster tree ;

3. Update optimality bounds:

    1) $M(D_i) := M(D_i) - M_j$;

    2) $m(D_i) := m(D_i) - m_j$;

4. Collect network status:

    1) $\forall n \neq i, n \in 1 \ldots k$

        Send status request to Leader(D_n) ;

    2) $\forall n \neq i, n \in 1 \ldots k$

        Collect answers $(n, N_n, M(D_n), m(D_n))$;

5. Ensure global balancing constraint:

$$\sum_{i=1}^{k} N_i < \sum_{i=1}^{k} M(D_i) \ ;$$

6. Generate candidate set $\mathscr{C}$;

7. Rank($\mathscr{C}$) ;

8. Select highest ranked (v^*, k^*), and migrate v^* to D_{k^*} ;

9. Reflect migration and new relocation:

1) $N_i := N_i - W(v^*)$;

2) $N_{k^*} := N_{k^*} + W(v^*)$;

3) Delete v^* from r_i and update ancestors' capacities ;

4) **if** $N_i > M(D_i)$ **then goto** step 6.

/* iterate until done */

10. Verify that the relocation holds:

Invoke ALLOCATE(r_i, R_i) ;

od ;

LEADER$(D_{k \ne i})$ **do**

1. Fetch the already allocated $\mathscr{S}$ and

append the incoming processes:

$$\mathscr{S} := \mathscr{S} \oplus \{ p_1, \ldots, p_s \} ;$$

2. $r_{k^*} := \text{cluster}(\mathscr{S})$;

3. ALLOCATE(r_{k^*}, R_{k^*}) ;

4. $N_{k^*} := N_{k^*} + s$;

od ;

end ;

We find the relocation approach very appealing from a fault tolerance point of view. However, this approach does not satisfy hard real-time system requirements because it does not take into account the deadlines in its clustering measure. The algorithm also ignores the impossibility of recovery through a roll-back (e.g., in its migration) in many cases.

12.7 SERVING NON-REAL-TIME TASKS BY A REAL-TIME SCHEDULER

When a deadline driven scheduler is employed, the execution of some aperiodic incoming requests may be delayed to a point where the responsiveness of the system is impractical. Let us note two methods of bandwidth preserving algorithms that can help in such cases [88].

In a *priority exchange* algorithm a task may exchange the priority previously assigned to it by a rate-monotonic priority scheduling algorithm with a lower priority task. It is very useful in cases of idling tasks whose turn to run comes although enabling conditions are absent. In such cases they exchange priority with one of the subsequent tasks, whose enabling conditions are satisfied. In other words, the idle task with the high priority gives its turn to run to a ready task with a lower priority. We can use this scheme and dedicate a periodic server (idle process) to deal with incoming aperiodic requests. In case a pending aperiodic request exists on the server's execution turn, it serves this request. Otherwise, it exchanges its turn with a subsequent periodic task whose enabling conditions hold.

Another method, the *deferrable server*, can also solve this problem. It is similar to the priority exchange algorithm, but when there are no pending aperiodic requests on the dedicated server turn, the deferrable server still holds its high priority until its run-time period elapses. The deferrable server is much simpler to implement; however, it produces a decrease in the worst case task scheduling bound.

12.8   HEURISTIC APPROACH IN SCHEDULING

In general, optimizing resource allocation under time and precedence constraints in a multi-processor environment is an NP-hard problem [103, 104]. This fact motivates the research for heuristics that provide suboptimal solutions for the hard real-time scheduling problem [121, 141, 156, 32, 158, 159, 160]. An example of a heuristic approach can be found in the Spring kernel local scheduler [140], whose goal is to schedule a set of tasks $\bar{\tau}$ in a system with r resources $\mathcal{R}$. Each resource is allowed to be required in one of the following three modes:

- exclusive,
- shared,
- not needed.

We can model each task $T \in \bar{\tau}$ by

- the time constraint which contains a computation time c_T and a deadline d_T,
- a vector of resource requirements $(T_R[1], \ldots, T_R[r])$, where the value of $T_R[i]$ $(i = 1, \ldots, r)$ reflects one of the above three resource modes; and
- a scheduled start time T_{sst}, determined from the above model characteristics of all the tasks.

In order to understand the suggested algorithm for scheduling, some terms must first be defined.

- A *partial schedule* is a subset of tasks in $\bar{\tau}$ whose start time has been assigned.
- A partial schedule $\mathcal{S}$ is *feasible* if

$$\forall T \in \mathcal{S} : T_{sst} + c_T \leq d_T$$

- A set of tasks is *schedulable* if there exists a feasible schedule for it.
- A feasible partial schedule is *strongly feasible* if all the schedules obtained from extending it one more level (with any one of the remaining unscheduled tasks) are also feasible.

The algorithm proposed here views the scheduling as a search problem. The search space is a tree whose root is an empty schedule, each intermediate vertex is a feasible partial schedule, and each leaf is a complete feasible schedule. The computational intractability of the problem leads to a heuristic approach to this search, using a heuristic function H to value a vertex in the search tree. The heuristic function H can be constructed as a linear combination of simple heuristics, whose weights are tailored to perform very close to an optimal solution.

The algorithm maintains the vectors EAT^s and EAT^e, which are the earliest available times of resources in shared and exclusive modes, respectively. It also calculates the earliest start time, T_{est}, for each task $T \in \bar{\tau}$ that remains to be scheduled.

Procedure scheduler (task_set: task_set_type;

      var schedule: schedule_type; **var** schedulable: boolean);

      /* task_set is the set of tasks to be scheduled. */

var EAT^s, EAT^e: vector_type;

      /* Resources earliest available times

        in share and exclusive modes. */

begin

      schedule $\leftarrow \phi$;

      schedulable $\leftarrow$ true ;

      $EAT^s \leftarrow EAT^e \leftarrow \mathbf{0}$;

      while ((task_set $\neq \phi$) $\wedge$ schedulable) **do begin**

          $\forall T \in$ task_set: calculate T_{est} ;

    if $\neg$ strongly-feasible(task_set, schedule) **then**

        schedulable $\leftarrow$ false ;

    else begin

$\forall T \in$ task_set: apply function H ;

$T' \leftarrow T$: $\min_{\forall T \in task\_set}(H(T))$;

$T'_{sst} \leftarrow T'_{est}$;

task_set $=$ task_set $-\{T'\}$;

schedule $\leftarrow$ append(schedule, T') ;

calculate new values for EAT^s and EAT^e ;

end

end

end;

The algorithm as presented above employs a simplistic model of tasks and resources. Some extensions allow this approach to handle the following cases:

- each resource has multiple instances, out of which each task may require one or more;
- tasks may be required to start only after a given instance of time in the future and;
- there are precedence constraints that are interpreted as an additional factor in the heuristic function.

12.9 IMPOSING PRECEDENCE AND RESOURCE REQUIREMENTS

In the previous sections we presented some ideas about resource restrictions and multiple resource instances. One of the above approaches represents resource restrictions with the preference matrix and the exclusion matrix. These matrices are used to eliminate unauthorized use and improper allocation of resources.

Interesting ways to express resource requirements have been presented to support the heuristic scheduling approach in Section 12.8. At each level of the search for a strongly feasible schedule, the scheduler updates a vector of the *dynamic resource demand ratio*

$$DRDR = (DRDR_1, \ldots, DRDR_r)$$

whose component i indicates the fraction of resource R_i to be used by the tasks not yet scheduled. Let us denote the set of tasks not yet scheduled as $\mathcal{T}$. Thus

$$DRDR_i = \frac{\sum_T(c_T : T \in \mathcal{T} \wedge T \text{ uses } R_i)}{\max_T(d_T : T \in \mathcal{T} \wedge T \text{ uses } R_i) - EAT_i}$$

where EAT_i is the earliest available time of resource R_i, and d_T and c_T are the deadline of task T and its computation time, respectively. In Section 12.8, when testing the condition

> **if** strongly-feasible(task_set, schedule) **then** . . .

one should check also

$$\forall_{i=1,\ldots,r} \; DRDR_i \leq 1$$

Note that all the resources are reserved for the whole computation time.

An extension of the above resource requirement management allows distinguishing exclusive and shared resources. Furthermore, if we allow preemption, then the computation time that really matters is the computation time still left to execute. Since a task can be in a preempted state, its unfinished execution time is certainly less than the whole task computation time. At each level of the search, the scheduler updates a vector of the *minimum resource demand ratio*

$$MRDR = (MRDR_1, \ldots, MRDR_r)$$

whose component i indicates the minimal fraction of resource R_i to be used by the tasks not yet scheduled. Denoting again the set of tasks not yet scheduled as $\mathcal{T}$, we can write

$$MRDR_i = \frac{\sum_{T \in R_i^{\text{exclusive}}}(c'_T : T \in \mathcal{T}) + \max_{T \in R_i^{\text{share}}}(c'_T : T \in \mathcal{T})}{\max_T(d_T : T \text{ uses } R_i \wedge c'_T > 0) - EAT_i}$$

The terms in this equation are the same terms defined for the $DRDR_i$ equation, except for c_T which is the remaining execution time of task T. We also note that the additional check defined for the $DRDR_i$ case is also valid for the $MRDR_i$ case

$$\forall_{i=1,\ldots,r} \; MRDR_i \leq 1$$

12.10   CONCLUDING REMARKS

Scheduling the tasks in real-time systems to meet hard deadlines is a problem which has received much attention and will continue to be the focus of much research. It is well recognized that finding the optimal solution requires a very large amount of computations. Therefore, we must use solutions that yield acceptable, feasible performance without causing very large overhead. In a dynamic environment the scheduler has to handle the processing requests as they are made. These environments put more severe constraints on the resource usage made by the computations of the scheduler. For static environments, the rate monotonic scheduling yields reasonable results provided we are willing to accept the constraints on the level of utilization for resources. In order to extend these results to the dynamic environments we must resort to heuristic approaches.

CHAPTER
13

VERIFICATION OF
SCHEDULABILITY

We start this chapter by defining the conditions that lead to a feasible schedule of job execution. In order to state these conditions and prove them, we use the definitions and notation introduced in Sections 4.1.2 and 4.3.1, as well as the time constraint definition as stated in Section 2.2. Based on the conditions for the existence of a feasible schedule, we then present an algorithm that verifies these conditions. The algorithm is invoked upon an arrival of a request to execute a job in the system. At that point we assume that the request can be represented as a convex time constraint. In the following section we prove some properties of this algorithm. We then extend the algorithm to the case of nonconvex time constraints, which is more complicated but allows more efficient resource management. The next section includes proof of some properties of the nonconvex algorithm. The chapter ends with some concluding remarks.

For allocation and schedule feasibility verification purposes, let us restrict the description presented in Section 4.3.1 by considering only the maximal durations of the constraints. The reason for this restriction is that, in verifying schedule feasibility when accepting a new request, we need to assume the worst case. Without this restriction we cannot guarantee future execution. Here again, the need to guarantee that future execution meets its constraints restricts the model. When we consider the allocation spectrum, it shows that the worst case means maximal time consumption by the already-accepted objects.

We apply this restriction only when we deal with guaranteeing future executions. We note that for temporal reasoning purposes we need the extended model, as defined above.

13.1 FEASIBLE SCHEDULE CONDITIONS

Let us denote the jth occurrence of time constraint i by $TC_i^{(j)}$, represented as the jth maximal convex subinterval of nonconvex interval TC_i. Let $P_i^{(j)}$ be a convex interval contained within $TC_i^{(j)}$,

$$(P_i^{(j)} \uparrow TC_i^{(j)}) \vee (P_i^{(j)} \ll TC_i^{(j)}) \vee (P_i^{(j)} \downarrow TC_i^{(j)}) \vee (P_i^{(j)} = TC_i^{(j)}).$$

Let us convert the definition of a time constraint in Section 2.2 to interval notation as follows:

1. $Taft(condition_1)^* \rightarrow begin_{min}(TC_i^{(j)})$.
2. $Tbef(condition_2)^\dagger \rightarrow end_{max}(TC_i^{(j)})$.
3. f_i periodicity $\rightarrow \forall j > 1: end_{max}(TC_i^{(j)}) - end_{max}(TC_i^{(j-1)}) = \frac{1}{f_i}$.
4. c_i computation time $\rightarrow \forall j \geq 1: \|P_i^{(j)}\| = c_i$.

The fact that the duration of $P_i^{(j)}$ may be less than that of $TC_i^{(j)}$ requires a more precise definition regarding the degree of freedom we have in sliding the interval $P_i^{(j)}$ within the interval $TC_i^{(j)}$.

DEFINITION 14. *The* laxity *of a (computation) convex interval* $P_i^{(j)} = \langle t_\alpha^P, t_\beta^P \rangle$ *that is constrained within a (window) convex interval* $TC_i^{(j)}$ *is defined by the pair (backward_slack, forward_slack), for which*

$$begin_{min}(P_i^{(j)}) = t_\alpha^P - backward\_slack,$$

$$end_{max}(P_i^{(j)}) = t_\beta^P + forward\_slack.$$

If no other constraints are imposed, then

$$backward\_slack = x_- = t_\alpha^P - t_\alpha^{TC},$$

$$forward\_slack = x_+ = t_\beta^{TC} - t_\beta^P.$$

Additional constraints that intersect the $TC_i^{(j)}$ window should be considered each time the laxity is derived.

Let TC_{in} be a time constraint whose schedule feasibility we want to test. Let all the other already-accepted time constraints, $TC_i^{(j)}$, have a feasible schedule. We first consider the case of single-occurrence time constraints with a contiguous computation requirement (hence convex), and then we analyze the bounds that guarantee schedule feasibility for nonconvex time constraints.

13.1.1 Convex Time Constraints

A single-occurrence time constraint defines a time interval in which an execution may take place. We consider this interval as a "window" in which we allow an

---

*Begin-time constraint.

$\dagger$ Deadline.

"occurrence" to happen. Let the window of occurrence of an incoming request be TC_{in}.

$$TC_{in} = \, < begin_{min}(TC_{in}), end_{max}(TC_{in}) >$$

In this window we must verify that, after satisfying the already accepted time constraints, we can schedule a convex subinterval of duration $\|P_{in}\|$. We note that P_{in} must be contained within TC_{in}. Since every constraint that the system accepts passes this verification, we can assume that the already-accepted time constraints have a feasible schedule. From these already-accepted time constraints we can construct a set of maximal convex subintervals, which we check over a *verification interval*

$$V = \, < t_\alpha^V, t_\beta^V >$$

Initially, the verification interval is set equal to the incoming constraint's window of occurrence. We simply reduce our problem to the interval where problems may be found. Hence, $V = TC_{in} = \, < begin_{min}(TC_{in}), end_{max}(TC_{in}) >$. Each subinterval that intersects V, say $TC_i^{(j)}$, has one of four possible relations with it:

1. $TC_i^{(j)} \varnothing V$; or
2. $(TC_i^{(j)} \uparrow V) \vee (TC_i^{(j)} = V) \vee (TC_i^{(j)} \ll V) \vee (TC_i^{(j)} \downarrow V)$; or
3. $TC_i^{(j)} \varnothing^u V$; or
4. $(TC_i^{(j)} \uparrow^u V) \vee (TC_i^{(j)} \gg V) \vee (TC_i^{(j)} \downarrow^u V)$.

Let $\mathcal{I}$ be the set of all the subintervals that intersect V. Let $\mathcal{I}_1$ be the subset of those that overlap V, $\mathcal{I}_3$ the subset of those that are overlapped by V, $\mathcal{I}_2$ the subset of those that are within V, and $\mathcal{I}_4$ the subset of those containing V. In that sense, intervals that satisfy the first relation belong to $\mathcal{I}_1$, those that satisfy the second relation belong to $\mathcal{I}_2$, and so on. We note that no interval can belong to more than one of these subsets, due to the mutually exclusive nature of the four relations.

If $\mathcal{I}_4$ is empty, we verify directly according to the boundaries of TC_{in}. Otherwise, we extend the verification window to the boundaries of the member of $\mathcal{I}_4$, which is not contained within any other member of $\mathcal{I}_4$. This extension requires appropriate extensions of $\mathcal{I}_1$, $\mathcal{I}_2$ and $\mathcal{I}_3$. Each of the members of $\mathcal{I}_4$ is moved to the appropriate subset as well. TC_{in} is of course in $\mathcal{I}_2$, which is the subset of those contained in the verification window.

We must now consider the computation intervals $P_i^{(j)}$, each of which is contained within its own occurrence window $TC_i^{(j)}$. In order to establish the cases that constrain the system the most, we must include within the verification window as much computation of each $P_i^{(j)}$ as possible. Thus, for worst case analysis, let us consider the case in which

$$TC_i^{(j)} \in \mathcal{I}_1 : P_i^{(j)} \downarrow TC_i^{(j)}$$

setting $x_+^{TC_i^{(j)}} \leftarrow 0$, and

$$TC_i^{(j)} \in \mathcal{I}_3 : P_i^{(j)} \uparrow TC_i^{(j)}$$

setting $x\_{i}^{TC_{i}^{(j)}} \leftarrow 0$. In doing so, we encounter the largest computation requirement possible within the verification window, due to of artificially reducing the laxity.

We can now create two new subsets $\mathcal{I}_1^o$ and $\mathcal{I}_3^o$, for which only the relevant portions of overlapping time constraints are accounted. In this action we omit the computation parts that are left out of the verification window, even after the above laxity reduction.

$$\mathcal{I}_1^o \equiv \{ TC_{i_o}^{(j_o)} \}$$
$$= \{< \max(begin_{min}(TC_i^{(j)}), t_\alpha^V), end_{max}(TC_i^{(j)}) >,\ TC_i^{(j)} \in \mathcal{I}_1\}$$
$$\mathcal{I}_3^o \equiv \{ TC_{i_o}^{(j_o)} \}$$
$$= \{< begin_{min}(TC_i^{(j)}), \min(t_\beta^V, end_{max}(TC_i^{(j)})) >,\ TC_i^{(j)} \in \mathcal{I}_3\}$$

For each of the subintervals in $\mathcal{I}_1^o$ and $\mathcal{I}_3^o$ the computation requirement $P_i^{(j)}$ is appropriately set to

$$\|P_{i_o}^{(j_o)}\| = \min(\|P_i^{(j)}\|, \|TC_{i_o}^{(j_o)}\|).$$

At this point each of the members of $\mathcal{I}_1^o$, $\mathcal{I}_2$ and $\mathcal{I}_3^o$ contains the maximal load it can impose over the verification window. Hence, we can formalize the condition for schedulability for both preemptive and nonpreemptive schedulers.

NONPREEMPTIVE SCHEDULING DISCIPLINE.

Condition 1. TC_{in} *is* nonpreemptively schedulable *if*

$$\forall i\ \forall j:\ TC_i^{(j)} \in \mathcal{I}^o :\ \exists x\_^{TC_i^{(j)}} \geq 0\ \exists x_+^{TC_i^{(j)}} \geq 0\ \exists x\_^{TC_{in}} \geq 0\ \exists x_+^{TC_{in}} \geq 0 :$$

$$P_{in} \bowtie P_i^{(j)}$$

where $\mathcal{I}^o$ *is the set union of* $\mathcal{I}_1^o$, $\mathcal{I}_2$ *and* $\mathcal{I}_3^o$. *In other words,*

$$\{P_{in}\} \widehat{\bowtie} \mathcal{P}^o$$

where $\mathcal{P}^o$ *is the set* $\{P_i^{(j)} : TC_i^{(j)} \in \mathcal{I}^o \}$.

An example of a verification that obeys Condition 1 is given in Figure 13.1. The verification interval (V) is TC_{in}, because $\mathcal{I}_4$ is empty. $\mathcal{I}_1$ contains one convex subinterval of TC_1, $\mathcal{I}_3$ contains one convex subinterval of TC_3 and $\mathcal{I}_2$ contains two convex subintervals of TC_2. It can be seen from this example that P_{in} demonstrates nonpreemptive schedulability, since it is disjoint from the disjoint occurrences of the relevant $P_i^{(j)}$'s ($i = 1,2,3$).

The totally-disjoint ($\widehat{\bowtie}$) requirement can hold either if the computation interval P_{in} is disjoint in its original placement, or if TC_{in} has enough laxity to allow a new placement of P_{in} to yield a disjoint relation. The time constraints of I^o that have either overlapping or containment relations with TC_{in} affect its laxity. However, their own laxities are affected by TC_{in} as well. Figure 13.2 demonstrates

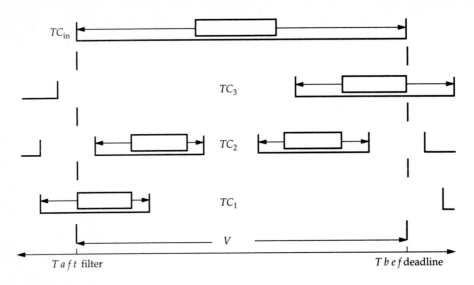

FIGURE 13.1
Verification of schedulability of TC_{in}.

a case of two overlapping constraints, $TC_A \varnothing TC_B$, whose laxities allow the disjoint relations. Let us consider the effects on the laxities. The backward slack of constraint B, x_-^B, is updated to $x_-'^B$, where

$$x_-'^B = \min(x_-^B, \min(t_\alpha^{P_B} - t_\alpha^{TC_B}, t_\alpha^{P_B} - (t_\beta^{P_A} - x_-^A)))$$

since P_B is constrained by P_A from the left. If $x_-'^B$ is negative, and P_B can be moved to the right (on x_+^B's account), the disjoint relation can still hold. This requires

$$x_-'^B + x_+^B > 0$$

However, P_A is constrained by P_B from the right. Hence, we have to update the forward slack of constraint A, x_+^A, to $x_+'^A$, where

$$x_+'^A = \min(x_+^A, \min(t_\beta^{TC_A} - t_\beta^{P_A}, (t_\alpha^{P_B} + x_+^B) - t_\beta^{P_A})).$$

Here again, a negative $x_+'^A$ can still produce the disjoint relation, by moving P_A to the left, if

$$x_+'^A + x_-^A > 0$$

EXAMPLES. Let us consider the two time constraints

$$(A, begin_{min}TC_A, P_A, 0, end_{max}TC_A)$$

$$(B, begin_{min}TC_B, P_B, 0, end_{max}TC_B)$$

Both constraints are sporadic, and thus have a zero frequency.

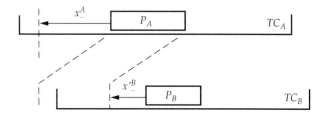

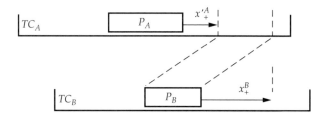

FIGURE 13.2
Laxity interaction of overlapping time constraints.

1. Let $TC_A = (2, 16)$, $P_A = (7, 10)$, $TC_B = (4, 17)$, $P_B = (8, 12)$. Let the laxities of these constraints be given, probably due to the effects of other constraints, as follows: $x_-^A = 4$, $x_+^A = 5$, $x_-^B = 3$, and $x_+^B = 3$. Since $TC_A \oslash TC_B$, let us check the effects these constraints have on each other. According to the above $x_+^{'A}$ and $x_-^{'B}$ are reduced to

$$x_+^{'A} = \min(5, \min(16 - 10, (8 + 3) - 10)) = 1$$
$$x_-^{'B} = \min(3, \min(8 - 4, 8 - (10 - 4))) = 2$$

x_-^A and x_+^B remain unchanged.

2. Let us consider a slightly different case. Let $TC_A = (2, 16)$, $P_A = (7, 12)$, $TC_B = (4, 17)$, $P_B = (8, 12)$. Let the laxities of these constraints be as follows: $x_-^A = 4$, $x_+^A = 3$, $x_-^B = 3$, and $x_+^B = 3$. Applying the same method as above, we get:

$$x_+^{'A} = \min(3, \min(16 - 12, (8 + 3) - 12)) = -1$$

Since $x_+^{'A} + x_-^A = -1 + 4 = 3 > 0$, we can shift P_A to the left and get $P_A = (6, 11)$, $x_-^A = 3$, and $x_+^{'A} = 0$. Thus,

$$x_-^{'B} = \min(3, \min(8 - 4, 8 - (11 - 3))) = 0$$

Figure 13.3 illustrates these examples.

PREEMPTIVE SCHEDULING DISCIPLINE. In a preemptive schedule the condition can be less demanding, in the sense that the interval allocated for TC_{in} does not have to satisfy convexity. Therefore, we can impose only duration constraints.

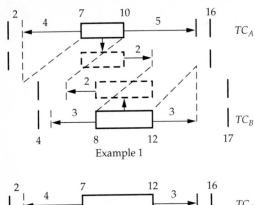

Example 1

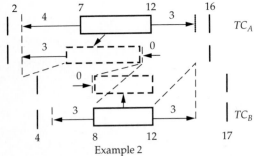

Example 2

FIGURE 13.3
Laxity computation example.

In order to analyze the requirements, we examine two time constraints TC_A and TC_B, that contain computation requirements P_A and P_B, respectively.

If the context switching can be assumed to take a negligible amount of time, then we can allocate a *resource portion* (γ_A, γ_B) per time unit during the time intervals TC_A and TC_B, respectively. Figure 13.4 explains how we derive the required resource portion. Let a constraint A have a period T, an occurrence window of duration TC_A, and a computation interval of duration P_A. Being allowed to execute P_A throughout the whole occurrence window, we can "spread" the execution accordingly. Doing so, we decrease our peak resource requirement portion from unity to P_A/TC_A. Thus, we can write

$$\gamma_A = \frac{\| P_A \|}{\| TC_A \|} \leq 1$$

$$\gamma_B = \frac{\| P_B \|}{\| TC_B \|} \leq 1$$

and still satisfy the requirements. In other words, satisfaction of the constraints is achieved due to

$$\int_{TC_A} \gamma_A \, dt = P_A$$

and analogously for P_B.

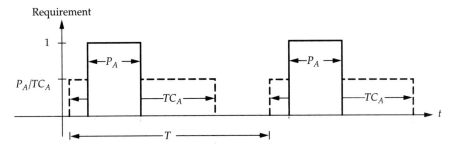

FIGURE 13.4
Spreading requirement in preemptable constraint.

When two or more constraints are not disjoint, one must satisfy an additional constraint. Resource portions cannot be allocated in a manner that exceeds the capacity of the resource (unity for a single resource). In other words, in all possible instances of resource requirement intersection, the following may be required to hold:

$$\gamma_A + \gamma_B + \cdots \le 1$$

However, this requirement is too strong for the following reasons. First, the assumption that the resource portion is a constant is unnecessary. Second, even for a nonconstant $\gamma(t)$ the convexity assumption is unnecessary, since we allow preemption. Therefore, a reasonable condition can be derived by checking that for intersecting requirement intervals, a single resource (or the inventory in the multiple resource case) has the "capacity" to respond. For intersecting TC_A, TC_B, and others, it can be formulated as

$$\int_{TC_A} \gamma_A(t)\, dt + \int_{TC_B} \gamma_B(t)\, dt + \cdots = \| P_B \| + \| P_B \| + \cdots$$

$$\le \| TC_A \sqcup TC_B \sqcup \cdots \|$$

Recalling the definition of the set of maximal convex subintervals[1], the condition we impose for accepting a time constraint TC_{in} is given below.

CONDITION 2. *Let V be the verification interval, derived from the duration of a time constraint TC_x, for which $TC_x = TC_{in}$ or $TC_x \gg TC_{in}$.*

Let $\mathcal{I}_V$ be

$$\mathcal{I}_V = \mathcal{I}^o \cup \{TC_{in}\} - \{TC_x\}$$

where $\mathcal{I}^o$ is the set union of $\mathcal{I}_1^o$, $\mathcal{I}_2$, and $\mathcal{I}_3^o$.

---

[1]See Definitions 8 and 10.

TC_{in} *is preemptively schedulable* if

$$\forall\, s_v \in \mathcal{S}(\mathcal{I}_V):\quad \sum_{\forall i\,:\,TC_i \in \mathcal{I}_V} \| s_v \sqcap P_i \| \;\leq\; \| s_v \|$$

$$\bigwedge$$

$$\sum_{\forall s_v \in \mathcal{S}(\mathcal{I}_V)} \| s_v \| \;\leq\; \| V \| - \| P_x \|$$

where s_v are the convex subintervals of $\mathcal{S}(\mathcal{I}_V)$.

Note that the first part of the condition requires that each maximal convex subinterval assures a "local" satisfaction of the constraints it intersects. Furthermore, those that the subinterval intersects must have a containment relation with it, since it belongs to the set of maximal convex subintervals of their union. The second part of the condition assures that within the whole verification window, we can accumulate enough resource portions "globally" to execute P_x. It is an acceptance test for P_x that does not have any role in the first part of the condition.

13.1.2 Nonconvex Time Constraints

In real systems, time constraints may have some arbitrary precedence relations between them. Grouping them into one time constraint, while forcing their execution to be carried out in a particular computation node [31], imposes a nonconvex resource requirement on that node. This nonconvex resource requirement is the set of maximal convex subintervals of the group of individual resource requirements. The time window in which this group is allowed to execute is the cover of the individual windows of the group. The result of the grouping is, therefore, a nonconvex time constraint. That fact is a good reason to extend the convex constraint schedulability conditions to the finite nonconvex case. Furthermore, a resource requirement may be discontinuous to begin with. A better utilization of the resource is expected if it can be released in the gaps between the subintervals in which it is needed, without conflicting with the prescheduled tasks in these subintervals.

Formally, a nonconvex time constraint differs from a convex one in the nature of its discontinuous computation interval. For an occurrence window TC_i we associate a nonconvex computation interval

$$P_i = \cup_j P_i^{(j)},\ \text{such that}$$

$$(\uplus_j P_i^{(j)} \uparrow TC_i) \vee (\uplus_j P_i^{(j)} \ll TC_i) \vee (\uplus_j P_i^{(j)} \downarrow TC_i) \vee (\uplus_j P_i^{(j)} = TC_i).$$

Let us extend the definition of laxity to include the nonconvex nature of the computation requirement.

DEFINITION 15. *The* laxity *of a (computation) nonconvex interval* P_i *that is constrained within a (window) convex interval* TC_i *is defined by the pair* $(x_-^{TC_i}, x_+^{TC_i})$, *such that*

$$x_-^{TC_i} = t_\alpha^{P_i^L} - begin_{min}(P_i^L) \le t_\alpha^{P_i^L} - t_\alpha^{TC_i} = t_\alpha^{\uplus P_i} - t_\alpha^{TC_i}$$

$$x_+^{TC_i} = end_{max}(P_i^R) - t_\beta^{P_i^R} \le t_\beta^{TC_i} - t_\beta^{P_i^R} = t_\beta^{TC_i} - t_\beta^{\uplus P_i}$$

where $P_i^L = \triangleleft P_i$ *and* $P_i^R = \triangleright P_i$

If no other constraints are imposed, the equality holds. Additional constraints that intersect with TC_i may reduce the laxity and then the inequality holds. Note that we have defined the laxity above in terms of $\uplus P_i$, which is a convex interval. Therefore, in case such a reduction occurs, it is done in the same way defined for a convex time constraint (and illustrated in Figure 13.2).

The schedulability is verified within the time interval where the computation is allowed to occur. In this window one must verify that after satisfying the already accepted time constraints, one can satisfy the constraint that is to be verified.

The construction of the set of intersecting intervals ($\mathcal{I}$) is similar to the process defined for convex time constraints, since the occurrence window is convex here, too. Hence, the subsets $\mathcal{I}_1$ to $\mathcal{I}_4$ are the same in the case of a nonconvex time constraint. Again we make the worst case assumptions, but here we base them on nonconvex relations between convex occurrence windows TC_i and their corresponding computation nonconvex intervals P_i. Thus,

$$\forall\, TC_i \in \mathcal{I}_1 : P_i \downarrow \{TC_i\}$$

setting $x_+^{TC_i} \leftarrow 0$, and

$$\forall\, TC_i \in \mathcal{I}_3 : P_i \uparrow \{TC_i\}$$

setting $x_-^{TC_i} \leftarrow 0$. The worst case is expressed here by having the largest computation requirement possible within the verification window, as in the convex time constraint case. Still, $\mathcal{I}_1$ and $\mathcal{I}_3$ include portions that are outside the verification window. Therefore, subsets containing only the portions of computation that are in the required verification window are created.

$$\mathcal{I}_1^o \equiv \{TC_{i_o}\}$$
$$= \{\, < \max(begin_{min}(TC_i), t_\alpha^V), end_{max}(TC_i) > \,,\ TC_i \in \mathcal{I}_1\}$$
$$\mathcal{I}_3^o \equiv \{TC_{i_o}\}$$
$$= \{\, < begin_{min}(TC_i), \min(t_\beta^V, end_{max}(TC_i)) > \,,\ TC_i \in \mathcal{I}_3\}$$

For each of the subintervals in $\mathcal{I}_1^o$ and $\mathcal{I}_3^o$ the nonconvex computation requirement P_i is appropriately set to

$$P_{i_o} = \{\, \uplus_j\, P_{i_o}^{(j)} \mid P_{i_o}^{(j)} = P_i^{(j)} \sqcap TC_{i_o},\ P_i^{(j)} \in P_i \,\}.$$

As in the convex time constraint case, we make here a basic assumption that the already-accepted time constraints are also schedulable. This assumption, along with the relations of the set of intersecting intervals and the verification window, allow us to formulate the conditions for schedulability of a nonconvex time constraint.

First, for the nonpreemptive schedule, we require a totally-$\bowtie$ relation between all the computations. This relation results in empty intersections among computation nonconvex intervals that correspond to the intersecting windows of occurrence.

CONDITION 3. *An incoming time constraint with an occurrence window TC_{in} and a nonconvex computation requirement P_{in} is nonpreemptively schedulable if*

$$\forall i \, \forall j : TC_i^{(j)} \in \mathcal{I}^o : \exists x_-^{TC_i^{(j)}} \geq 0. \; \exists x_+^{TC_i^{(j)}} \geq 0. \; \exists x_-^{TC_{\text{in}}} \geq 0. \; \exists x_+^{TC_{\text{in}}} \geq 0. :$$

$$\forall P_{i_o}^{(j)} \in \mathcal{P}^o : P_{\text{in}} \bowtie P_{i_o}^{(j)}$$

where $\mathcal{I}^o$ is the set union of $\mathcal{I}_1^o$, $\mathcal{I}_2$ and $\mathcal{I}_3^o$ and $\mathcal{P}^o$ is the set $\{P_{i_o}^{(j)} \mid TC_i^{(j)} \in \mathcal{I}^o\}$.

In the preemptive schedule, we also take into account the nonconvex nature of the computation intervals.

CONDITION 4. *Let the new constraint be a time constraint with an occurrence window TC_{in} and a nonconvex computation requirement P_{in}. Let V be the verification interval, derived from the duration of a time constraint TC_x, for which $TC_x = TC_{\text{in}}$ or $TC_x \gg TC_{\text{in}}$. Let $\mathcal{I}_V$ be*

$$\mathcal{I}_V = \mathcal{I}^o \cup \{TC_{\text{in}}\} - \{TC_x\}$$

where $\mathcal{I}^o$ is the set union of $\mathcal{I}_1^o$, $\mathcal{I}_2$ and $\mathcal{I}_3^o$.

TC_{in} *is preemptively schedulable if*

$$\forall s_v \in \mathcal{S}(\mathcal{I}_V) : \sum_{\forall i: TC_i \in \mathcal{I}_V} \sum_{\forall k: P_i^{(k)} \in P_i} \| s_v \sqcap P_i^{(k)} \| \leq \| s_v \|$$

$$\wedge$$

$$\sum_{\forall s_v \in \mathcal{S}(\mathcal{I}_V)} \| s_v \| \leq \| V \| - \sum_{\forall k: P_x^{(k)} \in P_x} \| P_x^{(k)} \|$$

where s_v are the convex subintervals of $\mathcal{S}(\mathcal{I}_V)$.

We note that, as in the convex interval case, the first part of the condition assures resource availability "locally," or at each maximal convex subinterval of the union of all of them. Yet, the computation that corresponds to the constraint that determines the verification window is missing this part. The second part of the condition assures the "global" resource availability, for the verification window constraint as well as for all the rest. Note that, practically, the difference between this nonconvex version and the convex version is in an additional summation that integrates the subintervals of the nonconvex interval.

13.2 ALGORITHMS PRINCIPLES

Throughout the rest of this chapter we propose algorithms based on the calendars and on the conditions of schedule feasibility proposed above. We introduce two algorithms, one for convex time constraints, and another for nonconvex time constraints.

The algorithms install a convex time constraint (or a nonconvex time constraint, respectively) into a calendar if its schedulability is verified according to conditions 1 and 2 (and similarly conditions 3 and 4). Although not explicitly stated in the algorithm, the access to the global variable representing the current calendar must be protected for mutual exclusion, to avoid concurrent accesses and false deduction. The PUSH_TC boolean function we propose is one of the service access points (SAPs) of the scheduler. Other SAPs might access the same calendar concurrently. In the system concept we proposed above, this mutual exclusion mechanism is a part of the *object* access mechanism of the *scheduler* that is implemented in its *joint*.[2]

Let us now explain the algorithms. Each algorithm contains four phases that are executed sequentially: the init phase, the classification phase, the update phase, and the test. The algorithms differ in the way they express the constraints. We note this difference in the declarations of the type **time_constraint** of the algorithms. In the convex constraint we find a field **P** that represents a convex time interval for the computation. In the nonconvex constraint we find a field **P** that represents a nonconvex time interval for the computation. Both algorithms view the rest of the constraint similarly. The filed **tc** represents the convex window of occurrence; the **back_slack** and **for_slack** fields represent the laxities; the **freq** field represents the frequency of a periodic constraint, and the **state** field supports a conditional insertion of the constraint in the calendar, for execution management. In later chapters we extend this model of time constraint to support fault tolerance and other requirements, but for the schedule feasibility test this model is sufficient.

In the init phase of the algorithm, the constraint that determines the verification window is set equal to the incoming constraint TC_{in}. Accordingly, the verification window itself, v, receives the proper value. The set of intersecting intervals is initialized to an empty set value.

The second phase of the algorithm is a **repeat** loop which classifies the four subsets of intersecting time constraints. It starts with initializing these four subsets to the empty set value. Then, for each constraint (i) through the whole calendar (the already accepted constraints), the algorithm generates an instance j

---

[2]See Part IV for implementation details.

which intersects v and is denoted $TC_i^{(j)}$. Each constraint instance passes through a classification switch which adds it to the proper subset, according to its relation with v. Note that for periodic tasks, the algorithm starts generating more instances after the first selection switch while iterating and selecting a proper subset for each generated instance. This iterative selection–generation is bounded by the verification window boundaries. Once the calendar is classified, we check if $\mathcal{I}_4$ is empty. If it is not, then there is at least one constraint that contains v. In such a case we update v to correspond to the maximal constraint in $\mathcal{I}_4$, the one that is not contained within any of the rest. The algorithm then performs another iteration of the **repeat** loop, now with the new window of verification. If on the other hand $\mathcal{I}_4$ is empty, then the **repeat** loop terminates.

The third phase of the algorithm updates the required computation intervals of the constraints that overlap from left ($\mathcal{I}_1$) and right ($\mathcal{I}_3$). These updates generate the maximal load of the constraints within the verification window, and they are represented in $\mathcal{I}_1^o$ and $\mathcal{I}_3^o$, respectively.

The fourth part of the algorithm is the schedule feasibility test corresponding to the above conditions. Since the schedule type is a parameter, tests for both preemptive and nonpreemptive schedulers are available. If the test result is positive, the incoming constraint is inserted into the calendar. In any case, the test result is returned.

13.3 SCHEDULE FEASIBILITY FOR CONVEX CONSTRAINT

Let us examine the algorithm for verification of schedule feasibility. It receives a parameter that defines the the scheduler's preemption **class** and a definition of the incoming time constraint. The algorithm uses a "global" calendar of already accepted constraints, and we emphasize again that the mutual exclusion is not shown here. As a boolean function it returns true when it finds a feasible schedule and false otherwise. On a true answer, a reservation for the incoming constraint is made to avoid ambiguity.

13.3.1 The Verification Algorithm

```
type class = {preemptive,non_preemptive };

type convex_time_interval = construct
   { begin: time_point ;
      end: time_point ;
      scale, bias: real };

type time_constraint = construct
```

{ tc: convex_time_interval ;

    back_slack, for_slack : real ;

    P : convex_time_interval ;

    freq : real ;

    state : integer };

global var *Already_Accepted*: **set** of time_constraints;

boolean function PUSH_TC(TC_{in}:time_constraint,

    schedule_type: class) ;

local var $I^o, I_1, I_2, I_3, I_4, I_1^o, I_3^o, I_V$: **set** of time_constraint ;

$TC_i^{(j)}, TC_x, constraint$: time_constraint ;

S_V: **set** of convex_time_interval ;

v, s_v: convex_time_interval ;

i, j, i_o, j_o, k, n: indices ;

/* Init PHASE */

$TC_x \leftarrow TC_{in}$;

$v \leftarrow TC_{in}.tc$;

$I^o \leftarrow \phi$;

/* Second PHASE:

Prepare verification interval and classify interference set

of already accepted time constraints. */

repeat

$I_1, I_2, I_3, I_4, I_1^o, I_3^o \leftarrow \phi$; $i \leftarrow 0$;

$\forall$ *constraint* $\in$ *Already_Accepted* **Do**

  if *constraint.freq* $\neq$ 0. **then Do**

    $j \leftarrow \lceil (v.begin - constraint.tc.end)/ constraint.freq \rceil$;

    $TC_i^{(j)}.tc.begin \leftarrow constraint.tc.begin + j/constraint.freq$;

    $TC_i^{(j)}.tc.end \leftarrow constraint.tc.end + j/constraint.freq$;

  oD ;

else Do

$\qquad j \leftarrow 0$; $TC_i^{(j)} \leftarrow constraint$;

$\quad$ **oD** ;

/* Classification switch */

while $TC_i^{(j)}.tc.begin < v.end$ **Do**

$\quad TC_i^{(j)}.tc \varnothing v \Rightarrow I_1 \leftarrow I_1 \cup \{TC_i^{(j)}\}$;

$\quad (TC_i^{(j)}.tc \uparrow v) \vee (TC_i^{(j)}.tc \ll v) \vee (TC_i^{(j)}.tc \downarrow v)$

$\qquad \vee (TC_i^{(j)}.tc = v) \Rightarrow I_2 \leftarrow I_2 \cup \{TC_i^{(j)}\}$;

$\quad TC_i^{(j)}.tc \varnothing^u v \Rightarrow I_3 \leftarrow I_3 \cup \{TC_i^{(j)}\}$;

$\quad (TC_i^{(j)}.tc \uparrow^u v) \vee (TC_i^{(j)}.tc \gg v) \vee (TC_i^{(j)}.tc \downarrow^u v)$

$\qquad \Rightarrow I_4 \leftarrow I_4 \cup \{TC_i^{(j)}\}$;

/* Next instance of periodic constraints */

$\quad$ **if** $constraint.freq \neq 0.$ **then Do**

$\qquad j \leftarrow j + 1$;

$\qquad TC_i^{(j)}.tc.begin \leftarrow constraint.tc.begin$

$\qquad\qquad + j/constraint.freq$;

$\qquad TC_i^{(j)}.tc.end \leftarrow constraint.tc.end$

$\qquad\qquad + j/constraint.freq$; **oD**

$\quad$ **else break** ;

$\quad$ **oD** ;

$\quad i \leftarrow i + 1$;

oD ;

if $I_4 \neq \phi$ **then Do**

$\quad TC_x \leftarrow max\_convex\_constraint(I_4)$;

$\quad v \leftarrow max\_convex\_interval(I_4)$;

oD ;

until $I_4 = \phi$;

/* Third PHASE:

Update the overlapping already-accepted constraints (I_1, I_3) to

contain only relevant portion within the verification interval. */

$\forall\, i\;\forall\, j\colon TC_i^{(j)} \in I_1\colon$ **Do**

    $TC_{i_o}^{(j_o)}.tc.begin \leftarrow \max\,(v.begin, TC_i^{(j)}.tc.begin)\;;$

    $TC_{i_o}^{(j_o)}.tc.end \leftarrow TC_i^{(j)}.tc.end\;;$

    $I_1^o \leftarrow I_1^o \cup \{TC_{i_o}^{(j_o)}\}\;;$

oD ;

$\forall\, i\;\forall\, j\colon TC_i^{(j)} \in I_3\colon$ **Do**

    $TC_{i_o}^{(j_o)}.tc.end \leftarrow \min(TC_i^{(j)}.tc.end, v.end)\;;$

    $TC_{i_o}^{(j_o)}.tc.begin \leftarrow TC_i^{(j)}.tc.begin\;;$

    $I_3^o \leftarrow I_3^o \cup \{TC_{i_o}^{(j_o)}\}\;;$

oD ;

$I^o \leftarrow \{TC_i^{(j)}\colon (TC_i^{(j)} \in I_1^o) \vee (TC_i^{(j)} \in I_2) \vee (TC_i^{(j)} \in I_3^o)\}\;;$

    /* Fourth PHASE:

Check schedulability condition and accept if possible. */

     if $schedule\_type$ = non_preemptive **then Do**

if ($result \leftarrow \forall\, i\;\forall\, j\colon TC_i^{(j)} \in I^o\colon$

    $\exists TC_i^{(j)}.back\_slack \geq 0.\,\wedge\,\exists TC_i^{(j)}.for\_slack \geq 0.$

    $\wedge\,\exists TC_{in}.back\_slack \geq 0.\,\wedge\,\exists TC_{in}.for\_slack \geq 0.\;\colon$

    $TC_{in}.P \bowtie TC_i^{(j)}.P$) **then**

      $Already\_Accepted \leftarrow Already\_Accepted \cup \{TC_{in}\}\;;$

    return($result$) ;

oD ;

if $schedule\_type$ = preemptive **then Do**

    $S_V \leftarrow \mathcal{S}(I_V \leftarrow I^o \cup \{TC_{in}\} - \{TC_x\})\;;$

    if ($result \leftarrow \forall\, s_v \in S_V\colon$

     $(\forall\, i\colon TC_i \in I_V\colon \sum_i \|\, P_i \sqcap s_v \,\| \leq \|\, s_v \,\|)$

     $\wedge\,(\sum \|\, s_v \,\| \;\leq\; \|\, v \,\| - \|\, TC_x.P \,\|)$) **then**

      $Already\_Accepted \leftarrow Already\_Accepted \cup \{TC_{in}\}\;;$

    return($result$) ;

oD ;

13.3.2 Correctness of Schedule Feasibility Guarantee

We assume that each of the already-accepted time constraints in the calendar has successfully passed the same schedule feasibility test. However, this property is valuable only if we show that a time constraint that has been accepted after others does not contradict this condition for the former time constraints. We consider the verification of a feasible schedule to be a *guarantee* of resource availability. Therefore, we start our discussion on the algorithm's properties with proving the maintenance of these guarantees, and then we prove the convergence of the algorithm. The following propositions (1 and 2) hold both for the convex time constraints (section 13.3) and the nonconvex ones (section 13.4).

MAINTENANCE OF GUARANTEES

Proposition 1. *An acceptance of a time constraint TC'' after TC' has already been accepted, maintains the guarantee given to TC'.*

> *Proof*
> Let us examine the following two complementary cases.

1. $TC'' \bowtie TC'$. We prove our claim by induction. If TC' is the only constraint in the calendar, being disjoint from TC'' clearly maintains the calendar unchanged. The trivial case of an empty calendar also holds. Now let us assume we have a finite number of time constraints in $\mathcal{I}$, the set union of $\mathcal{I}_1$, $\mathcal{I}_2$, $\mathcal{I}_3$ and $\mathcal{I}_4$, at the time we examine the acceptance of TC''. By the induction hypothesis, each of these constraints maintains the guarantees of the rest of the constraints in the calendar. Since there is no intersection between TC' and TC'', by the algorithm we have $TC' \notin \mathcal{I}$. Therefore, TC'' cannot affect TC', and its guarantee is maintained by the members of $\mathcal{I}$ that might be affected by TC''. Hence, the guarantee for TC' is maintained. The same argument is valid for both preemptive and nonpreemptive policies.

2. $TC'' \bowtie TC''$. When we examine TC'', the portion of TC' that might be affected is $TC' \sqcap TC''$. If this intersection equals either TC' or TC'', the whole computation requirement, P', is included within the verification window (either $TC' \in \mathcal{I}_2$ or $TC' \in \mathcal{I}_4$). On the other hand, if $TC' \in \mathcal{I}_1$ the algorithm sets $x_+^{TC'}$ to 0, while if $TC' \in \mathcal{I}_3$ $x_-^{TC'}$ is set to 0. The laxity reduction shifts the computation requirement into the verification window, without violating its constraint. Thus, the algorithm forces $TC' \sqcap TC''$ to consume the maximal resource requirements that it is capable to consume within the new verification window.

> In the preemptive policy, when the schedule feasibility criterion is examined, the time constraint accepted earlier is checked either as one member of the set of maximal convex subintervals or as the constraint that dictates the verification window, TC_x.

$$\exists s_v \in \mathcal{S}(\mathcal{I}_V) : TC' \sqcap s_v \neq \phi \bigvee TC' = TC_x$$

Hence, if schedule feasibility is verified, then TC' is guaranteed to hold with the maximal resource requirements of which it is capable to consume within the new verification window. Since its resource requirement can only be less than or equal to that, then the guarantee given earlier to TC' holds according to the test.

In the nonpreemptive case, P' is verified to have sufficient laxity as a member of $\mathscr{I}^o$, and therefore accepting P'' is possible only if the updated laxity of P' is not negative. Thus, a nonnegative laxity for P' ensures the guarantee given earlier.

CONVERGENCE OF THE ALGORITHM. The schedule feasibility verification algorithm contains a loop

$$\textbf{repeat} \ \cdots \ \textbf{until} \ I_4 \neq \phi,$$

which is an "unbounded" iteration, unless we prove otherwise.

Proposition 2. *The* **repeat** *loop is bounded to at most two iterations.*

Proof

There are two cases we must consider. In the first case the incoming time constraint TC_{in} is not contained within any other already-accepted time constraint in the calendar (the first three guards). In the second case there exists such an already-accepted time constraint (the fourth guard).

1. $\exists \, TC_i^{(j)} : TC_i^{(j)} \gg TC_{in}$. In this case v is initially set to TC_{in} and I_4 is initially set to ϕ. Since $\not\exists TC_i^{(j)} : TC_i^{(j)} \gg TC_{in}$, I_4 is not updated in the classification switch, and hence only one iteration is executed.

2. $\exists TC_i^{(j)} : TC_i^{(j)} \gg TC_{in}$. In this case too, v is initially set to TC_{in} and I_4 is initially set to ϕ. Since $\exists TC_i^{(j)} : TC_i^{(j)} \gg TC_{in}$, at the end of the first iteration

$$I_4 = \{TC_k'\} \,, \ k = 1, 2, \ldots$$

such that

$$\forall k : TC_k' \gg TC_{in}$$

We therefore set v to TC_{max}' such that

$$\not\exists TC_k' \in I_4 : TC_k' \gg TC_{max}'$$

and start the second iteration with reseting I_4 to ϕ. If the second iteration ends with $I_4 \neq \phi$, we have a contradiction. To demonstrate, say $I_4 \neq \phi$. Therefore,

$$\exists TC' : TC' \gg TC_{max}'$$

But then TC' also satisfies

$$TC' \gg TC_{in}$$

which implies

$$TC' \in \{TC_k'\} \,, \ k = 1, 2, \ldots$$

that contradicts the definition of TC_{max}'.

13.3.3 Properties of Schedule Feasibility Verification

CONVEX INTERVAL NONPREEMPTIVE SCHEDULING DISCIPLINE. In order to show that the guarantee provided by the nonpreemptive schedulability condition (Condition 1) holds for a convex time constraint, we show that two properties hold. First, consistency between the tentative schedule of the computation interval and the allowed window of occurrence is maintained. Second, an accepted constraint is not in conflict with the already-accepted constraints, and a schedule for all these time constraints exists.

Proposition 3. *If Condition 1 holds, each of the computation intervals of the incoming new time constraint and the already-accepted constraints is consistent with its allowed window of occurrence.*

Proof

   The definition of $laxity \geq 0$ in Condition 1, allows us to write

$$\forall P_i \in \mathcal{P}^o : P_i \uparrow TC_i \bigvee P_i \ll TC_i \bigvee P_i \downarrow TC_i \bigvee P_i = TC_i$$

and

$$P_{\text{in}} \uparrow TC_{\text{in}} \bigvee P_{\text{in}} \ll TC_{\text{in}} \bigvee P_{\text{in}} \downarrow TC_{\text{in}} \bigvee P_{\text{in}} = TC_{\text{in}}$$

Hence, executing the already-accepted subintervals $\{P_i\}$ and the incoming P_{in} at the order of the calendar through which the algorithm verified Condition 1 is not in conflict with any of the time constraints. This calendar is therefore a feasible schedule. Thus, this is a schedule in which each computation interval is within the occurrence window allowed for it.

Proposition 4. *If Condition 1 holds, the accepted constraint, TC_{in}, is not in conflict with any of the already accepted constraints in the calendar, and there exists a possible schedule of all of them.*

Proof

   The assumption that all the already accepted time constraints have been accepted by this algorithm, implies that

$$\forall i, j : P_i, P_j \in \mathcal{P}^o \wedge i \neq j : P_i \bowtie P_j$$

As shown in [7] and by the definitions in Section 4.1.2, from a disjoint relation $P_{\text{in}} \bowtie P_i^o$ one can infer the existence of an *idle* nonnegative interval T_x between the incoming computation P_{in} and each of the already accepted computations $P_{i_o} \in \mathcal{P}^o$. In other words, the positive result of the test in Condition 1 yields

$$\exists T_x : P_{i_o} \Uparrow T_x \Uparrow P_{\text{in}} \bigvee P_{\text{in}} \Uparrow T_x \Uparrow P_{i_o}$$

with $\| T_x \| \geq 0$. Let us examine the consequences of such an interval on each unshifted computation interval P_i that corresponds to each P_{i_o}.

   1. We note the trivial cases

$$\forall i, j : TC_i^{(j)} \in \mathcal{I}_2 \Rightarrow TC_i^{(j)} \in \mathcal{I}^o$$

   2. The existence of such a T_x for computation P_{i_o}, whose corresponding window of occurrence TC_{i_o} satisfies $TC_{i_o} \in I_1^o$, implies the existence of another interval T_y, for computation P_i.

$$\exists T_y : P_i \Uparrow T_y \Uparrow P_{\text{in}} \bigvee P_{\text{in}} \Uparrow T_y \Uparrow P_i$$

P_i's corresponding window of occurrence, TC_i, satisfies $TC_i \in I_1$. The existence of T_y is implied, due to the way I_1^o is constructed from I_1 by shifting P_i to the right to produce P_{i_o} and reducing the laxity $x_+^{P_{i_0}}$ to 0, such that

$$T_x \downarrow T_y \vee T_x = T_y$$

      3. Similarly, the following holds for the right side of the verification interval. If Condition 1 holds, then each computation interval has at least one possibility of being scheduled without a conflict with its constraint. Furthermore, as in the left side of the verification algorithm, Condition 1 implies

$$\exists T_x : P_{i_o} \Uparrow T_x \Uparrow P_{\text{in}} \vee P_{\text{in}} \Uparrow T_x \Uparrow P_{i_o}$$

for computation interval P_{i_o}, whose corresponding window of occurrence TC_{i_o} satisfies $TC_{i_o} \in I_3^o$. Hence, by the way I_3^o is constructed from I_3, we can have a T_y

$$T_x \uparrow T_y \vee T_x = T_y$$

such that

$$\exists T_y : P_i \Uparrow T_y \Uparrow P_{\text{in}} \vee P_{\text{in}} \Uparrow T_y \Uparrow P_i$$

for computation interval P_i, whose corresponding window of occurrence TC_i satisfies $TC_i \in I_3$.

The above cases include all the constraints that intersect TC_{in}. Therefore, we can conclude that if the condition holds for the shifted computation intervals, it definitely holds for the unshifted ones. Hence, a feasible schedule exists for the incoming constraint and for all the constraints that intersect TC_x (members of $\mathcal{I}_1$, $\mathcal{I}_2$ and $\mathcal{I}_3$).

CONVEX INTERVAL PREEMPTIVE SCHEDULING DISCIPLINE. Condition 2 constitutes a method for checking the feasibility of a preemptive schedule for an incoming convex time constraint TC_{in}.

Proposition 5. *If Condition 2 holds, then there is a feasible schedule of the already-accepted constraints in the calendar and the accepted constraint, TC_{in}.*

Proof
      The verification of schedulability must be examined for two possible cases. The first is the case in which the verification window equals the interval of occurrence of the new incoming time constraint. The second is the case in which it is not equal.

      1. $TC_x = TC_{\text{in}}$. From the first test in Condition 2 we know that $\forall s_v \in \mathcal{S}(\mathcal{I}_V)$, for those i's for which $s_v = \sqcup_i TC_i^o$

$$\| s_v \| \geq \sum_{\forall i(s_v)} \| P_i^o \|$$

Let P_i be the convex computation interval of time constraint TC_i, that has been "modified" in the algorithm to the relevant intervals in $\mathcal{I}^o$ to P_i^o and TC_i^o, respectively. Then, by summing the above we get

$$\sum_{\forall s_v \in \mathcal{S}(\mathcal{I}_V)} \| s_v \| \; \geq \; \sum_{\forall s_v \in \mathcal{S}(\mathcal{I}_V)} \sum_{\forall i(s_v)} \| P_i^o \| \; \geq \; \sum_{\forall s_v \in \mathcal{S}(\mathcal{I}_V)} \sum_{\forall i(s_v)} \| P_i \sqcap TC_{in} \|$$

The right side of the above equation originates in the construction of $\mathcal{I}_1^o$ and $\mathcal{I}_3^o$. The equality holds for $\mathcal{I}_2$, as well as for members of $\mathcal{I}_1^o$ and $\mathcal{I}_3^o$ whose computation intervals were already within the verification window. For those whose computation intervals were "pushed" into the verification interval, in a worst case simulation, inequality holds.

Hence, if the second test of Condition 2 holds for TC_{in}

$$\| TC_{in} \| \; = \; \| V \| \geq \sum_{\forall s_v \in \mathcal{S}(\mathcal{I}_V)} \| s_v \| \; + \; \| P_{in} \|$$

$$\geq \sum_{\forall s_v \in \mathcal{S}(\mathcal{I}_V)} \sum_{\forall i(s_v)} \| P_i^o \| \; + \; \| P_{in} \|$$

and we can conclude by replacing $\sum_{\forall s_v \in \mathcal{S}(\mathcal{I}_V)} \sum_{i(s_v)}$ with $\sum_{\forall i : TC_i \in \mathcal{I}^o}$ to get

$$\| TC_{in} \| \geq \sum_{\forall i : TC_i \in \mathcal{I}^o} \| P_i \sqcap TC_{in} \| \; + \; \| P_{in} \|$$

The above equation simply states that the verification interval is large enough to include all the required computations.

  2. $TC_x \neq TC_{in}$. In this case TC_{in} is a member of $\mathcal{I}_V$ and a "contained" relation holds for TC_{in} with respect to the verification window. Therefore, if the first test of Condition 2, then $\forall s_v \in \mathcal{S}(\mathcal{I}_V)$ for those i's for which $s_v = \bigsqcup_{i(s_v)} TC_i^o$

$$\| s_v \| \; \geq \; \sum_{\forall i(s_v)} \| P_i^o \|$$

In this case

$$TC_i^o \in \mathcal{I}^o \bigvee TC_i^o = TC_{in}$$

As in the first case, summing the durations of all the maximal convex subintervals yields

$$\sum_{\forall s_v \in \mathcal{S}(\mathcal{I}_V)} \| s_v \| \; \geq \; \sum_{\forall s_v \in \mathcal{S}(\mathcal{I}_V)} \sum_{\forall i(s_v)} \| P_i^o \|$$

where one of these $P_{i(s_v)}$ is P_{in}, and the others are members of $\mathcal{I}^o$. So, we can write

$$\sum_{\forall s_v \in \mathcal{S}(\mathcal{I}_V)} \| s_v \| \; \geq \; \sum_{\forall s_v \in \mathcal{S}(\mathcal{I}_V)} \sum_{\forall i(s_v)} \| P_i^o \| + \| P_{in} \|$$

As in the first case, the construction of $\mathcal{I}^o$ yields

$$\sum_{\forall s_v \in \mathcal{S}(\mathcal{I}_V)} \| s_v \| \; \geq \; \sum_{\forall s_v \in \mathcal{S}(\mathcal{I}_V)} \sum_{\forall i(s_v)} \| P_i^o \| + \| P_{in} \|$$

$$\geq \sum_{\forall s_v \in \mathcal{S}(\mathcal{I}_V)} \sum_{\forall i : TC_i \in \mathcal{I}^o - \{TC_x\}} \| P_i \sqcap TC_x \| \; + \; \| P_{in} \|$$

When the second test in Condition 2 holds, then

$$\| TC_x \| = \| V \| \geq \sum_{\forall s_v \in \mathcal{S}(\mathcal{I}_V)} \| s_v \| + \| P_x \|$$

Using our results from above

$$\| TC_x \| = \| V \|$$

$$\geq \sum_{\forall s_v \in \mathcal{S}(\mathcal{I}_V)} \quad \sum_{\forall i : TC_i \in \mathcal{I}^o - \{TC_x\}} \| P_i \sqcap TC_x \|$$

$$+ \| P_x \| + \| P_{\text{in}} \|$$

13.4 SCHEDULE FEASIBILITY FOR NONCONVEX CONSTRAINT

We now present the algorithm for verification of schedule feasibility of nonconvex time constraints. We have chosen to introduce it in a way similar to that of the convex time constraint algorithm, as a boolean function. The function, PUSH_TC, accepts a parameter that defines the the scheduler's preemption *class* and a definition of the incoming nonconvex time constraint. This algorithm also uses a "global" calendar of already-accepted constraints, for which we do not show the mechanism for mutual exclusion.

There are two main differences between the following algorithm for verification of schedule feasibility of nonconvex time constraints and the previous algorithm for convex time constraints. The first difference is in the structures and relations that represent the computation intervals. Note that the **P** field in the time constraint is nonconvex. Furthermore, every relation that refers to that field is a nonconvex interval relation, denoted by the proper symbol ($\wedge$).

The second difference is the detailed laxity update that we present here. We present it in the third phase of the algorithm, where we shift as much computation requirement as we can into the verification window. This shift is defined in detail here, to reflect the proper activities as required for a complete description.

13.4.1 The Verification Algorithm

type class $=$ {preemptive,non_preemptive} ;

type convex_time_interval $=$ **construct**

    {   begin: time_point ;

       end: time_point ;

       scale, bias: real } ;

type non_convex_time_interval $=$ **set** of convex_time_interval ;

type time_constraint $=$ **construct**

```
{  tc: convex_time_interval ;
   back_slack, for_slack : real ;
   P : non_convex_time_interval ;
   freq : real ;
   state : integer } ;
```

global var *Already_Accepted*: **set** of time_constraints;

boolean function PUSH_TC (*TC*$_{in}$:time_constraint,

        schedule_type: class) ;

local var $I^o, I_1, I_2, I_3, I_4, I_1^o, I_3^o, I_V$: **set** of time_constraint ;

P^o: **set** of non_convex_time_interval ;

$TC_i^{(j)}, TC_x$, *constraint*: time_constraint ;

S_V: **set** of convex_time_interval ;

s_v, v: convex_time_interval ;

i, j, i_o, j_o, k, n: indices ;

```
/* Init PHASE */
TCₓ ← TCin ;
v ← TCin.tc ;
Iᵒ ← φ ;
```

/* Second PHASE:

Prepare verification interval and classify interference set

of already accepted time constraints. */

repeat

$I_1, I_2, I_3, I_4, I_1^o, I_3^o \leftarrow \phi$; $i \leftarrow 0$;

∀ *constraint* ∈ *Already_Accepted* **Do**

  if *constraint.freq* ≠ 0. **then Do**

    $j \leftarrow \lceil (v.begin - constraint.tc.end)/ constraint.freq \rceil$;

    $TC_i^{(j)}.tc.begin \leftarrow constraint.tc.begin + j/constraint.freq$;

    $TC_i^{(j)}.tc.end \leftarrow constraint.tc.end + j/constraint.freq$;

  oD ;

else Do

$j \leftarrow 0$; $TC_i^{(j)} \leftarrow constraint$; **oD** ;

/* Classification switch */

while $TC_i^{(j)}.tc.begin < v.end$ **Do**

$TC_i^{(j)}.tc \oslash v \Rightarrow I_1 \leftarrow I_1 \cup \{TC_i^{(j)}\}$;

$(TC_i^{(j)}.tc \uparrow v) \vee (TC_i^{(j)}.tc \ll v) \vee (TC_i^{(j)}.tc \downarrow v)$

$\vee (TC_i^{(j)}.tc = v) \Rightarrow I_2 \leftarrow I_2 \cup \{TC_i^{(j)}\}$;

$TC_i^{(j)}.tc \oslash^u v \Rightarrow I_3 \leftarrow I_3 \cup \{TC_i^{(j)}\}$;

$(TC_i^{(j)}.tc \uparrow^u v) \vee (TC_i^{(j)}.tc \gg v) \vee (TC_i^{(j)}.tc \downarrow^u v)$

$\Rightarrow I_4 \leftarrow I_4 \cup \{TC_i^{(j)}\}$;

/* Next instance of periodic constraints */

if $constraint.freq \neq 0.$ **then Do**

$j \leftarrow j + 1$;

$TC_i^{(j)}.tc.begin \leftarrow constraint.tc.begin$

$+ j/constraint.freq$;

$TC_i^{(j)}.tc.end \leftarrow constraint.tc.end$

$+ j/constraint.freq$; **oD**

else break ;

oD ;

$i \leftarrow i + 1$;

oD ;

if $I_4 \neq \phi$ **then Do**

$TC_x \leftarrow max\_convex\_constraint(I_4)$;

$v \leftarrow max\_convex\_interval(I_4)$; **oD** ;

until $I_4 = \phi$;

/* Third PHASE:

Update the overlapping already-accepted constraints (I_1, I_3) to
contain only relevant portion within the verification interval. */

$\forall i \; \forall j : TC_i^{(j)} \in I_1 :$ **Do**

$TC_{i_o}^{(j_o)}.tc.begin \leftarrow \max(v.begin, TC_i^{(j)}.tc.begin)$;

$TC_{i_o}^{(j_o)}.tc.end \leftarrow TC_i^{(j)}.tc.end$;

$TC_{i_o}^{(j_o)}.P \leftarrow shift\_right\,(TC_i^{(j)}.P\,,\ TC_i^{(j)}.for\_slack)$;

$TC_{i_o}^{(j_o)}.for\_slack \leftarrow 0.$;

if $TC_{i_o}^{(j_o)}.tc.begin \leq (\lhd\ TC_{i_o}^{(j_o)}.P).begin$ **then**

$\quad TC_{i_o}^{(j_o)}.back\_slack \leftarrow \min(\,TC_i^{(j)}.for\_slack + TC_i^{(j)}.back\_slack\,,$

$\quad\quad\quad\quad (\lhd\ TC_{i_o}^{(j_o)}.P).begin - TC_{i_o}^{(j_o)}.tc.begin\,)$

else Do

$\quad TC_{i_o}^{(j_o)}.P \leftarrow TC_i^{(j)}.P \cap TC_{i_o}^{(j_o)}.tc$;

$\quad TC_{i_o}^{(j_o)}.back\_slack \leftarrow 0.$; **oD**

$I_1^o \leftarrow I_1^o \cup \{TC_{i_o}^{(j_o)}\}$;

oD ;

$\forall\, i\ \forall\, j\colon TC_i^{(j)} \in I_3\colon$ **Do**

$\quad TC_{i_o}^{(j_o)}.tc.end \leftarrow \min(TC_i^{(j)}.tc.end, v.end)$;

$\quad TC_{i_o}^{(j_o)}.tc.begin \leftarrow TC_i^{(j)}.tc.begin$;

$\quad TC_{i_o}^{(j_o)}.P \leftarrow shift\_left\,(TC_i^{(j)}.P\,,\ TC_i^{(j)}.back\_slack)$;

$\quad TC_{i_o}^{(j_o)}.back\_slack \leftarrow 0.$;

if $TC_{i_o}^{(j_o)}.tc.end \geq (\rhd\ TC_{i_o}^{(j_o)}.P).end$ **then**

$\quad TC_{i_o}^{(j_o)}.for\_slack \leftarrow \min(\,TC_i^{(j)}.for\_slack + TC_i^{(j)}.back\_slack\,,$

$\quad\quad\quad\quad TC_{i_o}^{(j_o)}.tc.end - (\rhd\ TC_{i_o}^{(j_o)}.P).end\,)$

else Do

$\quad TC_{i_o}^{(j_o)}.P \leftarrow TC_i^{(j)}.P \cap TC_{i_o}^{(j_o)}.tc$;

$\quad TC_{i_o}^{(j_o)}.for\_slack \leftarrow 0.$; **oD**

$I_3^o \leftarrow I_3^o \cup \{TC_{i_o}^{(j_o)}\}$;

oD ;

$I^o \leftarrow \{TC_i^{(j)}\colon (TC_i^{(j)} \in I_1^o) \vee (TC_i^{(j)} \in I_2) \vee (TC_i^{(j)} \in I_3^o)\}$;

$\quad \forall\, i\ \forall\, j\colon TC_i^{(j)} \in I^o\colon P^o \leftarrow \cup_{i,j}\, TC_i^{(j)}.P$;

/* Fourth PHASE:

Check schedulability condition and accept if possible. */

if *schedule_type* $=$ non_preemptive **then Do**

    if (*result* $\leftarrow$ ($\forall\, i\ \forall\, j\colon TC_i^{(j)} \in I^o$:

        $\exists TC_i^{(j)}.back\_slack \geq 0.\ \wedge\ \exists TC_i^{(j)}.for\_slack \geq 0.)$

        $\wedge\ \exists TC_{\mathrm{in}}.back\_slack \geq 0.\ \wedge\ \exists TC_{\mathrm{in}}.for\_slack \geq 0.\ :$

        $TC_{\mathrm{in}}.P \bowtie P^o$) **then**

            Already_Accepted $\leftarrow$ *Already_Accepted* $\cup\ \{TC_{\mathrm{in}}\}$;

    return(*result*) ;

oD ;

if *schedule_type* $=$ preemptive **then Do**

    $S_V \leftarrow \mathscr{S}(I_V \leftarrow I^o \cup \{TC_{\mathrm{in}}\} - \{TC_x\})$;

    if (*result* $\leftarrow \forall\, s_v \in S_V$:

        $(\forall\, i\colon TC_i \in \mathscr{I}_V\colon \sum_i \sum_{\forall k: P_i^{(k)} \in P_i} \|\, s_v \sqcap P_i^{(k)} \,\| \leq \|\, s_v \,\|)$

        $\wedge\, (\sum \|\, s_v \,\| \ \leq\ \|\, v \,\| - \sum_k \|\, P_x^{(k)} \,\|)$) **then**

            Already_Accepted $\leftarrow$ *Already_Accepted* $\cup\ \{TC_{\mathrm{in}}\}$;

    return(*result*) ;

oD ;

13.4.2   Properties of Schedule Feasibility Verification

The conditions for the feasibility of a schedule for nonconvex computation intervals, either for a nonpreemptive policy (Condition 3) or for a preemptive policy (Condition 4), are in a way generalizations of the conditions for the convex computation intervals. The convex computation interval can be represented as the single subinterval case of a nonconvex interval, and the reader can verify that the conditions become identical.

NONPREEMPTIVE SCHEDULING DISCIPLINE. In order to show that the guarantee provided by the nonpreemptive schedule feasibility condition, Condition 3, holds for nonconvex constraints, we show that two properties hold. These two properties are exactly as in the convex constraints case. First, consistency between a schedule of the computation interval and the allowed window of occurrence is maintained. Second, an accepted constraint is not in conflict with the already-accepted constraints, and a schedule of all these time constraints exists. We start with an examination of these properties for a nonpreemptive scheduling discipline.

Proposition 6. *If Condition 3 holds, each of the computation intervals of the incoming new time constraint and the already-accepted constraints is consistent with its allowed window of occurrence.*

Proof

From *laxity* ≥ 0 in Condition 3 and the definition of laxity, we can write

$$\forall P_i^{(j)} \in \mathcal{P}^o : \overset{\cup}{+}_j P_i^{(j)} \uparrow TC_i \vee \overset{\cup}{+}_j P_i^{(j)} \ll TC_i$$

$$\vee \overset{\cup}{+}_j P_i^{(j)} \downarrow TC_i \vee \overset{\cup}{+}_j P_i^{(j)} = TC_i,$$

and

$$\overset{\cup}{+}_j P_{\text{in}}^{(j)} \uparrow TC_{\text{in}} \vee \overset{\cup}{+}_j P_{\text{in}}^{(j)} \ll TC_{\text{in}} \vee \overset{\cup}{+}_j P_{\text{in}}^{(j)} \downarrow TC_{\text{in}} \vee \overset{\cup}{+}_j P_{\text{in}}^{(j)} = TC_{\text{in}}.$$

Using the schedule that is exactly the same as the calendar through which the algorithm is verified keeps each computation interval within the allowed occurrence window.

Proposition 7. *If Condition 3 holds, the accepted constraint, TC_{in}, is not in conflict with any of the already-accepted constraints in the calendar, and there exists a schedule of all these time constraints.*

Proof

The assumption that all the already-accepted time constraints have been accepted by this algorithm, and the property of preservation of the algorithm (Proposition 1), imply that

$$\forall i, j : P_i, P_j \in \mathcal{P}^o \wedge i \neq j : P_i \bowtie P_j.$$

As shown in [7] and by the temporal relations definitions in section 4.1.2, from a disjoint relation $P_{\text{in}} \bowtie P_i^o$, that is the positive result of the test in Condition 3, one can infer the existence of an *idle* interval T_x between the incoming computation P_{in} and each of the already accepted computations $P_{i_o} \in \mathcal{P}^o$. In other words

$$\forall k,n : P_{i_o}^{(k)} \in P_{i_o} \wedge P_{\text{in}}^{(n)} \in P_{\text{in}}$$

$$\exists T_x^{(k,n)} : P_{i_o}^{(k)} \Uparrow T_x^{(k,n)} \Uparrow P_{\text{in}}^{(n)} \vee P_{\text{in}}^{(n)} \Uparrow T_x^{(k,n)} \Uparrow P_{i_o}^{(k)}$$

with $\forall k, n : \| T_x^{(k,n)} \| \geq 0$

1. For every P_{i_o} that corresponds to $TC_{i_o} \in \mathcal{I}_2$ the existence of

$$\min_{k,n}(\| T_x^{(k,n)} \|) \geq 0$$

assures a feasible schedule.

2. For every $TC_{i_o} \in \mathcal{I}_1^o$, since every computation interval of $\mathcal{I}_1^o$ is a right-shifted version of a computation interval of $TC_i \in \mathcal{I}_1$, one can infer the existence of $\{T_y^{(k,n)}\}$, such that

$$\forall k, n : T_x^{(k,n)} \downarrow T_y^{(k,n)} \vee T_x^{(k,n)} = T_y^{(k,n)}$$

to support

$$\forall TC_i \in \mathscr{I}_1 : \forall k, n : P_i^{(k)} \in P_i \wedge P_{\text{in}}^{(n)} \in P_{\text{in}}:$$

$$\exists T_y^{(k,n)} : P_i^{(k)} \Uparrow T_y^{(k,n)} \Uparrow P_{\text{in}}^{(n)} \vee P_{\text{in}}^{(n)} \Uparrow T_y^{(k,n)} \Uparrow P_i^{(k)}$$

Thus, we can use this property to conclude $\| T_y^{(k,n)} \| \geq \| T_x^{(k,n)} \|$ that yields

$$\min_{k,n}(\| T_y^{(k,n)} \|) \geq 0$$

which assures a feasible schedule.

3. Similarly, for every $TC_{i_o} \in \mathscr{I}_3^o$

$$\forall k, n : T_x^{(k,n)} \uparrow T_y^{(k,n)} \vee T_x^{(k,n)} = T_y^{(k,n)}$$

Since $\| T_y^{(k,n)} \| \geq \| T_x^{(k,n)} \|$, we conclude

$$\min_{k,n}(\| T_y^{(k,n)} \|) \geq 0$$

which assures a feasible schedule.

Hence, all the constraints that intersect with TC_x (members of $\mathscr{I}_1$, $\mathscr{I}_2$, and $\mathscr{I}_3$) assure a feasible schedule.

PREEMPTIVE SCHEDULING DISCIPLINE.

Proposition 8. *If Condition 4 holds, there exists a schedule of the already-accepted constraints in the calendar and the accepted constraint, TC_{in}.*

Proof

The verification of schedulability has to be examined for two possible cases. The first is the case in which the verification window equals the interval of occurrence of the new incoming time constraint. The second is the case in which it is not equal.

1. $TC_x = TC_{\text{in}}$:

From the first test in Condition 4 we know that $\forall s_v \in \mathscr{S}(\mathscr{I}_V)$ for those i s for which $s_v = \sqcup_i TC_i^o$

$$\| s_v \| \geq \sum_{\forall i(s_v)} \sum_{\forall k: P_i^{(k)} \in P_i^o} \| P_i^{(k)} \|$$

Summing the above and considering the "unmodified" computation intervals $\{P_i\}$ we receive

$$\sum_{\forall s_v \in \mathscr{S}(\mathscr{I}_V)} \| s_v \| \geq \sum_{\forall s_v \in \mathscr{S}(\mathscr{I}_V)} \sum_{\forall i(s_v)} \sum_{\forall k: P_i^{(k)} \in P_i^o} \| P_i^k \|$$

$$\geq \sum_{\forall s_v \in \mathscr{S}(\mathscr{I}_V)} \sum_{\forall i: TC_i \in \mathscr{I}^o} \sum_{\forall n: P_i^{(n)} \in P_i} \| P_i^{(n)} \sqcap TC_{\text{in}} \|$$

If the second test in Condition 4 holds, then

$$\| TC_{\text{in}} \| = \| V \| \; \geq \; \sum_{\forall s_v \in \mathcal{S}(\mathcal{I}_V)} \| s_v \| + \| P_{\text{in}} \|$$

$$\geq \sum_{\forall s_v \in \mathcal{S}(\mathcal{I}_V)} \sum_{\forall i(s_v)} \sum_{\forall k: P_i^{(k)} \in P_i^o} \| P_i^{(k)} \| + \| P_{\text{in}} \|$$

so we can conclude and replace $\sum_{\forall s_v \in \mathcal{S}(\mathcal{I}_V)} \sum_{i(s_v)}$ with $\sum_{\forall i: TC_i \in \mathcal{I}^o}$ to get

$$\| TC_{\text{in}} \| \geq \sum_{\forall i: TC_i \in \mathcal{I}^o} \sum_{\forall n: P_i^{(n)} \in P_i} \| P_i^n \sqcap TC_{\text{in}} \| + \| P_{\text{in}} \|$$

2. $TC_x \neq TC_{\text{in}}$:

As in the above case, the first test in Condition 4 yields

$$\| s_v \| \; \geq \sum_{\forall i(s_v)} \| P_i^o \|$$

Here

$$TC_i^o \in \mathcal{I}^o \bigvee TC_i^o = TC_{\text{in}}$$

Summing

$$\sum_{\forall s_v \in \mathcal{S}(\mathcal{I}_V)} \| s_v \| \; \geq \sum_{\forall s_v \in \mathcal{S}(\mathcal{I}_V)} \sum_{\forall i(s_v)} \sum_{\forall k: P_{i(s_v)}^{(k)} \in P_{i(s_v)}^o} \| P_{i(s_v)}^{(k)} \|$$

where one of these $P_{i(s_v)}^o$ is P_{in}, and the rest are members of $\mathcal{I}^o$. Hence,

$$\sum_{\forall s_v \in \mathcal{S}(\mathcal{I}_V)} \| s_v \| \; \geq \sum_{\forall s_v \in \mathcal{S}(\mathcal{I}_V)} \sum_{\forall i(s_v): TC_i \in \mathcal{I}^o} \sum_{\forall k: P_{i(s_v)}^{(k)} \in P_{i(s_v)}^o} \| P_{i(s_v)}^{(k)} \| + \| P_{\text{in}} \|$$

As in the convex case, it can be extended to

$$\sum_{\forall s_v \in \mathcal{S}(\mathcal{I}_V)} \| s_v \| \; \geq \; \| P_{\text{in}} \|$$

$$+ \sum_{\forall s_v \in \mathcal{S}(\mathcal{I}_V)} \sum_{\forall i: TC_i \in \mathcal{I}^o - \{TC_x\}} \sum_{\forall n: P_{i(s)}^{(n)} \in P_{i(s)}} \| P_i^{(n)} \sqcap TC_x \|$$

From the second test in Condition 4

$$\| TC_x \| = \| V \| \; \geq \sum_{\forall s_v \in \mathcal{S}(\mathcal{I}_V)} \| s_v \| + \sum_{\forall k: P_x^{(k)} \in P_x} \| P_x^{(k)} \|$$

Using our results from above

$$\| TC_x \| \; \geq \sum_{\forall s \in \mathcal{S}(\mathcal{I}_V)} \sum_{\forall i: TC_i \in \mathcal{I}^o - \{TC_x\}} \sum_{\forall n: P_i^{(n)} \in P_{i(s)}} \| P_i^{(n)} \sqcap TC_x \|$$

$$+ \sum_{\forall k: P_x^{(k)} \in P_x} \| P_x^{(k)} \| + \sum_{\forall k: P_{\text{in}}^{(k)} \in P_{\text{in}}} \| P_{\text{in}}^{(k)} \|$$

13.5 CONCLUSION

The conditions and algorithms introduced above support the goals of guaranteeing that accepted jobs will meet their constraints. The jobs accepted can have convex as well as nonconvex computation requirements, all of which should be verified to allow a feasible schedule. The following chapter discusses an allocation scheme that is based on verification of a feasible schedule for every object in the computation. This combination of resource allocation and feasible schedule verification supports the requirements of "next generation" real-time systems.

The approach we present in this chapter has a conservative nature. This property is demonstrated by having the schedulability as a sufficient condition for guaranteeing deadlines, while rejection does not necessarily assure the nonexistence of a feasible schedule.

CHAPTER

14

RESOURCE
ALLOCATION

Allocation of resources in "next-generation" real-time operating systems requires several features in addition to those demonstrated by current systems, increasing the complexity of the resource allocation mechanisms. Allocation is closely related to scheduling, and both are based on *time* considerations, rather then on a static priority scheme. The allocation is fault-tolerance motivated, to support the application reliability goals. In addition, distributed system issues and adaptive behavior requirements further increase the complexity of the mechanisms.

We propose an allocation scheme that guarantees meeting the deadlines of each accepted job. In addition, this allocation scheme enhances fault tolerance, while supporting both damage containment and resiliency. It does this in cooperation with the schedulability verification mechanism introduced in Chapter 13, and with an object architecture, in which for each object there exists a *calendar* management that relates time to its execution. Another feature of this scheme is that it can be used for reallocation to restore the resiliency to its previous value after a failure has occurred.

We start this chapter with a description of the computation model we employ. Then we introduce the allocation algorithm. Each rule of the algorithm is first presented in principle and then in detail. We then examine the algorithm properties.

Before concluding this chapter, we present a way to use this algorithm as part of a recovery procedure, in order to restore resiliency after failure. The chapter closes with some concluding remarks.

14.1 DEFINITIONS AND FORMULATION

Let us start describing our proposed solution with a description of our model of a distributed computation and the problem of allocating resources to such a distributed computation.

14.1.1 Model Description

Let us consider a model in which computation is a system constructed from objects and resources. Let these objects and their relations be as those defined in Chapter 3. The objects that participate in a computation are related to each other via semantic links pointed to by the object joints. The temporal properties of each relation are expressed as either convex or nonconvex time intervals in a calendar within the relevant joint. In that respect, resources can also be viewed as objects. However, we distinguish between the two for differences in fault tolerance properties that relate to the monotonicity of faults. The distinction also relates to properties that concern damage containment in case of a fault. For these reasons we define a resource as an element that requires no other services, and whose failure mode is monotonic. Objects may require services from resources or other objects, and their failures can be either monotonic or transient.

The properties of the resources may allow us to model the system elements in terms of resource segments. For example, we may model one particular memory page as a resource, if we can detect a failure at this level of resolution. We may even be able to trigger an off-line recovery at the same level. On the other hand, if we cannot detect the failure at the page level, we may model the whole memory at a given locality as a resource, or even the whole locality (i.e., the processors, the memory, the devices, etc.) as a single resource. Therefore, we note the flexibility of this model in supporting a complete resolution spectrum of the system elements.

We allocate required resources to executing and "to-be-executed" objects, each having its own joint and calendar. These resources are physically linked according to their geographic and hardware constraints. However, in addition to resources, objects may need services that are provided by other objects, which in turn may need other services and resources, and so on. We represent this relationship with a graph, where objects and resources are nodes, and the relations between them are directed arcs. Note that resources are always the leaf-nodes, since a resource is not expected to need services from other resources.

The distinction between transient and monotonic faults, as expressed in our object / resource model, allows the use of two recovery mechanisms. We denote the most common one as *temporal redundancy*, in which we execute a "retry" effort upon a fault detection. This mechanism is perfectly suited for faults whose existence may be a transient phenomenon. It also permits roll-back recovery. Real-time constraints may conflict with temporal redundancy, however, because the time needed for recovery may not exist. Furthermore, in case of a monotonic failure, retrying is ineffective. In such cases only *physical*

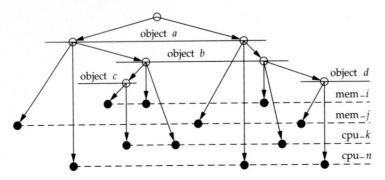

FIGURE 14.1
Temporal (*a, b*) and physical (*c/d*) redundancy.

redundancy can increase the system resiliency. Roll-forward recovery and the N-version programming are examples of such redundancy.

In Figure 14.1 we give an example of the two mechanisms. Objects *a* and *b* are allocated with temporal redundancy, while object *c* has a physical redundancy in object *d*. In the model defined below, resources are to be subjected only to physical redundancy, while redundancy of objects is defined by the computation designer. We note again that the reason for the above originates in the monotonic failures of resources.

One major obstacle that the allocation and relocation mechanisms must overcome is shown in Figure 14.2. Although objects B_1 and B_2 are physically redundant, as are objects C_3 and C_4, the allocation in the figure results in a 0-resilient computation. Any failure of one of the four resources results in a

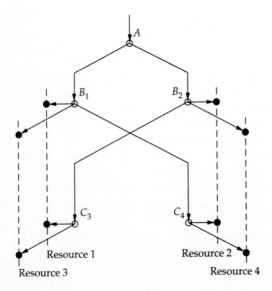

Resource 1   Resource 2   **FIGURE 14.2**

Resource 3   Resource 4   Wrong use of resources: 0-resiliency.

computation fault, since both redundant threads depend on all four resources. If B_1 is allocated with C_3, and B_2 with C_4, the outcome is a 1-resilient computation.

14.1.2 Conditions and Formulation

Let each executable object instance p have a set of resource requirements $\{R_i^{(p)} : 1 \leq i \leq k\}$ and a set of service requirements $\{S_i^{(p)} : 1 \leq i \leq n\}$, forming its *dependency set*, which we denote as DS_p. Restricting p with a time constraint TC_p implies a projected time constraint to each member of its dependency set. Each projection is a result of the temporal relation between p's execution and its requirements. A service requirement can be executed by another executable object instance, which can be chosen out of a set of alternatives. Hence, we can define the dependency set as follows.

Definition 16. *The* dependency set *of an object p with a time constraint TC_p is*

$$DS_{p,TC_p} = \{\{< R_i^{(p)}, TC_{R_i^{(p)}} >: 1 \leq i \leq k\}, \{S_i^{(p)} : 1 \leq i \leq n\}\}$$

where

$$S_i^{(p)} = \{< s_j^{(p)(i)}, TC_{S_i^{(p)}} >: 1 \leq j \leq M_i^{(p)}\}$$

and $M_i^{(p)}$ is the number of service alternatives of service requirement $S_i^{(p)}$.

Let us consider a graph that models the dependency relations between an object p and its requirements. We denote each relation by a directed arc from an object to a member of its dependency set. If a member of the dependency set is another object q, then q's dependency graph is a subgraph of p's dependency graph.

Definition 17. *The* dependency graph *of an object is a graph in which the object is represented as a node, and directed arcs connect this node to the dependency graphs of the members of its dependency set.*

We can also define the set of members in each subgraph as follows.

Definition 18. *A* reachability set *of an object p_i is the set of all objects p_k, such that there exists a finite path from p_i to p_k in the dependency graph of p_i.*

In Chapter 13 we demonstrated a way to guarantee against conflict among computation elements that share servers and resources by using calendars, while at the same time avoiding conflicts between each window of occurrence and its corresponding computation interval.

The schedulability conditions, Conditions 3 and 4, establish the means for defining object allocatability that does not violate a feasible schedule.

Condition 5. *An object p is* allocatable, *if it is* schedulable, *its resource requirements are* schedulable, *and for each of its service requirements there is at least one* allocatable *service alternative (in case the set of its service requirements is not an empty set).*

The above definition is recursive, implying that there must exist at least one object with an empty service requirement set in the reachability set of each allocatable object.

We now define the resiliency of an allocated computation to transient faults and to monotonic faults. But in order to do so, we must first define two special subgraphs of an allocated dependency graph.

Definition 19. *An* allocation graph *of an object is a subgraph of the object's dependency graph in which only allocatable objects and the schedulable resources are represented.*

Note that when the allocation graph of object p includes the object p itself, it also contains all the resource requirements and all the service requirements of p, due to the allocatability property.

Definition 20. *An* allocation alternative *of an object is a subgraph of the object's allocation graph in which for every service requirement only one service alternative is represented.*

Due to the definition of the allocation graph, the service alternatives represented in the allocation alternative are obviously allocatable.

We now have the tools that allow us to phrase the conditions for an allocation resiliency. The allocation resiliency we are interested in can guarantee a certain connectivity within our computation graph. Thus, we want to define resiliency to monotonic faults as well as to transient faults. In addition, we recall the example in Figure 14.2 to show how the following conditions avoid the obstacle presented there.

Condition 6. *An allocation for the execution of object p is n-resilient to monotonic faults if p is allocatable, and there exist at least $n + 1$ distinct allocation alternatives whose intersection with each other contains at most the node p.*

Let us emphasize that this condition excludes any resource requirement or service requirement of p from taking part in the intersection. This way, we base the execution of each distinct allocation alternative on a different resource and service. Furthermore, each allocation alternative demonstrates a complete damage containment from the other alternatives.

Let us now examine the condition for resiliency to transient faults. Since we allow multiple executions of instances of the same object on temporal redundancy, we must first define the allocation of each of these instances.

Definition 21. *An* allocatable instance *of an allocation alternative $\mathcal{A}_p$ of an object p is the the tuple $(\mathcal{A}_p, TC_p)$, where TC_p is the particular time constraint reserved for this allocation alternative.*

Using the above definition and recalling that a physical redundancy is also a temporal redundancy, we have the following condition.

Condition 7. *An allocation is n*-resilient *to* transient faults *if the computation is k-resilient to monotonic faults, and each of its k* + 1 *allocation alternatives,* $0 \leq i \leq k$, *have* τ_i *distinct allocatable instances, such that*

$$\sum_{i=0}^{k} \tau_i \geq n$$

The practical implication of the above condition can be stated informally in terms of the following allocation philosophy. Let us assume we invoke an allocator to achieve an objective of a given resiliency to transient faults. We may find out that the number of distinct allocatable instances at a given allocation alternative cannot support it. We can then use another allocation alternative to allocate additional allocatable instances. Thus, we use physical redundancy to support requirements for temporal redundancy.

14.2   ALLOCATION ALGORITHM

In this section we introduce our allocation algorithm, based on the definitions and conditions we have introduced above. But before providing the detailed algorithm, we use a condensed version of the algorithm to introduce the principles according to which it works.

Considering the *dependency graph* defined in Section 14.1.2, a leaf node is a node whose dependency set has an empty service requirement set. Recall that in the dependency graph the nodes are executable objects we want to allocate. As we will see later, a leaf node plays a special role in this allocation algorithm, and is responsible for generating the "*yes*" answers to the messages.

The *state* of an executable object during allocation can be *allocatable* or *non-allocatable*. An executable object is *allocatable* when it satisfies the allocatability condition as specified in Condition 5. Even when an executable object is non-allocatable, it is assumed to be capable of responding to the algorithm performed by the allocator.

We assume that the allocation algorithm is executed by allocators, each of which is invoked to test the satisfaction of Condition 5 by a particular object.[1] Therefore,we start by defining the invocation messages used in the algorithm, and go on to describe the principles of the algorithm.

14.2.1   Message Types Used

ALLOCATE (from, whom, TC, physical redundancy, temporal redundancy, to) is the initiator message

• *from,* initiating object Id;

---

[1]The assumption does not restrict the generality of the algorithm, but rather enriches its possible implementations. Allocators can be different instances of the same allocator (e.g., a recursive call), or different allocators executing concurrently.

- *whom*, **set** of alternative object_SAPs to be allocated;
- *TC*, time constraint;
- *physical redundancy*, degree of physical redundancy;
- *temporal redundancy*, degree of temporal redundancy;
- *to*, receiving allocator Id.

ALLOC_REQ (of, tag, from, whom, level, TC, to) is the query message

- *of*, initiator Id;
- *tag*, tag number of this *of*'s computation session;
- *from*, object_SAP that requests the service;
- *whom*, object_SAP whose service is requested;
- *level*, degree of temporal redundancy requested;
- *TC*, time constraint;
- *to*, receiving allocator Id.

ALLOC_REP (color, of, tag, from, whom, Δlevel, TC, to) is the feedback message

- *color*, yes / no;
- *of*, initiator Id;
- *tag*, tag number of this *of*'s computation session;
- *from*, object_SAP that replies;
- *whom*, object_SAP that requested the service from *from*;
- *Δlevel*, degree of temporal redundancy in debt;
- *TC*, time constraint;
- *to*, receiver Id.

14.2.2   Principles of Allocation Initiation

The following algorithm rule is implemented as an interface between the user who wants to initiate an allocation session and the allocator. This initiation rule can be implemented as either a special service access-point of the allocator or a dedicated server of another type. When we initiate an allocation session, we must specify its fault tolerance objectives, its set of alternatives in which the computation can be carried out, and the timing constraints for this computation. The initiation rule tries to reach the fault tolerance objectives by requesting allocation of constrained computation alternatives (from the set defined above). These computation alternatives must adhere to the physical and temporal redundancy defined by the user, as well as to the timing constraints.

We tag alternative subgraphs to allow concurrent allocation of dependency subgraphs while maintaining null intersection among them. To support the distributed allocation scheme, the computation *Id* and the graph *tag* are spread with the requests throughout the graph. We use the computation Id and tag as the means to control the connectivity of the graph.

The initiator (*me*) sends enough *ALLOC_REQ (. . .)* messages to allocate members of the alternative set defined by *whom*, and *me* now has to wait for eventual answers. In order to have a higher degree of concurrency, an artificial object joint is created. We note that *me* can be an allocator of the operating system, which we can use to serve many applications. Thus this artificial joint serves to keep *me* active while waiting to collect the answers when they arrive. It also allows choosing another alternative when the answer is negative.

Any decrease of physical redundancy is implicitly prevented by the algorithm. The physical redundancy is controlled through the INSERT_TC function (see Section 17.3.2) that does not reserve in a particular calendar two requests with the same *Id* and different *tags*. This property adheres to the null intersection requirement in Condition 6. Let us summarize the above principles in an algorithmic form, to phrase the initiation rule.

Upon receiving ALLOCATE (from, whom, TC, physical redundancy, temporal redundancy, me)

1. Create an artificial object (ROOT), whose dependency set consists of an empty set of resource requirements, and a set of service requirements whose cardinality equals the physical redundancy level required + 1. Distribute the alternatives of *whom* into these service requirements.
2. For every service requirement in ROOT
   (*a*) Select the first service alternative in the service requirement.
   (*b*) Send ALLOC_REQ for allocating the selected service alternative, distinguishing each service requirement with a different tag. The ALLOC_REQ asks for the temporal redundancy required, imposes the requested time constraint, and designates ROOT as the initiator of the allocation request.

14.2.3   Principles of Algorithm for Allocator

The following algorithm rules are implemented in all allocator instances in the system. They consist of actions responding to an *ALLOC_REQ (. . . , me)* message (allocation request), and actions responding to an *ALLOC_REP (. . . , me)* message (allocation reply).

An allocator receives an *ALLOC_REQ (. . . , whom, . . . , me)* message to allocate an executable object (*whom*). This object, *whom*, must have the *schedulability* property holding for itself and for its resources, for each of its "to-be-executed" instances. If it is schedulable, it forwards *ALLOC_REQ (. . .)* messages to allocate its service requirements in its dependency set. This *forward wave* of *ALLOC_REQ (. . .)* messages proceeds, propagating these messages until the propagation cannot continue. The forward wave stops if a requesting message reaches either an executable object which is *non-schedulable* or a leaf

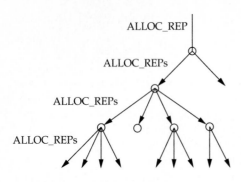

ALLOC_REP

ALLOC_REPs

ALLOC_REPs

ALLOC_REPs

ALLOC_REPs

FIGURE 14.3
Forward wave of ALLOC_REQ messages.

executable object which has no service requirements. Figure 14.3 describes the propagation of *ALLOC_REQ (. . .)* messages.

Real-time properties propagate through the time constraints sent in the *ALLOC_REQ (. . .)* messages to the service requirements and the timing requests imposed on the resource requirements. These constraints are projections of the incoming timing constraint. The projections are made according to the required temporal relations between the invoker's constraint and those imposed on the requirements. We assume that these relations are known in advance, and that they are *convergent*, as defined below.

Definition 22. *A* convergent *temporal relation sequence is a sequence of temporal relations* $(\mathcal{R}_{xy}, \ldots, \mathcal{R}_{yx})$ *that satisfies*

$$x\mathcal{R}_{xy}y \ldots \mathcal{R}_{zx}x' \ll x \bigvee x\mathcal{R}_{xy}y \ldots \mathcal{R}_{zx}x' = x \bigvee$$

$$\bigvee x\mathcal{R}_{xy}y \ldots \mathcal{R}_{zx}x' \uparrow x \bigvee x\mathcal{R}_{xy}y \ldots \mathcal{R}_{zx}x' \downarrow x$$

for time intervals x, y.

A convergent sequence of temporal relations assures bounded behavior of the sequence. If a constraint with a finite occurrence interval is related to itself through such a sequence, the result is contained by that interval. In other words, re-entrant invocation originated through external dependencies results in a projected constraint contained by the original constraint. Let us describe it with an example. Let x be the original constraint imposed on an object. This object requires a service from another object. The temporal relation between x and the constraint of the service, y, is $\mathcal{R}_{xy}$. Let us assume that the service itself requires another service, and let it be given by the original object constrained by x'. Let the relation between y and x' be $\mathcal{R}_{yx}$. This situation can be described as $x\mathcal{R}_{xy}\mathcal{R}_{yx}x'$. For a convergent $\mathcal{R}_{xy}\mathcal{R}_{yx}$ we are guaranteed that the occurrence interval of x' is contained within the occurrence interval of x.

Now let us examine how the *ALLOC_REP (. . .)* messages are generated. Consider the case in which we request to allocate an executable object *whom*, and the allocator verifies it or its resources to be *non-schedulable*. There is no point in verifying the *allocatability* of the resource requirements of *whom*. Therefore, the allocator generates an *ALLOC_REP (no, . . .)* message to the object that requested its service. On the other hand, let us consider the case where we request to allocate a leaf object *whom*, and the allocator verifies it and its resources to be *schedulable*. Having no resource requirements in *whom*'s dependency set, the allocator can generate an *ALLOC_REP (yes, . . .)* message to the object that requested its service.

Figure 14.4 describes the way in which the forward wave generates the backward wave. We attached indices to the messages in order to help ordering their occurrences.

The *backward wave* of *ALLOC_REP (. . .)* messages propagates in the following way. Let us start with the positive reply that requires some conditions to hold. First, both an executable object and its resource requirements must have been found *schedulable*. Second, this object must have received *all* the answers expected with a positive "color." Only then can the allocator send back a positive answer message *ALLOC_REP (yes, . . . , prev, . . .)* to the object that had requested the services. Thus, each node performs a boolean AND of all the positive answers. On the other hand, let us consider the case in which a requesting object exhausts all the service alternatives for any particular service request. It cannot meet its requirements, and it sends back a negative answer message *ALLOC_REP (no, . . . , prev, . . .)*. We note that in the latter case some services may have already been reserved (in particular, the object itself and the resources). We must remove these reservations to release them for other possible requests.

Between the two cases of generating the "yes" and "no" replies, we need to respond to other *ALLOC_REP (. . .)* messages. We have to note positive replies until all expected answers are verified positive. On the other hand, we have to invoke other alternatives as long as the object has not exhausted its service alternatives and the objectives are not satisfied.

Let us introduce the above principles in two reaction rules. The first presents the required reaction to an allocation request (the forward wave). The second presents the reaction to a reply (the backward wave).

Upon receiving ALLOC_REQ (of, tag, from, whom, temporal redundancy level, TC, me)

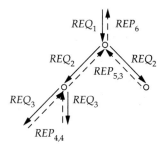

FIGURE 14.4
Backward wave of ALLOC_REP messages.

1. Iterate *my_level* successful iterations, trying to reserve an execution interval for *whom* in its calendar, and for its resource requirements in their calendars. The number of iterations is bounded by the required temporal redundancy level.

2. If no iteration was successful, send ALLOC_REP answering *no*.

3. Otherwise, if *whom* is a leaf-object (having no service requirements), send ALLOC_REP answering *yes*, indicating how many missing temporal redundancy instances there are according to *my_level*.

4. Otherwise (not being a leaf-object) do the following for every service requirement in *whom* dependency set:

   (*a*) Select the first service alternative in the service requirement.

   (*b*) Send ALLOC_REQ for allocating the selected service alternative, asking for the temporal redundancy *my_level*, projecting the proper time constraint according to the temporal relation between *whom* and the service.

5. Update the *whom* joint to include the proper information to deal with replies.

   Upon receiving ALLOC_REP (color, of, tag, from, whom, Δlevel, TC, me)

1. If the color is *yes*, and all the required temporal redundancy instances have been allocated, then mark this service requirement as *done*.

2. Otherwise, not having enough temporal redundancy instances, if there is another possible service alternative in the service requirement, do the following:

   (*a*) Select the next service alternative in the service requirement.

   (*b*) Send ALLOC_REQ for allocating the selected service alternative, requiring the unsatisfied temporal redundancy level (up to *my_level*), projecting the proper time constraint according to the temporal relation between *whom* and the service.

3. However, if there are no more service alternatives at that service requirement, the following two cases are distinguished:

   (*a*) If no alternatives at that requirement have been allocated, send ALLOC_REP answering *no* to the object that required the service of *whom*. In that case release *whom*, its resources, and the rest of the requirements.

   (*b*) If some alternatives at that requirement have been allocated, then decrease the level of temporal redundancy viewed by *whom*, to the lowest between its current view and the view seen by *from*. Then, mark this requirement as *done*.

4. If all service requirements are *done*, send an ALLOC_REP with positive answer to the object that required the service of *whom*, indicating the level of temporal redundancy as limited by *whom*'s view or its requirements.

Finally, we note the way in which the degree of temporal redundancy is maintained, in order to satisfy Condition 7. The temporal redundancy achieved by the object itself and its resources is bounded by the one requested from the service requirements. If a service alternative cannot satisfy the degree required by a requesting object, an additional alternative is invoked to satisfy the debt (the remaining redundancy), and so on, as long as there are alternatives. The requesting object is informed about the final debt in case one could not reserve the required redundancy. The sum of the redundancy achieved by the alternatives of a service requirement establishes the degree of that service requirement. The lowest degree achieved by a member of the service requirement is the one reserved. That way the informed requesting object can try to increase the degree by requesting another alternative. The principle here is to use *physical* redundancy when no more *temporal* redundancy can be achieved.

14.2.4 Local and External Variables

In the algorithm presented here we use some of the variables defined for the joint of an object (see Section 17.3.1) and the following local variables:

- my_level, the degree of temporal redundancy of this object;
- myΔlevel, the debt in temporal redundancy of this object;
- Δlevel, the debt in temporal redundancy of the service requirement;
- TC_{me}, time constraint of this object;
- R_i, a resource requirement;
- $\mathcal{R}_{R_i}$, the temporal relation between this object and resource requirement R_i;
- TC_i, the time constraint of the requirement as projected from TC_{me} using the temporal relation $\mathcal{R}$;
- S_i, a service requirement;
- $\mathcal{R}_{S_i}$, the temporal relation between this object and service requirement S_i;
- $s_j^{(i)}$, a service alternative of service requirement S_i;
- k, n are the number of requirements for resources and services, respectively.

14.2.5 The Allocation Algorithm

Upon receiving ALLOCATE(from,whom,TC,phys_deg,temp_deg,me)

begin

/* Creating an artificial ROOT and setting its parameters */

Let *whom* be associated with $\{p_1, \ldots, p_k\}$ with $k > phys\_deg$;

Construct a non-volatile auxiliary object *ROOT* with the following:

1. $DS_{ROOT,TC_{ROOT}} = \{\{R_i^{(ROOT)} : 1 \le i \le k\} \{S_i^{(ROOT)} : 1 \le i \le n\}\}$

where $\{R_i^{(ROOT)} : 1 \le i \le k\} = \phi$

and $S_i^{(ROOT)} = \{< s_j^{(ROOT)(i)}, TC > : s_j^{(ROOT)(i)} \in \{p_1, \ldots, p_k\}\}$.

2. $Id \leftarrow$ ROOT.

3. $prev \leftarrow from$.

4. $TC_{\mathrm{me}} \leftarrow TC$.

5. myΔlevel$\leftarrow 0$.

6. $s[i] \leftarrow s_1^i$, for $1 \le i \le phys\_deg$.

7. $Ans[i] \leftarrow off$, for $1 \le i \le phys\_deg$.

/* Distribute the request for the nonintersecting subgraphs,

each of which denoted with a different *tag*.

for $tag \leftarrow 1$ **to** $phys\_deg$ **step** 1 **do** send

$ALLOC\_REQ(ROOT,tag,ROOT,s_1^{(ROOT)(tag)},temp\_deg,TC,allocator)$;

od

end

Upon receiving ALLOC-REQ (Id, tag, from, whom, temp_deg, TC, me)

begin

my_level$\leftarrow 0$; I_M_O_K$\leftarrow$true;

$TC_{\mathrm{me}} \leftarrow$ construct($whom, TC, Id, tag$);

$TC_{\mathrm{me}}.level \leftarrow$my_level; $TC_{\mathrm{me}}.state \leftarrow$idle;

while (my_level$<$temp_deg)$\wedge$(I_M_O_K) **do**

/* Temporal redundancy reservations */

if INSERT_TC($whom, TC_{\mathrm{me}}$) **then**

/* Reserve necessary resources for *whom* */

$i \leftarrow 1$; R_is_O_K$\leftarrow$true ;

while $(i \le k)\wedge$(R_is_O_K) **do**

$TC_i \leftarrow$ project ($\mathcal{R}_{R_i}, TC_{\mathrm{me}}$) ;

$TC_i.level \leftarrow$my_level ;

if INSERT_TC(R_i, TC_i) **then**

$i \leftarrow i + 1$;

else /* cannot get them all: release guaranteed subset */

R_is_O_K$\leftarrow$false ;

$$\textbf{for } q \leftarrow 1 \textbf{ to } i \textbf{ step } 1 \textbf{ do}$$

$$\text{REMOVE\_TC } (R_q, TC_q) \; ;$$

od

I_M_O_K←false ;

REMOVE_TC $(whom, TC_{me})$;

fi

od /* resource reservation terminated */

else

I_M_O_K←false ;

fi

if (I_M_O_K) **then**

my_level←my_level + 1 ;

$TC_{me}.level$ ←my_level ;

fi

od

myΔlevel←my_level−temp_deg ;

if (my_level $= 0$) /* failed to reserve *whom* */ **then** send

ALLOC_REP(no, Id, tag, whom, from, myΔlevel, TC_{me}, allocator) ;

else /* my_level> 0, something was reserved */

   if ($\forall S_i \in DS(whom){:}S_i = \phi$) /* leaf-object */ **then** send

   ALLOC_REP(yes, Id, tag, whom, from, myΔlevel, TC_{me}, allocator) ;

   else /* non-leaf-object: invoke allocation of service requirements */

   prev ←*from* ;

   for $i \leftarrow 1$ **to** n **step** 1 **do**

   $TC_i \leftarrow$ project $(\mathcal{R}_{S_i}, TC_{me})$;

   send *ALLOC_REQ(Id, tag, whom, $s_1^{(whom)(i)}$,*

   my_level, TC_i, allocator) ;

   $s[i] \leftarrow s_1^{(whom)(i)}$;

   Ans[i] ← *off* ;

   od

/* In case allocator is reentrant: store in *whom* joint */

store $Id, prev, TC_{me}, my\Delta level, s[i = 1, \ldots, n], Ans[i = 1, \ldots, n]$;

fi fi

end.

Upon receiving ALLOC_REP(color, Id, tag, from, $s_j^{(whom)(i)}$, $\Delta level, TC, me$)

begin

Restore auxiliary variables according to $Id, tag, s_j^{(i)}$

/* $prev, TC_{me}, my\Delta level, s[i = 1, \ldots, n], Ans[i = 1, \ldots, n]$ */

if $(color = yes)$ **then**

    if $(\Delta level = 0)$ **then**

        $Ans[i] \leftarrow done$;

    else /* $\Delta level < 0$: more alternatives needed, some already reserved */

        $Ans[i] \leftarrow on$;

fi fi

if $(\Delta level < 0) \wedge (j < M^{(whom)(i)})$ **then**

    $TC_i \leftarrow$ project $(\mathcal{R}_{S_i}, TC_{me})$;

    send $ALLOC\_REQ(Id, tag, whom, s_{j+1}^{(whom)(i)}, -\Delta level, TC_i, allocator)$;

    store $s[i] \leftarrow s_{j+1}^{(whom)(i)}$;

elseif $(\Delta level < 0) \wedge (j = M^{(whom)(i)}) \wedge (Ans[i] = on)$ **then**

    $my\Delta level \leftarrow min(my\Delta level, \Delta level)$;

    $Ans[i] \leftarrow done$;

elseif $(\Delta level < 0) \wedge (j = M^{(whom)(i)}) \wedge (Ans[i] = off)$ **then**

        /* no alternative reserved release other requirements */

    send $UNLOAD(whom, TC_{me})$;

        /* see Section 17.3.4 */

    if $(Id \neq whom)$ **then** /* climb up to try again */ send

        $ALLOC\_REP(no, Id, tag, whom, prev, my\Delta level, TC_{me}, allocator)$;

    else /* ROOT failed to be allocated */ send

        $ALLOC\_REP(no, ROOT, tag, s[i], ROOT, my\Delta level, TC_{me}, prev)$;

    fi

else /* error in algorithm */

fi

if($\forall i$:$Ans[i] = done$) **then**

    if (*whom* $\neq$ *Id*) **then** send

        ALLOC_REP(yes, Id, tag, whom, from, myΔlevel, TC$_{me}$, allocator) ;

    else /* ROOT is properly allocated */ send

        ALLOC_REP(yes, ROOT, tag, ROOT, ROOT, myΔlevel, TC$_{me}$, prev) ;

            /* temporal redundancy debt in myΔlevel */

        delete ROOT;

fi fi

end.

14.3   ALLOCATION ALGORITHM PROPERTIES

Three major properties are discussed in this section: termination of the algorithm, correctness of allocatability when detected by the algorithm, and the achievement of the fault tolerance objectives when allocatability is confirmed.

14.3.1   Algorithm Termination

We start examining the algorithm's properties by considering the possibility of a nonterminating allocation session, in cases of allocating a particular object, p, with a finite reachability set. The finite number of members in p's dependency set implies a finite path from p to any member q in the set, and therefore within a finite time, an *ALLOC_REQ* (. . .) message sent from p will reach q. In addition, the finite reachability set implies a finite number of requirements. Furthermore, the finite reachability set implies that every path is either finite, or a close component, or a finite path ending with a close component. Therefore, these are the cases we examine below.

    Consider a path that starts at p, passes through one of its requirements, and is finite. It must eventually reach a leaf-node that has no requirements. There, the forward wave of *ALLOC_REQ* (. . .) messages is stopped, generating an *ALLOC_REP* (. . .) message that returns on the same path used by the forward wave.

    If p and its requirement q are both members of a closed component, then the following must occur. Object p inserts its incoming constraint $TC_{p^{(0)}}$ into its calendar, reserving an interval $P_{p^{(0)}}$ within this allowed window of occurrence. Then object p projects its incoming time constraint $TC_{p^{(0)}}$ into a constraint $TC_{q^{(0)}}$. Object q then inserts $P_{q^{(0)}}$ into its calendar, and passes the request. The request continues and returns back to p, since it is a closed component. The restriction on *convergent* temporal relations yields that the new arrival of the allocation request comes with a time constraint $TC_{p^{(1)}}$, which is contained within $TC_{p^{(0)}}$. Now p reserves another time interval $P_{p^{(1)}}$, which is of the same duration as $P_{p^{(0)}}$ and is definitely contained within $TC_{p^{(0)}}$. The same argument holds for the following occurrences of forwarding the *ALLOC_REQ (. . .)* messages. Note that the finite interval $TC_{p^{(0)}}$ can allow only a finite number of $P_{p^{(i)}}$ intervals to be reserved within its limits. Once this finite number is reached, and another reservation request within this window of occurrence arrives, p is not schedulable any more (both preemptively and nonpreemptively). When this case occurs, a negative reply *ALLOC_REP (no, . . .)* is sent back, and the forward wave is stopped.

The third case of a finite path that ends in a closed component is a combination of a finite delivery of *ALLOC_REQ (. . .)* followed by the above scenario.

Due to the above, we conclude that within a finite time the forward wave terminates, and only backward wave messages exist in the allocation session. Since each backward wave message uses the same path its corresponding forward wave message has passed in reverse direction, we conclude that within a finite time every *ALLOC_REQ (. . .)* to an alternative is answered by either a positive or a negative *ALLOC_REP (. . .)*. Having a finite number of alternatives for every requirement, and a finite number of requirements, yields the conclusion of the algorithm within a finite time.

Proposition 9. *The allocation algorithm terminates if the reachability set of ROOT is finite.*

14.3.2   Allocatability Correctness

There are only two possible "colors" for reply messages: a positive answer, the *ALLOC_REP (yes, . . .)* message, and a negative answer, the *ALLOC_REP (no, . . .)* message. The negative answer can be generated in two cases. The first is the case of a non-schedulable object that receives an *ALLOC_REQ (. . .)* message, where non-schedulability refers to the object itself or to one of its resource requirements. The second is the case of an object that receives *ALLOC_REP (no, . . .)* answers from all its alternatives for a specific requirement, and thus is known not to satisfy the allocatability condition. The positive answer is generated in the case of a schedulable leaf node that receives an *ALLOC_REQ (. . .)* message and immediately answers with a *ALLOC_REP (yes, . . .)* message. The positive answer propagates only when there were positive replies from all the service requirements of an intermediate schedulable node, and again schedulable refers to the object itself or to one of its resource requirements. Thus we conclude that each object that sends an *ALLOC_REP (yes, . . .)* message is either a schedulable leaf-node, and thus allocatable, or a schedulable intermediate node that received at least one *ALLOC_REP (yes, . . .)* message from each of its service requirements, and thus is allocatable. Hence, the following proposition:

Proposition 10. *A positive reply from the allocator of ROOT ensures the existence of a nonempty* allocation graph *of ROOT.*

14.3.3 Achievement of Fault Tolerance Objectives

In Section 14.1.2 we defined two types of redundancy, the temporal and the physical redundancy. Here we expand on these two concepts, and on their relations.

In the algorithm presented in Section 14.2, every request for allocating an object specifies the temporal redundancy level required. The temporal redundancy level propagates with some restrictions. Assuming there is no reason to request a service from a higher temporal redundancy level than the one achieved by the requesting object, each object first attempts to reach the required level itself. If it succeeds, the request propagates with no disturbance. Otherwise only a part of the request is forwarded, whose size equals the level achieved locally (my_level), and a "debt" of the size

$$my\Delta level = my\_level - required\_level$$

is generated. Note that, due to this definition, $my\Delta level$ is nonpositive. If all the service requirements achieve the redundancy level forwarded to them, then the local debt (myΔlevel) is reported in the backward wave message. If, however, an alternative does not succeed in reaching the objectives set for it by the requesting object, another alternative is invoked for increasing the temporal level. This alternative invocation continues as long as the temporal redundancy level for the service requirement does not reach the level achieved locally, and as long as there are alternatives. If there are no more alternatives, the local level is reduced to the lowest level achieved by the requirements, and the increased debt is reported in the backward wave message.

The above procedure provides the following result: an allocatable object that answers a request *ALLOC_REQ (. . .,temporal_deg, . . .)* positively with an *ALLOC_REP (yes , . . . , myΔlevel, . . .)*, has reserved at least temporal_deg + myΔlevel execution instances of itself and its resources, and its service requirements' answers reported on at least that amount. In other words, temporal_deg + myΔlevel distinct allocatable instances are reserved. Hence the following proposition:

Proposition 11. *A positive reply from the allocator of ROOT, ensures that Condition 7 holds to satisfy a resiliency to transient faults of an allocatable ROOT of*

$$temporal\_deg + my\Delta level(ROOT).$$

The physical redundancy is achieved by verifying that there are at least *physical_deg* allocation graphs that do not intersect each other, except in ROOT.

The nonintersecting nature is achieved by maintaining that amount of distinct *tags* for the computation allocated *Id*. The INSERT_TC function that is used to verify it assumes every object and every resource has a calendar, each of which is maintained by instances of INSERT_TC and REMOVE_TC. The implementation of the tags separation as service requirements of ROOT serves two goals. First, *physical_deg* replies with different tags are received into a boolean AND. Second, in case one alternative fails, another one can be chosen for an allocation retry.

Proposition 12. *A positive reply from the allocator of ROOT, ensures that Condition 6 holds to satisfy a resiliency to monotonic faults of an allocatable ROOT of physical_deg.*

14.4   REALLOCATION UPON FAILURE

14.4.1   Rationale

Let us recall our model of the system resources, denoted as

$$\mathcal{V}_P = \{R_1, \ldots, R_K\}$$

These vertices are connected with a set of communication links $\mathcal{E}_P$ to form a graph

$$\mathcal{G}_P = (\mathcal{V}_P, \mathcal{E}_P)$$

The dependency set of every object p in the system, contains a resource requirement $\{R_i^{(p)} : 1 \le i \le k\}$, such that

$$\{R_i^{(p)} : 1 \le i \le k\} \subseteq \mathcal{V}_P$$

Methods have been suggested to partition $\mathcal{G}_P$ into clusters of resources used to monitor each other in order to detect a monotonic failure. Each of these clusters is called a *detection unit*, denoted D_i, and we assume that the participating resources communicate with each other using some kind of detection protocol. We make no assumption here about the detection protocol. However, our previous assumption on keeping calendars in a non-volatile storage, suggests a possibility of retrieving the unsatisfied temporal guarantees for the faulty resource.

Although we have shown that the resiliency objectives are satisfied, we suggest an enhancement to allow recovery of the resiliency after a fault occurs. Unused resources in the system may be used to continue the execution of objects that are a part of the failed physical redundancy set. A reallocation of that alternative as a substitute to the faulty one can be easily implemented with the tools described above for the allocation. A retrieval of the calendar of the faulty resource (or object), allows invoking the reallocation with a negative ALLOC_REP, and thus triggering the search of another alternative. If such an alternative is found, ROOT (and thus the owner who requested the computation) is only informed about the recovery via a positive ALLOC_REP message. Otherwise, ROOT is informed with a Δlevel that results from the fault.

14.4.2 Algorithm for Detection Unit D_i

Upon detecting failure (obj.sap: $\uparrow$ object, TC_{in}:time_constraint)

begin

                inform members of D_i ;

                retrieve *calendar(obj.sap)* ;

                $\forall TC_i \in calendar(obj.sap)$: **do**

                        Get auxiliary variables according to *obj.sap* joint ;

                              /* $Id_i, tag_i, prev_i$ are restored */

                        myΔlevel$\leftarrow -1$;

                                send *ALLOC_REP(no, Id_i, tag_i, $prev_i$, obj.sap,*

                      myΔlevel, TC_i, allocator)

    ;

    od

    end

14.5 Concluding Remarks

In real-time systems, the resource management plan—the allocation—must be closely related to the scheduling, and both are based on *time* considerations, rather then on a static priority scheme. In addition to this characteristic, the allocation scheme we have presented in this chapter is fault-tolerance motivated. As such, it copes with the application's reliability goals, ensuring a user specified resiliency to failures while supporting both *temporal redundancy* and *physical redundancy* requirements. This approach allows dealing with *monotonic faults* and with *transient faults* in distinguished manner.

    The proposed allocation scheme accomplishes the hard real-time goal of guaranteeing a deadline satisfaction in case the job is accepted. In addition, it supports fault-tolerance objectives in both damage containment and resiliency requirements. It does it in cooperation with the schedulability verification mechanism, and with the object architecture discussed in Chapter 13 and Chapters 3 and 4, accordingly. An additional feature of this scheme is its use for reallocation while restoring the resiliency after a failure occurred.

CHAPTER
15

COMMUNICATION

This chapter introduces real-time issues related to a very important resource in a distributed system: the communication subsystem. We start with a characterization of delays in the communication subsystem, examining specifically the delay in a typical local area network. We then turn to the problem of the predictability of the temporal behavior of the communication subsystem. We introduce two approaches to real-time communication: synchronous and virtual-time CSMA.[1] After examining the problems of heterogeneous systems, we conclude with a proposal for a comprehensive solution of bounded semantic links.

15.1 NETWORK CHARACTERISTICS

Let us now examine the temporal behavior of our communication network. Since real-time systems require predictable behavior from their communication subsystems, let us construct a model of the communication delay. In order to be more specific, we examine the case of a local area network (LAN), but analysis of other networks can be carried out in the same manner. We base our model on the following observation. We can decompose the errors in estimating communication delays into deterministic and non-deterministic parts. Let us assume that our system performs a type of distributed algorithm whose performance is strongly influenced by temporal uncertainties. We can also assume there is an enhanced algorithm that can utilize knowledge on the deterministic part of the communication delay. The enhanced algorithm can compensate for the deterministic part, thereby reducing the error term to the non-deterministic part. The clock synchro-

---

[1]Carrier sense multiple access.

nization algorithms are good examples of such algorithms. The reader can find the error terms of some examples in Chapter 2.

In order to derive a LAN timing error model, we first examine the LAN architecture as defined by hierarchical models [138]. Both the OSI seven-layer model, and the IEEE 802 standards are built on top of a physical layer. The second layer in the OSI model is the link layer, which is represented in the IEEE model by two layers: the medium access control (MAC) and the logical link control (LLC). All these layers constitute the local network (LN) protocols. On top of the local network layers, the higher layers provide a modular and flexible design environment, but they also introduce delay and timing control problems.

15.1.1 The Network Interface

Each of the nodes in the system is connected to the communication network through a network interface (NIU). The network interface interconnects three items: the logical link protocol that executes on the host, the devices to which (or from which) the data should be delivered (or obtained), and the communication medium. We describe a general network interface unit in Figure 15.1.

The network interface contains servers and drivers. The device servers *get* data from the output devices, while the drivers *put* data to the input devices. We denote the time required for these actions t_{get} and t_{put}, respectively.

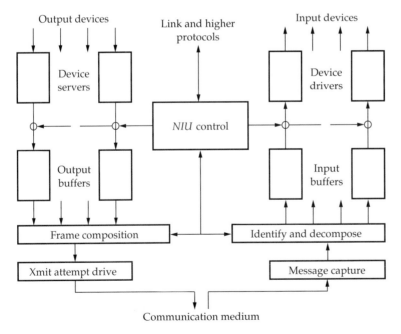

FIGURE 15.1
Network interface unit (NIU).

Data segments that are transferred between the devices and the communication medium are *buffered* in input and output buffers. The NIU-control controls the buffering, allowing buffer filling at the convenience of the protocol, for reasons such as acknowledgments and flow control. We denote the time a message "waits" at the buffers as t_{buf-in} and $t_{buf-out}$, respectively.

The NIU also *composes* the frames for transmission by dividing a long message into fragments and appending the proper head/tail to the message. We denote the time required for this action as t_{comp}. Similarly, when a message is received, it must be identified ("is it for me?") and *decomposed* by removing the head/tail. We denote this time by t_{decomp}. Both t_{comp} and t_{decomp} contain CRC treatment (generation or check, respectively).

The transmission of a message involves gaining control of the communication medium. In a CSMA/CD system, *attempts* to transmit may result in collisions, followed by retransmissions according to the persistence of the unit. In a token network, the unit *waits* for a free token before attempting transmission. In some other architectures the unit waits for its time-slot to transmit. We denote the time that elapses from the moment a message is composed to the moment its successful transmission starts as $t_{attempt}$.

Once a successful message transmission starts, it takes t_{xmit} time units to transmit it. After a propagation delay of $t_{propagate}$, it reaches its receiving NIU. The *capture* mechanism receives the message, an action that consumes $t_{receive}$ time units.

The economical benefits in serving a number of devices with one NIU raise some timing uncertainties. We cannot know the state of NIU-control at the time a message arrives, either from a device or from the communication medium. Hence, it is difficult to predict how long its response time is going to be. Furthermore, the fact that the logical link protocol is not synchronized with NIU-control introduces additional time uncertainties :

- Upon sending, from initiation to xmit/attempt.
- Upon receipt, from capture to link protocol interruption.

We denote the time from identification ("it is for me!") to interruption of the logical link protocol by t_{signal}. We can also express this time as $t_{buf-in} + t_{put}$, in case we have to deliver data to an input device. But in case a message is purely a control function, the NIU-control can inform the Link protocol in a shorter way, as observed in Figure 15.1.

15.1.2 Communication Elements and Timing Uncertainties

We describe a general scheme of the actions that produce communication delays in Figure 15.2. The delay is generated and accumulated from the moment a host initiates a specific activity (e.g., reading a clock) to the moment a remote variable is updated (e.g., clock difference). In the general case, we assume there can be

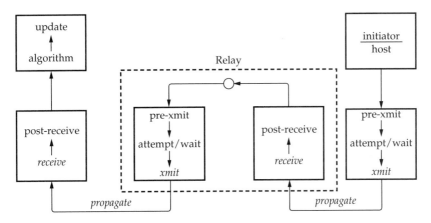

FIGURE 15.2
Delay model for a LAN.

an indirect connection between the two communicants. In such a case relays are needed. For $n - 1$ relays, n propagation delays are accumulated during a message transfer.

Let us describe the delay contributors according to the layered architecture of a local area network. In order to simplify the description, we start with a restriction of a homogeneous implementation. In other words, all the NIU's and protocols are the same in all the sites. All the communication connections are the same as well. Later, we relax this restriction.

PHYSICAL LAYER. The delay from *xmit* to *propagate* to *receive* depends on properties of the physical layer

- bandwidth,
- topology,
- medium technology.

The above, along with the frame size, produce a highly predictable delay. We parameterize and express this delay as

$$t_{xmit} + t_{propagate} + t_{receive}$$

MAC LAYER. The MAC additional activities consist of the following:

- The attempt/wait phase in the transmission part.
- The frame composition in the pre-xmit phase.
- The frame identification and decomposition in the post-receive phase.

We parameterize and express this additional delay as

$$t_{attempt} + t_{comp} + t_{decomp}$$

LINK LAYER. The link layer initiates sending a message from a device, or a data delivery to a device. Its activities can start (in case some conditions are satisfied, as discussed below) t_{signal} time units after NIU-control identifies a particular message that has arrived. Additional activities in this layer consist of the following:

- Moving data from the device to the NIU.
- Filling the output buffer.
- Filling the input buffer.
- Moving data from the NIU to the device.

We parameterize and express this additional delay as

$$t_{get} + t_{buf-out} + t_{buf-in} + t_{put}$$

Additional time is required for composition of an outgoing frame at that level, as well as for decomposition of an arriving frame. Similarly, if we use buffering at that level, we introduce an additional delay.

15.1.3   A Communication Delay Model

In the specific implementation of a network, we merge the delays due to composition, decomposition and buffering of all levels as if they were generated by one level of the hierarchy. Yet, in order to complete our model, we need to account for another delay, the one introduced by the application program. We denote it as $t_{algorithm}$.

To summarize our delay model, let us assume the following:

- One application initiates transmission to another.
- There are $n - 1$ communication relays between the source and the destination, as described in Figure 15.2.
- No recovery mechanism retransmits a lost message without a proper update of its content, since messages have time meaning.
- $t_{attempt}$ contains the contention effects.

We can derive a bound for the total delay of delivering a message from node i to node j, μ_i^j, by summing the maximal value of the contributors:

$$t_{algorithm} + n \times (t_{pre-xmit} + t_{attempt} + t_{xmit} + t_{propagate} + t_{receive} + t_{post-receive})$$

where

$$t_{pre-xmit} = t_{get} + t_{buf-out} + t_{comp}$$

$$t_{post-receive} = t_{decomp} + t_{buf-in} + t_{put}$$

This bound is too large for any real-time system so we will examine an alternative approach in which a large portion of the above bound is known a priori and is compensated for.

Now we can remove the restriction on having identical elements, and we can write the delay μ_i^j of a message from i to j through the relays r_1 to r_{n-1} as the following sum (instead of the above multiplication)[2]

$$
\begin{aligned}
\mu_i^j = \ & t_{\text{comp}}[i] + t_{\text{attempt}}[i] + t_{\text{xmit}}[i] + t_{\text{propagate}}[j] \\
& + \ t_{\text{receive}}[j] + t_{\text{decomp}}[j] + t_{\text{signal}}[j] + t_{\text{algorithm}}[j] \\
& + \sum_{k=r_1}^{r_{n-1}} (t_{\text{comp}}[k] + t_{\text{attempt}}[k] + t_{\text{xmit}}[k] \\
& + \ t_{\text{propagate}}[k] + t_{\text{receive}}[k] + t_{\text{decomp}}[k] + t_{\text{signal}}[k])
\end{aligned}
$$

The adequacy of LAN architecture to real-time applications has been examined mainly in qualitative ways [89]. However, the predictability of any network (including LAN) temporal behavior needs some quantitative measures. Such measures allow the expression of the communication delay for every particular message. We must note that, in a real-time system, a late delivery of a particular message can cause a system failure.

The elements in the above equation contain, in general, a deterministic and a non-deterministic part in each of the terms. The non-deterministic parts cannot be compensated for, but must have bounds in order to assure on-time delivery. We will consider this issue later in this chapter. However, each of the deterministic parts of the elements can be parameterized for a specific system configuration and used later in compensation procedures. We have shown the principle of such a compensation regarding clock synchronization algorithms, in Section 2.4. There, we expressed the communication delay μ_i^j as a sum of a predictable part $\hat{\mu}_i^j$ and an uncertainty $\Delta\mu_i^j$,

$$
\mu_i^j = \hat{\mu}_i^j + \Delta\mu_i^j
$$

Under a proper discipline, we can maintain most of the terms in the delay summation highly predictable. The major contributor to the communication delay uncertainty is

$$
\Delta\mu \approx \sum_{k=i}^{j-1} t_{\text{attempt}}^{(k)}
$$

One way to help keep all the other terms predictable and compensated is through the use of mechanisms of urgency and priority only for messages with

---

[2]The indices relate each parameter to a participant node in the network. The index i stands for the source, the index j for the destination and k for the relays. In the rest of the document we omit the indices for better readability.

deadlines. Information for the compensation is also available. For example, in IP [117] and ICMP [118], the compensation may use the routing information that the timestamp option field contains. We introduce some solutions to these requirements in the following sections.

15.2 PROTOCOLS FOR REAL-TIME COMMUNICATION

In real-time communication we need a timely delivery of messages as well as correct data transfer between sender and receiver. In many cases a message that arrives too late is useless, even though the data transfer is correct. We can, therefore, associate deadlines with real-time messages, as we do with any other real-time computation activity. Association of deadlines with messages has various interpretations in the literature. Since communicating processes may gain their knowledge of time from different clocks, the reference of the deadlines must be properly defined. Furthermore, if both send and receive actions have deadlines, the relationship of one to the other must be defined.

In this section we describe two approaches to deal with real-time communication at the data-link layer of the layered communication model, each concerning a different level of the data link layer. We start with a protocol that governs access to the communication medium. The example we introduce deals with a medium that allows contentions between different senders. We then describe activities at the logical-link layer, emphasizing real-time issues of synchronous communication protocols.

15.2.1 Protocols with Contention

Carrier sense multiple access (CSMA) protocols are widely used as medium access control (MAC) protocols. These protocols allow contention between senders that use the communication medium. The set of computation elements (processes) that share the communication medium may have conflicts in gaining control over it. When two processes transmit simultaneously over this medium, the information is jammed, causing a *collision*. CSMA-CD (collision detection) protocols assume such collisions are detectable.

A special class of CSMA protocols, which demonstrates advantages in its relatively low collision ratio, includes the *virtual-time* CSMA protocols (VTC-SMA [105]). In this class, each of the communicating nodes maintains two clocks, a real-time clock, $T_P(t)$, and a virtual-time clock, $T_V(t)$. The real-time clock runs all the time according to a monotonic algorithm, as described in Chapter 2. When the virtual clock runs, its speed, $a_V(t)$, is higher than that of the real-time clock, $a_P(t) \approx 1$. However, the virtual clock runs only when the communication medium is idle. Once the communication medium becomes busy, the virtual clock stops and is synchronized with the real-time clock when the communication medium becomes idle again. The use of these two clocks at each communicating node supports handling the "send time" of messages according to a time-based criterion.

Let us examine a protocol, called VTCSMA-L [157], that associates a deadline with each message. Let us denote the time in which a message M must reach a destination j by d_M (deadline of M). In addition, let us denote the message length (in time units) by L_M and the estimated communication delay between sender i and destination j by $\hat{\mu}_i^j$. Therefore, the latest time to start sending this message is

$$begin_{max}(M) = d_M - \hat{\mu}_i^j - L_M$$

The laxity of sending M at time t is then

$$x_+^M = d_M - \hat{\mu}_i^j - L_M - t$$

The VTCSMA-L protocol achieves a network-wide transmission policy of minimal-laxity-first, using the following principle. When the sender's virtual clock equals $begin_{max}(M)$, it sends the message M. Since $a_V(t) > a_P(t)$, the virtual clock shows "time to send has arrived" before the real-time clock, as long as the medium is idle. The ratio $a_V(t)/a_P(t)$ is a protocol parameter, whose value we can determine according to the system peak load.

Let us now review the protocol's rules. Let "wait_queue" be a queue of messages waiting for transmission. We assume that the messages in the queue are ordered according to their current laxities (the lowest laxity at the front). This assumption is taken care of by the *insert* command in the algorithm. Let the medium detector show the value busy or the value idle, according to the medium status. We also assume that a collision detector works continuously. The following four rules implement this protocol.

1. *Upon request to transmit* (M, d_M)

    begin

        $begin_{max}(M) \leftarrow d_M - \hat{\mu}_i^j - L_M$;

        if (medium = idle) $\wedge$ $(T_V(now) \geq begin_{max}(M))$

            then /* Immediate transmission */

                send(M) ;

            else /* Insert to the queue according to laxity */

                $x_+^M \leftarrow begin_{max}(M) - T_P(now)$;

                insert (M, x_+^M) ;

        fi

    end

2. *Upon detection of (medium = idle)*

> **begin** /* Reset virtual clock and reset indicator */

$$T_V(now) \leftarrow \rho \leftarrow T_P(now) ;$$

/* Remove late messages which are lost */

for $\forall\, i \in$ wait_queue **do**

if $begin_{max}(i) > T_P(now)$

then

remove i from wait_queue ;

od   fi

end

3. *Upon collision detection while transmitting M*

/* Employ a random recovery to retransmit

as a contention resolution rule,

assuming there is still time to do it */

begin   /* – pick a new $begin_{max}(M)$ from interval, */

$$begin_{max}(M) \leftarrow random(T_P(now), d_M - \hat{\mu}_i^j - L_M) ;$$

/* – then, update laxity, */

$$x_+^M \leftarrow begin_{max}(M) - T_P(now) ;$$

/* – then, insert to the queue properly. */

$$insert\ (M, x_+^M) ;$$

end

4. *Virtual-clock ticks*

begin

while medium$\neq$busy **do**

$$T_V(now) \leftarrow a_V(now) \times (T_P(now) - \rho) ;$$

$candidate \leftarrow$ front(wait_queue) ;

if $begin_{max}(candidate) = T_V(now)$

then /* Send by minimal-laxity-first */

remove *candidate* from wait_queue ;

send *candidate* ;

od   fi

end

The algorithm does not guarantee that messages will meet their deadlines because of the possibility of inappropriate contention resolution. However, its solution employs a time-based reasoning which is equivalent to scheduling shared resources in minimal-laxity discipline. The proper tuning of the ratio $a_V(t)/a_P(t)$ can give "near optimal" results in systems with small load variance.

15.2.2   Synchronous Protocols

Some languages require synchronous communication protocols, enforcing a *rendezvous* of the sender and the receiver of each message [1, 64]. The receiver must wait for the message in order to receive it. The sender must wait for ensuring the correct arrival of the message at the receiver.

In the Ada[3] language [1], parallel processes are called *tasks*. Each task may have some *entries*, which are called from other tasks. Two tasks interact by first synchronizing, then exchanging information and finally continuing their individual activities. This synchronized meeting to exchange information is called *rendezvous*. Let us examine the influence of the way we implement this interaction on a system's real-time properties.

The functionality required from the interaction mechanism must be served both locally and remotely. Therefore, assuming there are kernel primitives that support this mechanism, we may require the following behavior from the primitives to support the rendezvous concept [48].

1. When a task invokes the kernel to interact with another task, the invoked primitive executes in the processor on which the calling task resides.
2. If the called task resides on the same processor as the calling one, all the required information concerning the called task is available.
3. If the called task resides on a different processor, the primitive that has been invoked sends a request to that processor. In this request it specifies the calling processor, the called task, and the requested operation. The request service procedure at the remote site will then invoke the kernel primitive that corresponds to the requested operation, in order to complete the interaction.

There are some implementations that support the above requirements. The comparison criteria can be minimizing system overhead, and the task blocking time.

---

[3]Ada is a registered trademark of the U. S. Department of Defense (Ada Joint Project Office).

Server rendezvous is the first implementation we consider. The calling task remains suspended until the called task executes the *accept* body. For this implementation, a single copy of the accept body is sufficient. This copy should be stored in the private memory of the accepting processor. In order to complete the rendezvous, the mechanism invokes the scheduler *twice* if the entry calling execution precedes the accept execution, and *three times* otherwise. We note that each scheduler invocation may result in a context switch. A remote invocation requires *one* or *two* inter-processor request signals, necessitating *two* or *four* scheduling operations, respectively. Server rendezvous may carry out parameter passing through shared memory.

The second implementation we consider is the *procedural call* rendezvous. Here, the calling task always executes the accept body. There are two ways in which one can obtain accessibility of the accept body. The first is by keeping an exact copy of the accept body on each private memory of the processor that runs the calling task. The second is by storing the accept body in the shared memory. The shared memory solution resembles the *server* solution in communication cost. The replication solution may be ineffective or impossible if a resource needed for the accept body is only available to a particular processor. In this implementation, no special mechanism of parameter passing is needed, since the caller executes the accept body.

Order of arrival rendezvous [48], is an implementation that reduces the scheduling points required. Here, the accept body is a part of the execution of the last task to join the rendezvous. In single processor systems, only *two* scheduling points are needed. In the case of tightly-coupled multiple processor system, *one* inter-processor request signal and *two* scheduling operations are needed to complete a rendezvous. However, the difficulties in resource allocation we have pointed out in the *procedural call* approach exist here, too.

The differences between the three rendezvous implementation approaches emphasize the significance of the compiler-level implementation. The implementation has significant effects on the temporal behavior of programs as well as on the communication load of a system.

In all these approaches, the basic problem of guaranteeing timely message delivery is absent. Let us therefore add to the above mechanisms some criteria for communication correctness. Due to the nature of synchronous communication, these criteria differ slightly from those of asynchronous communication. We note that both sender and receiver must reach conclusion on correctness before each continues its computation. We can state the correctness of synchronous communication in two conditions:

1. the sender and receiver must agree on the correctness of the data transfer, and
2. the agreement must be reached within the respective deadlines.

Let us examine a system in which a process i initiates a rendezvous with process j, in order to transmit a message M from i to j. Each process has access to a local clock. Recalling the time provided from these clocks, as defined earlier

$$T_p(t) = a_p(t)C_p(t) + b_p(t), p = i, j$$

we can define safeness of on-time delivery. Let us assume that the sender i has a deadline $d_i^{(M)}$ to conclude on either success or failure of sending M ($d_i^{(M)}$ is in real-time terms, not local). Respectively, j has a deadline $d_j^{(M)}$ to conclude on the success of receiving M. Let us consider three protocols that take these deadlines into account.[4]

The *clock drift* protocol clock drift protocol compensates for the the clock drifts and the estimated delays by constraining the send execution

$$begin_{\max}(send_M) = (1 - \delta a_i)(d_j^{(M)} - \max(\mu_i^j) - L_M) - \delta b_i$$

Note that j must have advertised its deadline, or else i cannot know $begin_{\max}(send_M)$ that satisfies j. Any later start of sending M cannot assure j will receive it before $d_j^{(M)}$.

The *clock rate* protocol clock rate protocol uses an advertisement of a relative period j is willing to wait, say ω_j. Let $T_i(0)$ be the time in which i received ω_j. Compensating for the clock rate differences and the delays constrains the send execution

$$begin_{\max}(send_M) =$$

$$T_i(0) - (1 + \delta a_i)(\max(\mu_i^j) + \max(\mu_j^i) + L_M) - \delta b_i + \max \frac{(a_i(t)}{a_j(t))\omega_j}$$

Here one compensates for the delay of the advertisement, as well as for the clock differences.

The *last call* protocol carries out no advertisement. The receiver, j, just sends a "last call" message to the sender, i, notifying the sender the time after which satisfying $d_j^{(M)}$ cannot be assured. The receiver is therefore constrained by

$$begin_{\max}(last\_call) = (1 - \delta a_j)(d_j^{(M)} - \max(\mu_i^j) - \max(\mu_j^i) - L_M) - \delta b_j$$

In the above three protocols, both the sender and the receiver can make provisions for exception handling after a deadline miss. This is the case with these protocols when using local deadlines instead of real-time ones [87]. On a deadline miss detection, a process invokes the exception handling, being unable to satisfy the two conditions of correct communication. Let us note that failure to meet the deadlines, although these protocols are used, can still originate at a lower-level protocol. For example, the use of the contention protocol at the the MAC level may still create collisions that may fail the logical link protocol time provisions.

---

[4]These three protocols are examined in local time interpretations in [87].

15.3 HETEROGENEITY AND REPRESENTATION

Let us now turn to issues of higher level layers in the communication layered structure. On top of the local network (LN) layer we find the *transport* layer. The major tasks of this layer are to ensure error-free and in-order message delivery, with no message losses or duplications. Most communication protocols support the error-free objective with checks and retransmissions. As discussed in Chapter 14 on resource allocation, a "retry" can be useless if there is a deadline associated with an execution. The same problem exists in communication. Therefore, the transport layer, just like the allocation mechanism, must provide means for physical redundancy in the absence of temporal redundancy. Note that when we employ physical redundancy, we transmit message duplications in parallel. These messages must use different paths, to assure some degree of improved reliability. In such a case, we expect duplication even in non-faulty cases. There are very simple solutions to this problem, such as indexing, timestamps, and other message descriptors that support idempotency. Later in this chapter we present another way to support the physical redundancy.

The *session* layer, usually built on top of the transport layer, supports connection establishment and disconnection for a session. Such a task cannot be a part of a real-time computation that is deadline bounded. We therefore consider connection establishment as an allocation of a virtual circuit and the proper depositories. Not that we must base this allocation on time, as in the case of local resources.

Most modern computer embedded systems use microprocessors at various control points of the plant they control. This approach allows specialization at a low level of the system architecture, while maintaining generality at higher levels. Computer embedded systems of this nature demonstrate a heterogeneous set of computing devices that interact with each other. Any specialization according to local metrics may lead to heterogeneity of the computing devices. For example, an output device that deals with serial (one bit) data streams does not necessarily need a 32-bit word computer. We must make the decision on the word size of this computer according to the tasks and expected load of this device. Therefore, we require our operating system to support such heterogeneous environments. The *representation* layer, in the open system interface definitions, is one answer to this requirement. However, its cost in time is cumbersome. Another solution is the use of *typed messages*.

Communication via type messages requires an a priori agreement on the structure of the message. Each typed message contains fields in an a priori specified order. The internal fields of the message have specified sizes and meanings, and the source and destination of the message share this interpretation. This property helps real-time system requirements in an additional way. We have shown above a model of the communication delays and ways to overcome them using their predictable temporal properties. Defining the message fields before its transmission lets us know its length (L_M) precisely. Thus, we know the time required to transmit it. As we show in the next section, it also helps us to reserve communication resources. In addition, we can use this predictability to allocate communication resources in a virtual circuit well before run time.

15.4 BOUNDED SEMANTIC LINKS

Let us recall the object architecture from Chapter 3. Objects relate to each other through time constrained invocations, whose temporal behavior we have discussed and examined. However, timing analysis is only one aspect. Let us now add to the invocation its logical requirements. We first examine the case of an invocation of a local object, and propose a passive link to support these logical requirements. We then examine the case of a remote invocation, and extend the link to an active one, through the use of an *agent* object for the remote service. In local and remote invocations, and invoking object transfers a parameter block to the invoked object. We consider the parameter block as a typed message, defined by the proper service access point of the invoked object. In that sense, the use of one-way typed messages for invocations seems to suit this need. One proposed way to implement such invocations at the invoking object program is [108]:

send $<$ *typed_message* $>$ to $<$ *object* $>$ at $<$ *time_constraint* $>$.

We note that the mechanism that supports these invocatsion needs to support additional tasks as well, as discussed below.

15.4.1 Passive Links

Semantic links establish the relations between objects. Each invocation relation has both temporal and logical properties. The temporal properties determine the duration in which the link is active. The logical properties determine the invocation type, as determined by the parameters transferred from the invoking object to the invoked one. Through these properties, the semantic link becomes the justification in our object architecture. It is located between the justifier and the justificand, pointed by both and pointing to both. After the binding process initializes the context, these pointers allow a one-step addressing mode. The invoking object updates the link directly. The invoked object gets the parameters directly from the link.

Now, let us consider the case of an invoking object whose time constraint does not intersect the constraint of the invoked one. One of the tasks of the semantic link is, therefore, to buffer the parameter block of this invocation. Figure 15.3 shows an example of disjoint execution intervals of the invoking object (TC_x) and the invoked on (TC_y). The temporal relation between these computations is $\mathcal{R}_{xy}$. This relation involves the third subinterval of P_x and the second subinterval of P_y. Therefore, the semantic link must cover the earliest possible P_x (denoted P'_x) and the latest possible P_y (denoted P'_y). Note that the temporal relation $\mathcal{R}_{xy}$ is a non-convex one, and specifies the required subintervals which the link serves.[5]

---

[5]If we define relations between the convex windows of occurrence, the link duration is $TC_x \uplus TC_y$.

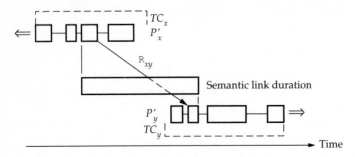

FIGURE 15.3
Duration of semantic link.

The strong type checking in a semantic link is helpful in reducing exceptions on the invoked object side. Let us assume that, upon link creation, the link contains a default value for each of its internal elements. The involving object updates elements in the link only after they pass the type checks. Therefore, there is no need for an end-to-end acknowledgement in this mechanism, an acknowledgement which requires the execution of the invoking and invoked objects to overlap.

The simplest way to implement such a local link is as a passive buffer. The invoking and the invoked objects share the buffer. The invoking object updates the buffer (writer access) and the invoked object uses the buffer as its input parameter block (reader access). In Chapters 16 and 17 we introduce an example of such implementation.

15.4.2   Agents

Distribution computations require stronger support in their semantic links. The changes are due to two major characteristics of distributed systems: communication requirements for remote relations, and system heterogeneity. However, all the previous arguments still hold. Therefore, we consider the distributed support to be an extension of the local semantic link, rather than a different type of link. The advantage of such an approach is the coherent view it gives the user for both local and remote invocations.

Although the user does not distinguish between local and remote invocations, the operating system does. In Chapter 3 we examined some remote service considerations, and presented the *agent* object. Since the agent resides on the invoking object's site, the invocation of the agent is treated locally. Thus, we achieve the required transparency of executing remote invocations in the maintenance of this server representative. However, the need to deal with remote execution and communication issues is now the agent's responsibility. The agent must agree with the "parent" object on a feasible schedule for the invocation, and reserve the time in the remote object calendar. In addition, the agent must provide the required interface for communication and remote reservations. The communication servers involved in this invocation must verify their feasibility accordingly. Each agent, therefore, has both the parent remote service and the communication servers as members of its dependency set.

We want the agent to play its role in interfacing remote servers while supporting the system heterogeneity, along with achieving the above transparency. Since different localities may have different interpretations of the same data, the agent must provide "on-line" translation to the strongly typed communication. The agent, as a representative of the remote server in the local site, is certainly the proper choice for that translation.

In order to support the remote relations, the semantic link must be an active link. The agent object is the source of this active behavior. The invoking object invokes the agent with a local link. During the allocation binding phases, the agent verifies that both the communication servers and the remote service have the feasibility to perform the proper execution. We note here that since the semantic link is size-bounded and strongly typed, the parameter block transfer is bounded, too.

15.5   CONCLUDING REMARKS

It is essential that the appropriate communication mechanisms be provided in any distributed system. When such a system is to be used for real-time applications, severe constraints have to be placed at the design and the implementation of the communication system. We have proposed the mechanisms of the semantic link and the agent to provide the communication support in a distributed heterogeneous environment.

PART
IV

OPERATING
SYSTEM
IMPLEMENTATION

THE MARUTI
OPERATING
SYSTEM

Let us now consider an implementation of the ideas introduced in the previous parts: a "next generation" operating system called MARUTI [93]. We start with an introduction that explains this operating system's principles. We then review its components and their invocation entries, the service access points.

16.1 INTRODUCTION

The MARUTI is a hard real-time, distributed and fault-tolerant operating system. As a hard real-time operating system, it must provide a guarantee to each of its accepted jobs that it can satisfy the associated deadline. In addition, it must support distribution of computations and allocate resources in a manner supportive of the fault-tolerance goals of its accepted jobs.

16.1.1 Objectives

MARUTI is built as a modular system, to allow design, analysis, and verification of temporal and logical properties of the elements executable by the system. The architecture of MARUTI emphasizes the *autonomy* of various elements of the system. Thus, MARUTI supports server replacement for the ease of maintenance. *Temporal predictability* is achieved by encapsulation of the services within localities that support predictable time bounds. Along with this encapsulation, the use of explicit time expressions in decisions regarding execution control further strengthens this predictability.

Many real-time applications require the temporal predictability in addition to the deadline guarantees and response time requirements. For example, control applications need to enforce *lead* and *lag* parameters in order to achieve proper stability requirements. Therefore, MARUTI imposes both start-time and finish-time constraints on periodic as well as on aperiodic computations.

Let us examine the principles according to which MARUTI is designed, and continue with an introductory description of the system.

16.1.2 Approach and Principles

The MARUTI operating system is an *object*-based system, supporting the goal of encapsulation of services. Related objects in MARUTI are semantically linked between object *joints*, as defined in Chapter 3 and described in Figure 16.1. Remote related objects are locally linked to each other through local *agents* of the remote objects. Each local agent is responsible for the communication between its locality and its corresponding remote service. An agent is also responsible for representing the remote service in schedule feasibility verification and reservation schemes [90]. The object architecture and the use of joints allow each access to an object to be indirect but with a fixed length access path. The binding philosophy of the operating system supports this objective. Access to an executing object is an invocation of a particular service of that object. The joint allows many users to access a particular service, assuring mutual exclusion along with consistency control. This object architecture is an important principle of the MARUTI design, and it significantly influences its properties.

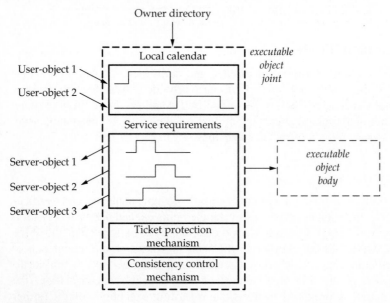

FIGURE 16.1
A single access server object.

The second principle of MARUTI is the use of *calendar*—data structures that are parts of the object joints. These data structures are used to implement sets of non-convex time intervals, and allow verification of schedule feasibility, reservation of guaranteed services, and synchronization. Additional mechanisms support projections of time constraints between different localities, each of which has access to a different time server. These projections maintain the required event ordering and assure the satisfaction of time constraints. Time limited reservation mechanisms and object state control allow reservation of service before loading.

Another principle in MARUTI design is the use of *bounded semantic links* to express relations between objects. The links support the user and owner existential justifications of a server object. Thus, they avoid deletion of the server by an owner as long as users are linked to it. Due to the semantic links, exceptions and validity tests are reduced to a minimum after establishing a link. The links are established by binding and loading processes which we will discuss in detail later in this section. The protection mechanisms are used during the link establishment, establishing authorization to allow a direct access afterwards. Links to remote objects, representing relations with these remote objects, are established with their local agents.

Jobs in MARUTI are invoked through executable objects. The system reactivity requirement demands accepting incoming new jobs while executing already-accepted and guaranteed jobs. This requirement justifies the next principle adopted in our design: supporting *on-line* and *off-line* execution disciplines. Guaranteed jobs execute under the on-line discipline. Objects with unpredictable execution-time bounds, including non-real-time jobs, execute under an off-line discipline. MARUTI carries out an off-line execution only when no real-time job can execute. An off-line job execution can be preempted by the on-line scheduler, since such execution can have an unbounded execution time. The scheduler uses the time service for the preemption.

Fault tolerance is an integral part of MARUTI. Each object's joint contains a consistency control mechanism to manage alternatives (redundant executable objects) or replicas (mainly redundant non-executable objects). The resource allocation algorithm supports a user defined connectivity of the computation graph, where redundancy can be established in time (execute again) or in space (parallel execution of alternatives). In addition, physical redundancy can help a node and link survive monotonic failures, using roll-forward recovery techniques. The system provides critical services with forum and quorum protocols. Under a physical-redundancy discipline, the communication subsystems use a node-to-node acknowledgement scheme, to avoid long end-to-end delays.

The MARUTI kernel is a collection of server objects. The kernel is "booted" at the system initialization, and resides in core throughout the active life time of the system. There are interactions among various servers of the kernel. Each server is subjected to a defined set of operations and operates on a defined set of other objects. Services provided by the kernel are interrupt handling, time service, scheduling, loading, and communication service. All the other services are viewed at higher levels, commonly referred to as the application or the service level. The services provided at higher levels are allocation, binding, login service, name service, directory service, and file service.

Different jobs in MARUTI may share objects or resources (which are also considered as objects). In order to provide a complete temporal management MARUTI uses *calendars*. A calendar is a data structure maintained and manipulated by the scheduler and contains the timing information about this object.

16.1.3 What's New?

The MARUTI design concept directly addresses the needs of "next generation" real-time systems as discussed previously in the book. MARUTI differs from other existing operating systems in some of its basic principles. Some of the major differences are listed below.

- MARUTI is an object-based operating system, with an architecture that supports real-time system requirements with a very high degree of determinism and predictability in its temporal behavior.
- It is a distributed operating system, maintaining the properties of transparency of actual distribution of resources from the user for both the computational resources used and the way fault tolerance is handled.

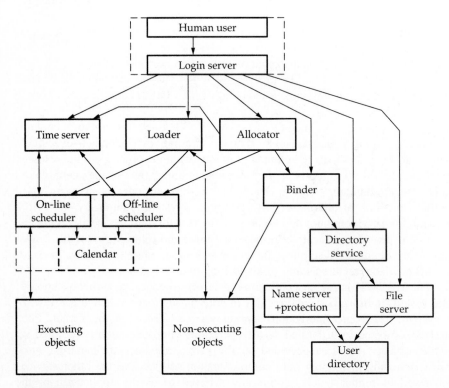

FIGURE 16.2
MARUTI: user's view of management.

- The system is driven by a time constraint model that imposes restrictions both on beginnings and on ends of executions, unlike many other systems that deal solely with the ends (deadlines).
- Requests for invocations of services that are accepted and acknowledged are guaranteed to satisfy their time constraints.
- MARUTI gives a coherent solution to tasks that are of a conventional type and to tasks that are interrupt-driven. Most of the other designs of real-time systems are not suitable for interrupt-driven tasks and may violate deadlines because of interrupts.
- The MARUTI architecture supports a reactive system definition. External requests are expected throughout the execution of already-accepted ones, providing means for verifying their schedule feasibility, and binding the requests to proper servers and resources.

An overview of an execution invocation of a MARUTI's component as seen by a user is described in Figure 16.2. In the next section we present the components that participate in such execution invocations. We note that the block that encounters the human user and its log_in server can be replaced by any user object which requires services of other objects or resources.

16.2   MARUTI COMPONENTS

MARUTI's components are server objects. Each object provides a set of services, that can be invoked through a defined service access point (SAP). We have already noted the collection of objects, called the *kernel*, that is core resident throughout the operation of the system. Each object that requires the service of another object must first bind itself to that object via a semantic link. The interconnections of the kernel members are kept active all the time, to avoid the need to re-bind them.

16.2.1   Kernel Components

INTERRUPT HANDLER. Each execution of an interrupt service is reserved as any other object. But, it is different in that it requires an event occurrence (the interrupt) as an enabling condition for its execution. A detailed example of such a handler is described in Chapter 3.2.1.

  MARUTI interrupt handler has three SAPs for defining the server, removing a server, and serving upon an interrupt occurrence.

- Interrupt Definition. This service access point adds a member to the *Interrupt_Map*, a data structure implemented as an ordered and balanced tree. The nodes of the tree are tuples

$$< device\_identifier, object\_server >$$

The insertion of the new member is by an insertion algorithm (e.g., [75, Chapter 6.2.3]) that keeps the tree ordered and balanced.

- Interrupt Removal. Activation of this SAP undoes the operation done by the SAP.
- Interrupt Handler. Only a very simple action is performed in response to an interrupt. This action must demonstrate a short and predictable temporal behavior. First, MARUTI masks all interrupts while handling the current response. Then, the interrupt service object's state is changed to an active one, indicating that the interrupt has already occurred. After these simple, short and time-deterministic operations are carried out, control is returned to the interrupted execution and interrupts are enabled. It is important to note that resources (or objects) are always reserved for the interrupt service before the interrupt occurs. The reservation is done through the interrupt definition SAP. However, it differs from a regular reservation in that it sets the service in an idle state.

Figure 16.3 describes this concept of interrupt handling and serving as employed in MARUTI. The interrupt-handler's two off-line SAPs allow definition and removal of interrupt servers. Its on-line SAPs allow only access to joints according to the *Interrupt_Map*. In such an access, the handler changes the object's state to active on the proper interrupt arrival. The servers are linked to the proper calendars, and the on-line schedulers pass control to them accordingly.

TIME SERVICE. The time service provides the knowledge of time to executing objects, considering past, present and future relations. We discussed these three

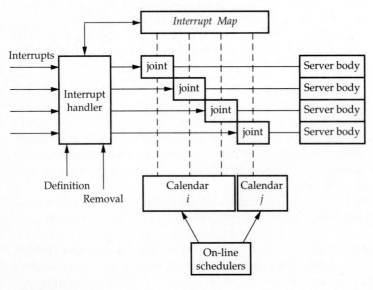

FIGURE 16.3
Interrupt handling and serving.

considerations in Section 4.2. We associate synchronization and event ordering with the past, since they involve events that have already occurred. In this aspect, the time server must assure that any two clocks in the system differ from each other in the lowest possible value. We associate the provision of the knowledge of the global (universal) time with the present. Here, we require each clock in the system to have a small knowledge error. In other words, we want each time knowledge to be close to the global (universal) time. Time service must also deal with future projections. This issue is of extreme importance in hard real-time systems. Here, allocation decisions are made in accordance with events that have not yet occurred, but are programmed to occur in a known time interval in the future.

The MARUTI time service is implemented as a *time provider*. In Chapter 11 we discussed the advantages of such implementation. Therefore, MARUTI supports the following SAPs in the time server:

- AWAKE_AT, a service access point that invokes the timer to awake a specified object at a specified time.
- AWAKE_AFTER, similar to AWAKE_AT, but in relative time units instead of absolute ones. This SAP is commonly called the PIT (programmable interval timer) service.
- GET_TIME, establishes a connection to a provider. This SAP provides the served object with a link to an address of a particular provider. Current time and the error bounds can be read from the area pointed by this link.
- SET_TIME, allows changing of "political time" as in time zone interpretation.
- AGREE_ON_FORUM, initializes a forum of participants in clock synchronization. An important parameter in the forum establishment is the degree of fault tolerance required. The accuracy of the service is also a property that is affected by the properties of the individual participants in the quorum. Hence, an upper-level service whose goal is to set an accuracy level of time may use this SAP.
- GIVE_BOUNDS, for predicting inaccuracies in the future, the time server provides future time bounds through the worst case time analysis.

SCHEDULER. The scheduler is invoked each time a job finishes a time-quantum to give control of the resource to another instance (if one exists). The scheduler then picks a next instance from a calendar according to the scheduling policy (e.g., least-slack, earliest deadline, etc.). The calendar is ordered according to a key that reflects the time constraints and the scheduling policy.

The allocator invokes the scheduler for a schedule feasibility check of a requested time constraint. Upon a positive verification of the feasibility, the scheduler reserves the resource for the requesting user. This reservation prevents conflicts between different users. There is a timeout for this reservation. After reservation has been made, a user must still invoke the scheduler in order to allow the execution to start. If such an invocation fails to arrive on time, the reservation is canceled, and the time constraint is removed from the calendar.

The invocation for execution comes from the loader, or by an automatic bind-allocate-load-execute sequence.

In MARUTI architecture, the scheduler is independent of the allocator. The scheduler uses a calendar to pass control to the next available job, if the state of the job allows it. The following SAPs are provided for the scheduler:

- INSERT_TC is used to insert a time constraint (TC) into the calendar with a non-operative state, using the PUSH_TC algorithms from Chapter 13. For a periodic time-constraint, an automatic PUSH_TC of its next instance is done by the EXIT SAP.
- REMOVE_TC removes a time constraint from the calendar. For example, the reservation with timeout scheme in allocation can be written as

$$AWAKE\_AT(now + time\_out, REMOVE\_TC(constraint))$$

- EXIT causes the execution of each instance of a time constraint to be terminated by the invocation of the scheduler's EXIT service. This SAP passes control of the resource to another instance, as dictated by the calendar and the scheduling policy.
- CHANGE_TC_STATE allows the change of the state of a time constraint in an object's calendar. Possible invocation sources include the loader, interrupt handler, and the object itself.

LOADER. The main task of the loader is to load jobs into the memory and to convert the unbounded indirect addresses into direct or bounded indirect ones. The loader also loads the redundant alternatives of an object, as dictated by the fault tolerance scheme employed. Note that alternatives which have already been reserved by the allocators are not necessarily loaded. Such reservations can also be removed. Therefore, the SAPs required for the above service support both loading and unloading.

- LOAD invokes a sequence of CHANGE_TC_STATEs (from idle to active) of reserved time constraints in calendars. In addition, the address of each loaded object is converted to direct address.
- UNLOAD invokes a sequence of REMOVE_TCs of time constraints from calendars in which time was reserved for these constraints.

COMMUNICATION. MARUTI provides two basic communication mechanisms to support the semantic links. Objects residing at the same site communicate via shared buffers. Remote objects communicate via message passing. Default value assignment and updates of semantic links support the principles discussed in Section 15.4. In addition, the communication subsystem provides synchronization ability that supports the time service.

Because of the stringent timing requirements, communication protocols tested with MARUTI are forced to take into account the deadline guarantee.

The LAN (local area network) low-level communication layers are implemented in the kernel. Higher layers of the communication protocols are either included within or invoked by *agent* objects at application layers.

The communication media are considered as resources of the system, and as such a reservation calendar must be established for each of them. The calendar is placed at each end-point of the communication and a service is reserved according to the agent requirements. The policy adopted resembles a virtual circuit path allocation.

In addition to the time critical communication, asynchronous communication is supported for off-line jobs. These services have no guarantee for their temporal behavior. They execute when no time critical communication is scheduled.

16.2.2   Application Level Components

ALLOCATOR. Preallocation of all required services and resources is needed in order to support the guarantee given to meet the deadline. The allocation scheme takes into account the interval union of all the possible resource requirements. Thus, it allocates resources for the set of maximal convex subintervals that result from that union.

The main concern of the allocator is the fault tolerance restrictions imposed on the computation. The goal of the allocator is to create a computation graph with a required degree of connectivity. In order to satisfy this goal, let us consider a simple allocation scheme. Let us divide the allocation into two phases:

1. the verification phase, and
2. the selection phase.

This scheme is a little simpler than the one described in Chapter 14, but it conveys the ideas implemented in MARUTI.

The verification phase is carried out for each alternative service. When a request for an allocation arrives, the allocator needs to extract the requirements of the computation from the required server's joint (see Figure 16.1). Then the allocator invokes a PUSH_TC on the server's calendar and the calendars of the resources required by it. As discussed in Chapter 13, this invocation uses the off-line scheduler. Allocation requests are then sent for all the services required by the server if it is verified to be allocatable. If a schedule feasibility verification holds for the local resource requirements and all the required services, a positive allocatability answer can be returned. The answer is sent by the allocator on behalf of the server to the initiator of the allocation request. Once a reservation is justified, the allocator can invoke the binder to create a semantic link between the initiator and the server object.

The selection phase chooses participants in the computation from the objects that answered positively in the verification phase. We introduced MARUTI's verification phase of the allocation algorithm in Chapter 14. We will discuss in detail MARUTI's selection approach later in Section 17.2. It is more complicated than the above, but it combines the two phases into one, and thus gives faster responses. In both approaches, it is apparent that the allocation must be an off-line service, because it has an unbounded execution time.

BINDER. The binder is responsible for "connecting" the justification links, as well as for verifying that the semantic relation is properly established. The resulting addresses are still not absolute, and only the loader will change them to be such. The binder installs the addresses it extracts from the directory service. Remote binding is done through agents, one at each side of the communication media. Locally, links of remote binding are established from an object to a local agent. A semantic binding requires the binder to attach the proper mechanisms for parameter exchanges to each side of the semantic link. The mechanism includes a default value set for each parameter.

A special task of the binder is to bind alternatives and replicas. This task requires attaching proper voting mechanisms needed for combining outputs of redundant computation paths. On the other hand, it requires attaching a consistency control protocol needed for updating replicas and invoking redundant computation paths. These redundancy control mechanisms are application dependent by their nature. Different applications usually have different interpretations for consistency, as well as for voting or result acceptance.

Each execution termination invokes an UNBIND operation in an off-line discipline to remove the justifications. An object without any justification is deleted.

Special data structures can be constructed by binding passive objects to construct hierarchical data bases. Binding the data structures is carried out independently of the allocation process.

LOG_IN SERVICE. The login server is the interface between MARUTI and users. It is invoked by a LOG_IN command, to load the directory owned by the user identified within the LOG_IN parameters. It executes thereafter as an off-line object, whose major task is *command interpretation*. Each logged-in user has an active log_in service object executing throughout the log_in session. This server includes the command interpreter, the port driver, and the links to the user-owned objects and to public objects. It is removed by a LOG_OUT command.

The command interpreter scans a conversation buffer. After identifying a command delimiter, the command interpreter invokes the service requested in the command. In case there is an illegal pattern in the command, the command interpreter invokes an exception handler. We describe this two-fold service and the way it switches from device mode to owner mode in Section 17.2.

DIRECTORY SERVICE. A directory is treated as an object. Each user's directory contains pointers to the objects owned by that user, establishing the owner justification links. When an owner deletes the justification for one of its object's existence, the result may be an object with no justification at all. The property of having no justification must propagate to objects that are justified by unjustified justifiers.

The protection mechanism is associated with each of the links between objects. Authorization of access for the use of the specific object is enabled using a ticket oriented mechanism.

The directory service in MARUTI has the following access points:

- DIRECTORY_SELECT;
- DIRECTORY_ENTRY_INSERT;
- DIRECTORY_ENTRY_REMOVE;
- DIRECTORY_LIST;
- OBJECT_CREATE;
- OBJECT_DELETE;
- OBJECT_LOCATE (i.e. FIND).

FILE SERVICE. The file service allows reading or writing elements of a passive object. (In a file system, one may consider a line or a character as such elements.) The MARUTI file server provides the following SAPs:

- DISPLAY_CONTENT;
- GET_STATUS;
- FETCH_SUB-OBJECT (i.e., READ);
- INSERT_SUB-OBJECT (i.e., WRITE).

NAME SERVER. The name server uses the directory services and the file service in order to carry out its own service. The name server bridges the different name domains, from human oriented names (strings) to machine oriented names (addresses). At all these domains, when an identifier is forwarded, the name service provides the proper translation, if such an object exists.

The names should be of limited size, otherwise the search space for the names is large and one cannot bound the time required in order to find the identifier. This limitation in the size of the identifier implies name reutilization, since there are no arbitrarily large number of identifiers available.

CHAPTER
17

OPERATIONAL ISSUES AND EXAMPLES

In this chapter we continue with a description of MARUTI's operation style and consider a scenario of job acceptance. To better understand these aspects, we first consider the mechanisms that support the distribution and the control transfer in scheduling the jobs. Then, we examine some detailed examples in which we present these mechanisms.

17.1 EXECUTION AND DISTRIBUTION CONSIDERATIONS

17.1.1 Scheduling Queues

All the resources in the system—even those of hardware type—are controlled by server objects. Each server's calendar represents the guarantees given to user objects so far. In MARUTI, we treat a processor as a resource; hence, the scheduler manipulates its calendar. In this calendar, we maintain entries for on-line guaranteed jobs. At the end of an instance of a time constraint, the scheduler picks the next on-line instance of a time constraint from the calendar. If there is no on-line job to execute in the calendar, an off-line job may receive control. The off-line jobs are preemptable by definition in MARUTI. One way to preempt an off-line job is by the use of one of the awake SAPs. We set the awake time according to the next on-line instance of a time constraint.

We may consider the calendar as a queue of on-line jobs, while requiring a different queue for off-line jobs. We require the additional queue for two reasons. First, an off-line job cannot be *reserved* in the calendar. Second, we want to reduce search in the calendar to a minimum. Furthermore, we may apply different scheduling schemes to the different queues. For fairness and efficiency, MARUTI has the following three queues for a resource:

1. The on-line time constraints' calendar.
2. The "off-line for on-line" jobs queue.
3. The off-line jobs queue.

Different divisions can be made for prioritizing the off-line jobs. However, the on-line jobs are always at the highest priority, represented in the resource's calendar. Special provisions may be made in the calendar to handle the failure modes.

Figure 17.1 describes the way in which MARUTI's on-line scheduler transfers control to off-line jobs. Completion of execution of P_A invokes the on-line scheduler through its exit SAP. This service access point checks and finds out that until $begin_{min}(P_B)$ it can execute no other real-time job. Therefore, it sets a preemption timer to $begin_{min}(P_B) - \delta$ by

$$AWAKE\_AT(begin_{min}(P_B) - \delta, \ on\_load(B()))$$

and passes control to the off-line queue scheduler. Here δ is the time required to load object B, in case we have not loaded it already, and to serve the preemption. The time server preempts the off-line job accordingly, and B receives control on time.

17.1.2 Remote Services

Typically, we establish communication between two sites due to service requests from one object to another in a remote site. MARUTI's communication subsystem

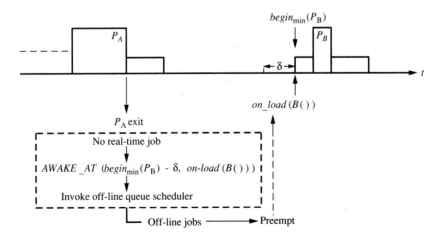

FIGURE 17.1
Control transfer from on-line to off-line.

employs virtual circuits as its discipline. We distinguish between two communication types, object migration and service requests. The latter type is carried out under real-time constraints. We assume that, after servicing the request, the server sends a response back to the request originator.

Each object in a remote site must have a local representative in each of the sites that expects it to provide some service. We call these representatives *agents*. Each agent is responsible for the reservation of a time interval in its master object's calendar. We can therefore replace the invocation relations described in Figure 16.2 by agents, as described in Figure 17.2.

Since communication must preserve real-time properties, the media involved in the communication must also use a reservation scheme. This implies having a calendar for each of the media sections between two allocated nodes.

We can carry out the creation of agents for remote objects in various ways. One way is an automatic generation of agents after an object requests service from a remote object. We must specify the path to the latter and present a capability ticket for the access. The operating system then creates the agent and initiates the communication process. This generation requires a prior check of the capability. Another way is the creation of agents before the execution of the requesting object.

Protection is also a concern of the communication service, since the media through which the requests and responses travel are unprotected. We need a mechanism to encode information and decode it properly in the destination site. Therefore, encryption techniques may also be necessary.

The lower levels of the communication service form a part of the operating system kernel. This part mainly concerns node-to-node transmission and reception. Communication subsystems must also support functions that deal with the translation of elements in heterogeneous distributed systems or networks. After a syntactic link is establish by the binder, the semantic link has a major role in the communication. For example, if one subsystem sends an integer to another, the other subsystem must receive the same integer. The same interpretation of the information sent is essential, regardless of the way in which each machine represents integers. The semantics of the transferred elements must agree at both end points of the communication. Thus, the agent translates the elements it transmits whenever needed, to agree with the representation at the destination site.

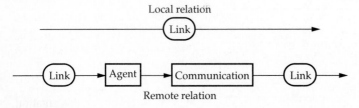

FIGURE 17.2
Local versus remote relation.

During execution time, when any service is invoked, its computation execution and the communication transfer times are bounded. The computation time is known *a priori*. The transfer time is also bounded due to the timely allocated virtual circuits, as implemented in the allocation and scheduling schemes.

17.2 JOB ACCEPTANCE IN MARUTI

Now that we have reviewed the execution and distribution considerations, let us consider the way MARUTI accepts a job. We start with a description of MARUTI after its boot terminates successfully. We then continue with a review of the log_in of a user. We consider the execution of a server object, and finally we extend it to an execution of an actor or an agent object.

17.2.1 MARUTI After Boot

The image seen at a given locality (a processing node in a distributed environment) after the boot process terminates is characterized by the following:

1. MARUTI *kernel* is loaded, and it stays core resident "forever" from the memory-manager's point of view. The kernel includes the servers, buffers for devices (assumed to be DMA accessed), resource scheduler(s) and calendars, and space for *on-line* and *off-line* queues. In the loaded kernel, we also find the interrupt handler, the defined interrupt tables, and service routines. The kernel also contains a *system directory*, which is a list of pointed tickets to a set of publicly accessible objects owned by the system.

   In order to support acceptance of incoming invocation requests, designated resources are reserved periodically as an idle "server." We have examined a mechanism of *priority exchange* to assure a starvation-free response, as well as sufficient on-line/off-line queue enablements.

   In addition to the above idle server, the system loads two object types for execution. The system attaches log_in servers to control units (TTY or CONSOLE) and executes the periodic services of the local time server.

2. The periodic service access points of the *time server* are in their resource calendars after carrying out an INSERT_TC. Since these are interrupt-driven services, each of them is initially in an idle state. On interrupt occurrence, the interrupt handler will change to an active state. The synchronization service starts executing after carrying out a FORUM and QUORUM protocol. This protocol selects remote servers that participate in the distributed synchronization algorithm.

3. Each *log_in server* is queued in the off-line queue. It only allows the LOG_IN SAP to be invoked. Since the log_in server at this state has a device orientation, we denote this mode as a *device mode*.

17.2.2 MARUTI After LOG_IN

After a LOG_IN is successfully completed, the log_in server changes its mode to an *owner-mode* after loading the proper owner directory. This directory is a list of pointers and tickets to the owner's objects. In addition, the directory may point to objects owned by others for which this owner has acquired accessing tickets sometime in the past. At this stage the log_in server acts as a command interpreter (CI), allowing activation and manipulation of objects with the proper authorization checks.

Let us now classify the executable objects into groups and discuss their execution. A *server object* is characterized by being subjected to operations of other objects, and not acting on any other executable object. An *actor object* is characterized by not being subjected to any operations of other objects, and acting on other executable objects. An *agent object* is characterized by being subjected to operations of other objects and acting on other executable objects. We will start the discussion about execution with server objects.

17.2.3 Executing a Server Object

In order to execute a *server object*, we take the following steps:

- Allocate resources and kernel servers for this object.
- Establish semantic links to required kernel servers.
- Invoke the loader or set it by INSERT_TC to load the server object in the future.[1]

We view the *allocator* as an application-level service, and therefore it must be loaded first. Since the allocator is not a time-bounded computation, we load it to be queued in the "off-line for on-line" queue. The loading and execution of the allocator set up the following sequence of steps in the system:

1. A loader image is queued to the *on-line/off-line* queue with parameters that describe whom to load (allocator) and its parameter block (whom to allocate). We can express this action as

   off/on_load (allocate (xyz.SAP$_{abc}$, time constraint))

   The above action results in loading the allocator to the "off-line for on-line" queue. It is loaded with parameters that relate to object *xyz*, in its *SAP$_{abc}$* access point, and a time constraint which describes the allowed occurrence window. In a design allowing the use of multiple loaders and multiple allocators, the loader image uses a designated memory space in which

---

[1] If the implementation includes a memory manager object, one can insert the loader execution in the manager's proper page calendar. In addition, a CHANGE_TC_STATE of the object's joint is inserted in the calendars of the object's resources.

these allocators reside. This space is bounded, and hence in the above case may require a context switching.

2. We need not invoke the binder for allocating resources to a server object. We assume that the semantic links of the allocator to the kernel servers are pre-established and are activated by the loader. If that is not the case, then the allocator must invoke a binding activity and exit. Such an invocation is a binder SAP that terminates with an invocation of the allocator to continue.

3. At this point, the allocater is loaded and its required semantic links to the kernel are bound. Now, the allocator invokes the mechanisms for schedule feasibility verification of the resources. If reservations are not confirmed, then a negative response is sent to the initiator. In a simple case, a message is sent to the proper display driver. In the next section a more complicated case is described: that of invoking a REPLY SAP of the initiating allocator with a negative parameter. In addition, if there is a subset of resources for which reservation has been confirmed, UNLOAD invocations are activated to the members of this subset.

4. If the schedule feasibility verification returns a positive reservation, we must consider two possibilities. When the begin-time constraint of its window-of-occurrence is soon enough (decided according to memory management policy) we have a simple case. There is a good reason to load the allocated object at this point. Otherwise, a future load execution is reserved with the INSERT_TC of the memory manager. This manager may execute on the same CPU, depending on the architecture. We note that the reservation may reduce the laxity of the original time constraint. Thus, a positive REPLY may include the final time constraint, and the *resource subtree* that was actually allocated.

The above scenario ends with either a positive or a negative REPLY. We note two conceivable cases for the positive REPLY. First, reservations can be made both for the server and the loader for a later loading and execution. Second, the server can be loaded in an active state for an immediate execution.

The following section describes how the above principle is extended to deal with objects that require the services of other objects.

17.2.4 Executing an Actor (or Agent) Object

In order to execute an *actor* or an *agent object*, the previous scenario must be extended to include the following steps:

• Allocate resources and kernel servers for this object.
• Allocate resources and kernel servers for the service requirements (and agents) of this object's dependency set.
• Establish semantic links between all participants.
• Invoke the loader or set it by INSERT_TC to load all the participating objects in the future.

This scenario can be summarized as an extension of the previously proposed scenario, with some differences as noted below:

1. The allocator invokes the schedule feasibility verification, testing itself and its required resources. If reservations are not confirmed, then a negative response is sent to the requiring allocator. The negative response invokes the requiring allocator's REPLY SAP with a negative parameter.

2. The binder is invoked to establish the semantic links to the service requirements that the actor (agent) object needs. To do that, the allocator employs the "call" invocation, as described in the previous scenario. The allocator invokes a binding activity and exits. The invoked binder SAP exits itself via invoking the allocator again to continue.

3. The loader image is queued to the *on-line/off-line* queue exactly as above.

4. Let us now consider the case in which a positive reservation is returned by the schedule feasibility verification. Following this response, the allocator invokes allocation of its service (agent) requirements, and exits.

5. Each of the invoked allocators then performs accordingly, exiting after a REPLY of this allocator is invoked by it.

6. After all the required REPLY invocations have arrived at this allocator from the allocators it has invoked, it invokes the REPLY of its requiring allocator with either a positive or a negative answer. The positive answer may include the updated time constraint (as a result of the laxity reduction) and the subgraph of computation as seen by this allocator. The subgraph is composed of its own resources and its service requirements that answered positively.

The above scenario extends the one introduced for a server object to an allocation scheme resembling the one introduced in Chapter 14. When the "root" of a computation graph (an actor object invoked by a user) receives positive reservation confirmations from its dependency set, the computation is allocatable. At this point, the actor can respond positively to the user and invoke the loading of its view of the computation subgraph—the whole computation graph.

17.3 SOME EXAMPLES OF DESIGN

Let us examine some detailed examples of design and implementation. These examples emphasize the combined use of the schedule feasibility verification and the fault-tolerant allocation scheme. We start with the definition of variables that are a part of the object's joint. We then introduce functions that insert a time constraint into a calendar, or remove it. The INSERT_TC function uses the algorithm PUSH_TC from Chapter 13, and supports the connectivity maintenance of the allocation algorithm from Chapter 14. We then consider the loader functions for loading and unloading an executable instance of an object.

17.3.1 Variables of Object's Joint

Three variables allow controlling object execution while providing guarantees to meet the constraints: the calendar, the schedule type, and the dependency set. Another auxiliary variable is the *wait_set* which contains a set of fields for each of its members to support allocation concurrency (see Figure 17.3).

An object's joint contains a *calendar*, which is an ordered set of accepted time constraints. Each *time_constraint* in the MARUTI operating system contains some fields that support the allocation and some that support the schedule feasibility tests. Two fields, *Id* and *tag*, allow controlling the connectivity of the computation graph. The *level* field identifies the temporal redundancy characteristic of the constraint. Along with these three allocation-oriented fields, six additional fields support the schedule feasibility tests. The *tc* field represents the window of occurrence, and the *P* field represents the computation interval. The *back_slack* and *for_slack* fields represent the laxity of *P*, and *freq* is the frequency of that constraint. The *state* field describes the object state due to this constraint and support execution control.

An external scheduler manipulates the calendar, according to a parameter *Sched_Type*. This parameter defines the scheduling type, which can be either preemptive or non-preemptive. The object's owner cannot change this parameter as long as the calendar is not empty.

The *dependency_set* of the object is a set of k resource requirements and n service requirements. Each *resource_requirement* contains four fields. R_R^{in} and R_R^{out} are temporal relations and R is a convex_time_interval. The pointer to the particular resource is ↑resource. A *service_requirement* is a set of *service_alternatives*, each of which also contains four fields. R_s^{in} and R_s^{out} are temporal relations, and s is a convex_time_interval. Finally, ↑object_SAP is a pointer to the specific service. We need these fields in order to support the constraint projection mechanisms, as defined in Section 4.3.1.

The constraints with incomplete allocatability tests are members of the *wait_set*. Each of these constraints corresponds to a set of fields in the object's joint. These fields allow concurrent execution of the rules of the allocatability tests, as defined in Chapter 14. The first field, *prev*, identifies the object which required the invocation. This field keeps a pointer that allows sending an answer to the proper object. The *Id* and *tag* fields represent the computation identifier and the thread indicator of that computation Id, respectively. The tag indicates the physical alternative of this computation to which the invocation belongs. The TC_{me} field is the time constraint as imposed on this object, and out of which the allocator projects the constraints for the dependency set. The next field, myΔlevel, is the temporal redundancy index. This index shows the number of instances still needing to be allocated.

We require two vectors to control the allocation query. The first vector, $s[n]$, has n components that are service_alternatives. Each alternative $s[i]$ is the last allocatable instance in service requirement $S^{0(i)}$ examined so far in the allocation session. The second vector, $Ans[n]$, contains n indicators, each of which can have a value of "off," "on," or "done." We described in Chapter 14 the way in which these vectors are manipulated by the allocator.

Figure 17.3 summarizes the above, as reflected in the MARUTI design.

type   time_constraint = **construct**

     { Id: computation identifier ;

     tag: thread indicator of computation Id ;

     level: redundancy index ;

     tc: convex_time_interval ;

     back_slack, for_slack : real ;

     P : non_convex_time_interval ;

     freq : real ;

     state : integer } ;

type   resource_requirement = **construct**

     { R_R^{in}: temporal relations ;

     R : convex_time_interval } ;

     ↑ resource ;

type   service_alternative = **construct**

     { R_s^{in}, R_s^{out}: temporal relations ;

     s : convex_time_interval } ;

     ↑ object_SAP ;

type   service_requirement = **set** of service_alternatives ;

type   *schedule_type* = (preemptive, non-preemptive) ;

type   Answer_Wait_Indicator = (off, on, done) ;

variables

     calendar : ordered **set** of time_constraints ;

     Sched_Type : *schedule_type* ;

     dependency_set : **set** of k resource_requirements and n service_requirements ;

auxiliary variables

     wait_set : **set** of **construct**

{ prev: ↑ object_SAP ;

  Id: computation identifier ;

  tag: thread indicator of computation Id ;

  TC_{me}: time_constraint ;

  myΔlevel: redundancy index ;

  $s[n]$: **set** of n service_alternatives ;

  $Ans[n]$: **set** of n Answer_Wait_Indicators } ;

FIGURE 17.3
Typical joint variables in MARUTI.

17.3.2 Inserting Time Constraint into a Calendar

DESCRIPTION. The boolean function INSERT_TC in Figure 17.4 is a part of the scheduler. The scheduler is one of the objects that form the operating system kernel. A user can invoke it for some off-line requests, as defined in Section 16.2. Any invocation of the scheduler to insert a new execution constraint uses this function. The boolean INSERT_TC returns the *true* value if the scheduler accepts the required constraint, and *false* if it does not. Acceptance of a requirement results in a new calendar of the object. This new calendar contains the required constraint in addition to the constraints that were already accepted. Rejection of the request leaves the calendar unchanged. The insertion leaves the newly accepted constraint in an idle state, and only the loader will change its state to active.

In order to adhere to the required time constraint, INSERT_TC calls the schedule feasibility verification function PUSH_TC. The latter returns true upon acceptance that supports a feasible schedule, and false upon rejection. INSERT_TC activates PUSH_TC only in cases that agree with the connectivity requirements of the computation. The invoked object may be able to serve some paths of the communication graph. In other words, it may be a member of the dependency sets of more than one participant in the computation. The allocation algorithm distinguishes between computation subgraphs that must not intersect by tagging them. Therefore, INSERT_TC applies the schedule feasibility test only if there is no previous reservation that belongs to another subgraph. This condition requires confirmation of the absence of another reservation with the same computation *Id* and a different *tag*.

This function locks the calendar before verification to avoid ambiguity and to assure mutual exclusion. In order to allow execution of already-accepted requests, the lock grants dispatchers with access to the calendar. The scheduler dispatchers change the calendar only in omitting already-executed constraints and in advancing periodic instances. These changes agree with the already-given guarantees, and therefore, we can ignore them. However, in order to simplify this issue, we assume here that while locking we produce a working copy of the calendar, called *already accepted*. The calendar stays marked as locked until this function unlocks it. During this period, the lock allows no off-line access for insertion or removal of constraints.

We characterize temporal redundancy instances as those whose level is higher than 1. The cases of insertion of such instances must establish the proper consistency control. If one instance fails, the next retry must use the proper semantic links, and sometimes we must employ "undoing" actions. The function refers to such principles without details because they strongly depend on policies adopted by the application.

type *schedule_type* = (preemptive, non-preemptive);

boolean function INSERT_TC (obj.sap: ↑ object,

$\qquad$ TC_{in}:time_constraint) ;

var

$\quad$ Already_Accepted : **set** of time_constraints ;

$\quad$ Sched_Type : *scheduler_type* ;

$\quad$ constraint : time_constraint ;

$\quad$ result : boolean ;

begin

$\quad$ lock calendar(obj.sap) ;

$\qquad$ /* Already_Accepted ← calendar(obj.sap) */

$\qquad$ /* Sched_Type ← obj.sap scheduler_type */

$\quad$ **if** ($\exists$ constraint $\in$ Already_Accepted:

$\qquad$ TC_{in}.Id = constraint.Id $\wedge$ TC_{in}.*tag* $\neq$ constraint.tag)

$\quad$ **then** /* prevent computation connectivity reduction */

$\qquad$ result ← false ;

$\quad$ **else**

$\qquad$ result ← PUSH_TC(TC_{in},Sched_Type) ;

$\qquad$ /* see Sections 13 and 13.4 */

$\qquad$ **if** (result) $\wedge$ (TC_{in}.level $\neq 1$)

$\qquad$ **then** $\forall$ constraint $\in$ Already_Accepted |

constraint.Id $= TC_{in}$.Id

$\bigwedge$ constraint.Id $= TC_{in}$.tag :

setup consistency control (see [36, 101]) to obey

1. identical non-determinism resolution, and

2. identical order of sericing input requests.

fi   fi

unlock calendar(obj.sap) ;

return(result) ;

end

FIGURE 17.4
Design example: inserting time constraint.

17.3.3   Removing Time Constraint from Object's Calendar

DESCRIPTION. The following example, the REMOVE_TC boolean function as described in Figure 17.5, undoes the results of the previous INSERT_TC. It returns the false value when it cannot find the required constraint in the calendar, and the true value otherwise. This function is another off-line entry of the scheduler, with a locking access to the object's calendar exactly as in the INSERT_TC. This scheduler part is invoked with the same two parameters used by INSERT_TC. The first is a pointer to the invoked object's joint, and the second is the constraint to be removed. The calendar of the pointed object must contain this required constraint, or else the function returns false.

When a reservation for such a constraint does exist in the calendar, REMOVE_TC removes the constraint. The removal includes an update of the consistency control links. In some applications, these control links may form a consensus cycle in which the consensus forum and quorum need updates. We only remove one of the temporal redundancy instances here. Thus, this function becomes useful in cases where we want to remove some instances and leave others.

An example of such a case appears in Chapter 14 in the allocation algorithm. In the rule corresponding to an ALLOC_REQ invocation, the allocator iterates for reserving the required temporal redundancy. For each temporal redundancy alternative, we require a set of schedulable resources and a set of allocatable services. We note that these requirements are checked concurrently. Therefore, let us consider the case in which one resource is not schedulable or one service is not allocatable. Here, we may receive a negative reply from INSERT_TC after making some reservations for the object and for other resources. In that case, it is reasonable to release the reservations which we cannot load anyway. Therefore, the allocator invokes REMOVE_TC for the incomplete reserved set, in case it cannot reserve a complete set.

boolean function REMOVE_TC (obj.sap: ↑ object,

TC_{in}:time_constraint);

var

Already_Accepted : **set** of time_constraints ;

constraint : time_constraint ;

result : boolean ;

begin

lock calendar(obj.sap) ;

/* Already_Accepted ←calendar(obj.sap) */

if (∃ constraint ∈ Already_Accepted: TC_{in} = constraint)

then

∀ constraint ∈ Already_Accepted |

constraint.Id = TC_{in}.Id

∧ constraint.tag = TC_{in}.tag:

rearrange consistency control

(see Section 17.3.2 and [35, 100]) ;

Already_Accepted ← Already_Accepted $-\{TC_{in}\}$;

result ←true ;

else

result ←false ;

fi

unlock calendar(obj.sap) ;

return(result) ;

end

FIGURE 17.5
Design example: removing time constraint.

17.3.4   Loading and Unloading Time
Constraint in Object's Calendar

DESCRIPTION. The allocation and the feasible schedule verification employ a reservation scheme to support the guarantees. This scheme requires assigning a state to an object for each reserved constraint. The state allows distinguishing between reservations made while querying feasibility and those authorized to execute. The mechanism that implements the change of the state from a "pending reservation" to an "authorized to execute" is the CHANGE_TC_STATE. This mechanism belongs to the set of operations that change an object state, as defined in Chapter 3. The CHANGE_TC_STATE changes the object state for a particular reserved time constraint to a specified value. Let us restrict the set of object states to *idle* and *active*. The CHANGE_TC_STATE is a scheduler service access point, since we restricted the access to calendars in MARUTI only to the scheduler.

The *loader* is the operating system's object that controls the activation of idle allocated objects to active ones. The loader receives a pointer to the object it must activate, and thus it can access the proper calendar using CHANGE_TC_STATE. The loader also receives as a parameter the time constraint that identifies which instance in that calendar to activate. The knowledge of the object and the time constraint allows a complete identification of that instance.

Since in MARUTI we use distributed dependency sets out of which we build the computation graph, activation of an object may imply activation of a subgraph. The invoking object does not know which resources and services an invoked server uses. Therefore, when we execute a load request for an object, we must interpret it as a request to load the object resources and service requirements as well. We can retrieve all the required data regarding the object's allocation graph from the regular and auxiliary variables of the joint of the object. From the dependency set information, it projects the proper time constraints for the resources and services. From the auxiliary variables, it finds allocated alternatives.

The resources and the object itself are directly activated by invoking the scheduler, through its CHANGE_TC_STATE service access point. The service requirements need an invocation of a loader themselves, and since they are not leaf nodes in the computation graph, they may also need resources and services. The time constraints of both the resources and the services are projected, and thus the identification of the loaded (or unloaded) instances is complete.

The example designs in Figure 17.6 and Figure 17.7 demonstrate the above principles.

local variables

   Already_Accepted : **set** of time_constraints ;

   constraint : time_constraint ;

Upon receiving LOAD (obj.sap: ↑ object, TC_{in}:time_constraint) :

begin

   using joint(obj.sap):

     Let $DS_{\text{obj.sap,TC}} = \{\{< R_i, TC_{R_i} > : 1 \le i \le k\}$

          $\{S_i : 1 \le i \le n\}\}$

     where $S_i = \{< s_j^{(i)}, TC_{S_i} > : 1 \le j \le M^{(i)}\}$.

    for $r \leftarrow 1$ **to** k **step** 1 **do**

       $TC_{R_r} \leftarrow$ project(R_{R_r}, TC_{in});

       CHANGE_TC_STATE ((R_r, TC_{R_r}),active) ;

   od

     CHANGE_TC_STATE ((obj.sap,TC_{in}),active);

    for $r \leftarrow 1$ **to** n **step** 1 **do**

       $TC_{S_r} \leftarrow$ project(R_{S_r}, TC_{in}) ;

       for $q \leftarrow 1$ **to** $(J: J \le M^{(r)} \wedge s[r] = s_J^{(r)})$ **step** 1 **do**

          LOAD($s_q^{(r)}, TC_{S_r}$) ;

     od od

   end

FIGURE 17.6
Example design.

local variables

   Already_Accepted : **set** of time_constraints ;

   constraint : time_constraint;

Upon receiving UNLOAD (obj.sap: ↑ object, TC_{in}:time_constraint)::

begin

   using joint(obj.sap):

     Let $DS_{obj.sap,TC} = \{\{< R_i, TC_{R_i} > : 1 \le i \le k\}$

          $\{S_i : 1 \le i \le n\}\}$

     where $S_i = \{< s_j^{(i)}, TC_{S_i} > : 1 \le j \le M^{(i)}\}$.

for $r \leftarrow 1$ **to** k **step** 1 **do**

  $TC_{R_r} \leftarrow$ project(R_{R_r}, TC_{in});

  REMOVE_TC (R_r, TC_{R_r});

od

REMOVE_TC (obj.sap, TC_{in});

for $r \leftarrow 1$ **to** n **step** 1 **do**

  $TC_{S_r} \leftarrow$ project(R_{S_r}, TC_{in});

  for $q \leftarrow 1$ **to** $(J: J \leq M^{(r)} \wedge s[r] = s_j^{(r)})$ **step** 1 **do**

    UNLOAD($s_q^{(r)}, TC_{S_r}$);

od od

end

FIGURE 17.7
Example design.

17.4 CONCLUDING REMARKS

MARUTI is a hard real-time operating system that supports the requirements of distributed and fault-tolerant systems. This operating system provides a guarantee to each of its accepted real-time jobs to meet the deadline associated with the job. MARUTI allocates its resources in a manner that supports the fault tolerance goals of its accepted jobs. MARUTI uses semantic links to establish the proper relations between objects, and calendars introduce the time notion explicitly into the allocation scheme.

 MARUTI achieves temporal determinism with encapsulation of the services within objects, along with the use of explicit time expressions both for start-time and for finish-time constraints on periodic, as well as on aperiodic, computations.

PART
V

EPILOG

CHAPTER
18

CONCLUSION

This book focuses on *real-time systems* whose correctness depends not only on their logical and functional behavior, but also on their temporal properties. It further focuses on properties that are not demonstrated by current real-time computing systems, yet are needed by "next generation" real-time systems. The latter systems will be very complex because of their distributed architecture, they will be required to have a very long lifetime, and they will consider the case of not satisfying logical or timing constraints of the computation as an unrecoverable failure [140].

This book suggests a methodology for designing "next generation" real-time operating systems. The methodology originates in the needs that arise from real-time systems design in general and real-time programming in particular. No specific hardware architecture is assumed. The results obtained are adequate to the spectrum in which a computing node can be built as a multi-processor, multi-memory unit, or a single memory and processor unit. In addition, the methodology can be applied to both homogeneous and heterogeneous systems.

The main thread of the methodology proposed here does not use the *nondeterministic interleaving* model in describing concurrency, a method that has presented many difficulties in analyzing temporal properties of computations. The proposed approach is based on the use of a *deterministic interleaving* model which is well suited for controlling the temporal behavior during the execution. This model also supports specification and verification of the temporal requirements and their guarantee to hold during execution.

The methodology is based on the use of *objects* as the system's elements. Time properties are assigned to objects with *calendars*. This approach is the first innovation presented in this book. The objects architecture achieves both fault containment and deterministic temporal behavior objectives through the use of the calendars and the associated management scheme. The achievement of a *guaranteed* execution of an object is obtained using a *schedule feasibility verification* scheme that controls the scheduling of both the objects and their resources. A fault-tolerance motivated *resource allocation* scheme ensures a user-specified resiliency to failures, supporting both *temporal redundancy* and *physical redundancy* requirements.

Note that the main thrust of the work here has been on schedule verification and not on the design of a scheduler. Such a scheduler has to take into account not only the requirement of guaranteed temporal behavior, but other physical and logical characteristics. It is well known that the generation of an optimal, dead-line-driven schedule requires a significant computational expense and hence the resources and time. A feasible schedule is generated by the schedule verification scheme proposed here and may be used as a simple schedule.

Some issues raised in this book need further exploration. The schedulability, as verified in this book, is a sufficiency condition for guaranteeing deadlines. Rejection, on the other hand, does not necessarily contradict the existence of a feasible schedule. Examination of the conservative approach and possible tradeoffs is left for further research. Another issue left for future work is the analysis of the algorithm performance in terms of response time and system overhead. These performance characteristics strongly depend on the already-accepted jobs in the system and their properties.

MARUTI is an experimental implementation of a particular design for a hard real-time operating system that is carried out according to the methodology suggested in this book. The specifications of modules in this implementation have shown interesting properties of the high degree of concurrency that can be achieved in multi-processor systems when accepting new jobs. Some other implementation examples have also been examined. Verification of schedule feasibility has been tested with a statistical population of input requests. However, since the properties of the algorithm are proved formally, the confirmation received by these experiments does not provide any new insight.

The methodology demonstrated in this book has been introduced to potential users and designers of such systems, both in the academic world and in industrial research and development facilities. The encouraging results demonstrate many possible benefits over current approaches, benefits that enhance the hard real-time properties of systems along with providing the means for designing applications.

BIBLIOGRAPHY

[1]   *Reference Manual for The Ada Programming Language*, US DOD (ANSI) MIL–STD 1815a–1983, February 1983.

[2]   Agrawala, A. K., and Levi, S.-T., *Objects Architecture for Real-Time, Distributed, Fault Tolerant Operating Systems*, IEEE Workshop on Real-Time Operating Systems, pp. 142–148, Cambridge MA, July 1987.

[3]   Ajmone-Marsan, M., Balbo, G., and Conte, G., "A Class of Generalized Stochastic Petri Nets for Performance Evaluation of Multiprocessor Systems," *ACM Trans. on Computer Systems*, Vol. 2 (2), 93–122, May 1984.

[4]   Alford, M., "A Requirement Engineering Methodology for Real Time Processing Requirements," *IEEE Trans. on Software Engineering*, Vol. SE–3 (1), 60–69, January 1977.

[5]   Allchin. J. E.. and McKendry, M. S., *Synchronization and Recovery of Actions*, Second ACM SIGACT-SIGOPS Symposium on Principles of Distributed Computing, Montreal, Canada, August 17–19, 1983.

[6]   Allen, J., "Maintaining Knowledge about Temporal Intervals," *Communications of the ACM*, Vol. 26 (11), 832–843, November 1983.

[7]   Allen, J., and Hayes, P., *A Common Sense Theory of Time*, Proceedings of the Ninth International Joint Conference on Artificial Intelligence (IJCAI), pp. 528–531, Los Angeles, CA, August 18–23, 1985.

[8]   Almes, G. T., Black, A. P., Lazowska, E. D., and Noe, J. D., "The Eden System: A Technical Review," *IEEE Trans. on Software Engineering*, Vol SE–11 (1) 43–59, January 1985.

[9]   Anderson, G., "The Coordinated Use of Five Performance Evaluation Methodologies," *Communications of the ACM*, Vol. 27 (2), 119–125, February 1984.

[10] Apt, K., Francez, N., and De Roever, W., "A Proof System for Communicating Sequential Processes," *ACM Trans. on Programming Languages and Systems*, Vol. 2 (3), 359–385, July 1980.

[11] Astrom, K. J., *Computer Controlled Systems*, Prentice Hall, Englewood Cliffs, NJ, 1984.

[12] Baker, T. P., and Jeffay, K., *Corset and Lace*, Proceedings of Real-Time Systems Symposium, pp. 158–167, San Jose, CA, December 1987.

[13] Balbo, G., Bruell, S., and Ghanta, S., "Combining Queueing Network and Generalized Stochastic Petri Nets Models for the Analysis of Some Software Blocking Phenomena," *IEEE Trans. on Software Engineering*, Vol. SE–12 (4), 561–576, April 1986.

[14] Barbacci, M. R., and Wing, J. M., *Specifying Functional and Timing Behavior for Real-Time Applications*, Technical Report CMU–CS–86–177, Department of Computer Science, Carnegie Mellon University, Pittsburgh, PA, November 1986.

[15] Bayer, R., Graham, R., and Seegmuller, G. (editors), Flynn, M., Gray, J., Jones, A., Lagally, K., Opderbeck, H., Popek, G., Randell, B., Saltzer, J., and Wiehle, H., *Operating Systems: An Advanced Course*, Springer-Verlag, Berlin, Federal Republic of Germany, 1979.

[16] Berry, G., Cosserat, L., *The ESTREL Synchronous Programming Language and Its Mathematica Semantics*, Ecole Nationale Supérieure des Mines de Paris, France, March 1986.

[17] Berry, G., Couronné, P., and Gonthier, G., *Synchronous Programming of Reactive Systems: An Introduction to ESTREL*, Ecole Nationale Supérieure des Mines de Paris, France, 1987.

[18] Birman, K. P., and Joseph, T. A., *Reliable Communication in an Unreliable Environment*, TR85–694, Department of Computer Science, Cornell University, Ithaca, NY, July 1985.

[19] Birman, K. P., Joseph, T. A., Raeuchle, T., and El-Abbadi A., "Implementing Fault Tolerant Distributed Objects," *IEEE Trans. on Software Engineering*, Vol. SE–11 (6), 502–508, June 1985.

[20] Bochmann, G., *Distributed Systems Design*, Springer-Verlag, Berlin, Federal Republic of Germany, 1983.

[21] Booch, G., "Object-Oriented Development," *IEEE Trans. on Software Engineering*, Vol. SE–12 (2), 211–221, February 1986.

[22] Brinch, Hansen P., *The Architecture of Concurrent Programs*, Prentice Hall, Englewood Cliffs, NJ, 1973.

[23] Brinch, Hansen P., *Operating Systems Principles*, Prentice Hall, Englewood Cliffs, NJ, 1973.

[24] Browne, J. C., and Dafni, G. J., *TOBS — A High Performance Object Based System*, Department of Computer Science, University of Texas at Austin, November 19, 1987.

[25] Browne, J. C., and Dafni, G. J., *Early Binding in Object Oriented Systems*, Department of Computer Science, University of Texas at Austin, November 23, 1987.

[26] Caspi, P., and Halbwachs, N., "A Functional Model for Describing and Reasoning Time Behavior of Computer Systems," *Acta Informatica*, Vol. 22 (6), 595–628, March 1986.

[27] Chandy, K. M., Browne, J. C., Dissly, C. W., and Uhrig, W. R., "Analytic Models for Rollback and Recovery Strategies in Data Base Systems," *IEEE Trans. on Software Engineering*, Vol. SE–1 (1), 100–110, March 1975.

[28] Chandy, K., Misra, J., and Haas, L., "Distributed Deadlock Detection," *ACM Trans. on Computer Systems*, Vol. 1 (2) 144–156, May 1983.

[29] Charniak, E., and McDermott, D., *Introduction to Artificial Intelligence*, Addison Wesley Publishing Company, Reading, MA, 1985.

[30] Chen, B., and Yeh, R., "Formal Specification and Verification of Distributed Systems," *IEEE Trans. on Software Engineering*, Vol. SE–9 (6), 710–722, November 1983.

[31] Cheng, S., Stankovic, J., and Ramamrithan, K., *Dynamic Scheduling of Groups of Tasks with Precedence Constraints in Distributed Hard Real-Time Systems*, Proceedings of Real-Time Systems Symposium (IEEE), pp. 166–174, New Orleans, LA, December 2–4, 1986.

[32] Chintamaneni, P. R., Yuan, X., Agrawala, A. K., and Tripathi, S. K., *Scheduling Tasks in Real-Time Systems*, Technical report CS–TR–1991, Department of Computer Science, University of Maryland, February 1988.

[33] Chu, W. W., and Lan, L. M-T., "Task Allocation and Precedence Relations for Distributed Real-Time Systems," *IEEE Trans. on Computers*, Vol. C–36 (6), 667–679, August 1987.

[34] Coolahan, J., and Roussopoulos, N., "Timing Requirements for Time Driven Systems Using Augmented Petri Nets," *IEEE Trans. on Software Engineering*, Vol. SE–9 (5), 603–616, September 1983.

[35] Cooper, E. C., "Replicated Procedure Call," *ACM Operating Systems Review*, Vol 20 (1), 44–55, January 1986.

[36] Courvoisier, M. et al., *Task Synchronization in Distributed Real Time Control Systems*, IEEE Proceedings—Real Time Systems Symposium, pp. 83–88, Miami Beach, FL, December 1981.

[37] Cristian, F., "Exception Handling and Software Fault Tolerance," *IEEE Trans. on Computers*, Vol. C–31 (6), 531–540, June 1982.

[38] Cristian, F., "Correct and Robust Programs," *IEEE Trans. on Software Engineering*, Vol. SE–10 (2), 163–174, March 1984.

[39] Cristian, F., Aghili, H., Strong, R., and Dolev, D., *Atomic Broadcast: from Simple Message Diffusion to Byzantine Agreement*, IEEE Fifteenth Fault Tolerance Computing Symposium (FTCS), pp. 200–206, 1985.

[40] Davari, S., and Dhal, S. K., *An On-Line Algorithm for Real-Time Task Allocation*, Proceedings of Real-Time Systems Symposium (IEEE), pp. 194–199, New Orleans, LA, December 2–4, 1986.

[41] Davidson, S. B., Gracia-Molina, H., and Skeen, D., "Consistency in Partitioned Networks," *Computing Surveys*, Vol. 17 (3), 341–370, September 1985.

[42] De Marco, T., *Structured Analysis and System Specification*, Yourdon Press, New York, NY, 1978.

[43] Dijkstra, E. W., "Cooperating Sequential Processes," (in Genuys, F., editor, *Programming Languages*, pp. 43–112), Academic Press, New York, NY, 1968.

[44] Dijkstra, E. W., *A Discipline of Programming*, Prentice Hall, Englewood Cliffs, NJ, 1976.

[45] Dowling, J., *Some Methods and Tools for Real Time Software Validation*, Proceedings of the Twelfth IFAC/iFIP Workshop on Real-Time Programming, pp. 81–86, Hatfield, UK, March 29–31, 1983.

[46] Farby, P. S., "Capability Based Adressing," *Communication of the ACM*, Vol. 17 (7), 403–412, July 1974.

[47] Ferguson, D., Kar, G., Leitner, G., and Nikolaou, C., *Relocating Processes in Distributed Computer Systems*, IEEE Proceedings of the Fifth Symposium on Reliability in Distributed Software and Database Systems, pp. 171–177, Los Angeles, CA, January 1986.

[48] Garetti, P., Laface, P., and Rivoira, S., *Multiprocessor Implementation of Tasking Facilities in Ada*, Proceedings of the Twelth IFAC/IFIP Workshop of Real Time Programming, pp. 97–102, Hatfield, UK, March 29–31, 1983.

[49] Garey, M. R., and Johnson D. S., "Scheduling Tasks with Nonuniform Deadlines on Two Processors," *Journal of the ACM*, Vol. 23 (3), 461–467, July 1976.

[50] Gelenbe, E., and Derochette, D., "Performance of Rollback Recovery Systems under Intermittent Failures," *Communication of the ACM*, Vol. 21 (6), 493–499, June 1978.

[51] Gelenbe, E., "On The Optimum Checkpoint Interval," *ACM Journal*, Vol. 26 (2), 259–270, April 1979.

[52] Gelenbe, E., Finkel, D., and Tripathi, S. K., "Availability of a Distributed Computer System with Failures," *Acta Informatica,* Vol. 23, 643–655, 1986.

[53] Gifford, D. K., "Weighted Voting for Replicated Data," *ACM Operating Systems Review*, Vol. 13 (5), 150–162, December 1979.

[54] Gomma, H., "Software Design Method for Real Time Systems," *Communications of the ACM*, Vol. 27 (9), 938–949, September 1984.

[55] Gomma, H., *ADARTS—An Ada Based Design Approach for Real Time Systems*, SPC–TR–88–021, Technical Report Version 1.0, Software Productivity Consortium, Reston, VA, August 1988.

[56] Gora, W., Herzog, U., and Tripathi, S., "Clock Synchronization on the Factory Floor," (to appear in *IEEE Trans. on Industrial Electronics*) Proc. of Workshop on Factory Communication, NBS, March 1987.

[57] Gusella, R., and Zatti, S., *TEMPO—Time Services for the Berkeley, Local Network*, Report No. UCB–CSD83–163, Computer Science Division, University of California, Berkeley, CA, December 1983.

[58] Gusella, R., and Zatti, S., *The Accuracy of Clock Synchronization Achieved by TEMPO in Berkeley UNIX 4.3BSD*, technical report, Computer Science Division, University of California, Berkeley CA, December 1986.

[59] Haase, V., "Real Time Behavior of Programs," *IEEE Trans. on Software Engineering*, Vol. SE–7 (5), 494–501, September 1981.

[60] Harel D., *Statecharts: A Visual Approach to Complex Systems*, CS84–05, Weitzman Institute of Science, Rehovot, Israel, February (December) 1984.

[61] Harel, D., and Pnueli, A., "On The Development of Reactive Sysytems," (in Apt, K., editor, *Logics and Models of Concurrent Systems*, pp. 477–498, Springer-Verlag, Heidelberg, Germany,1985), Weitzman Institute of Science, Rehovot, Israel, January 1985.

[62] Heninger, K., "Specifying Software Requirements for Complex Systems: Techniques and

Applications," *IEEE Trans. on Software Engineering*, Vol. SE–6 (1), 2–13, January 1980.

[63] Hoare, C. A. R., "Monitors: An Operating System Structuring Concept," *Communications of the ACM*, Vol. 17 (10), 549–557, October 1974.

[64] Hoare, C. A. R., "Communicating Sequential Processes," *Communications of the ACM*, Vol. 21 (8), 666–677, August 1978.

[65] Holmes, V. P., Harris, D. L., and Piorkowski, K. M., "Current Status of the Hawk Operating System," *IEEE Workshop on Real-Time Operating Systems*, pp. 78–82, Cambridge, MA, July 1987.

[66] *iRMK^{TM} Version 1.1 Real-Time Kernel*, and *iRMX^{TM}286 Release 2.00 Operating System*, Intel Corporation, Santa Clara, CA, June 1987.

[67] Jahanian, F., and Mok, A., *Safety Analysis of Timing Properties in Real Time Systems*, Department of Computer Science, University of Texas at Austin, September 15, 1985. (To appear in *IEEE Trans. on Software Engineering*.)

[68] Jahanian, F., and Mok, A., *A Graph-Theoretic Approach for Timing Analysis in Real-Time Logic*, Proceedings of Real-Time Systems Symposium (IEEE), pp 98-108, New Orleans, LA, December 2-4, 1986.

[69] Jensen, E. D., Locke, C. D., and Tokuda, H., *A Time Driven Scheduling Model for Real-Time Operating Systems*, Proceedings of Real-Time Systems Symposium (IEEE), pp. 112–122, San Diego, CA, December 3–6, 1985.

[70] Joseph, T. A., and Birman, K. P., "Low Cost Management of Replicated Data in Fault Tolerant Distributed Systems," *ACM Trans. on Computer Systems*, Vol. 4 (1), 54–70, February 1986.

[71] Kain, G. Y., "On Access Checking in Capability Based Systems," *IEEE Trans. on Software Engineering*, Vol. SE–13 (2) 202–207, February 1987.

[72] Kar, G., Nikolaou, C., and Reif, J., *Assigning Processes to Processors: A Fault Tolerant Approach*, Proceedings of 14th International Conference on Fault Tolerant Computing Systems (FTCS), pp. 306–309, Kissimmee, FL, June 1984.

[73] Karp, R. M., "Reducibility Among Combinatorial Problems," (in Miller, R. E., and Thatcher, J. W., editors, *Complexity of Computer Computations*) pp. 85–104, Plenum Press, New York, NY, 1972.

[74] Kleinrock, L., *Queueing Systems*, John Wiley and Sons, New York, NY, 1975.

[75] Knuth, D. E., *The Art of Computer Programming*, (Sorting and Searching, Vol. III), Addison-Wesley Publishing Company, Reading, MA, 1973.

[76] Kodres, U., "Analysis of Real Time Systems by Data Flowgraphs," *IEEE Trans. on Software Engineering*, Vol. SE–4 (3), 169–178, May 1978.

[77] Ladkin, P., *Primitives and Units for Time Specification*, Proceedings of the Fifth National Conference on Artificial Intelligence (AAAI), pp. 354–359, Philadelphia, PA, August 11–15, 1986.

[78] Ladkin, P., *Time Representation: A Taxonomy of Interval Relations*, Proceedings of the Fifth National Conference on Artificial Intelligence (AAAI), pp. 360–366, Philadelphia, PA, August 11–15, 1986.

[79] Lakshman, T. V., and Agrawala, A. K., "Efficient Decentralized Consensus Protocols," *IEEE Trans. on Software Engineering*, Vol. SE–12 (5), 600–607, May 1986.

[80] Lamport, L., "Time, Clocks and Ordering of Events in a Distributed System," *Communications of the ACM*, Vol. 21 (7), 558–565, July 1978.

[81] Lamport, L., "Using Time instead of Timeout for Fault-Tolerant Distributed System," *ACM Trans. on Prog. Lang. and Systems*, Vol. 6 (2), 254–280, April 1984.

[82] Lamport, L., "On Interprocess Communication," parts I and II, *Distributed Computing*, Vol. 1 (2), 77–101, Springer-Verlag, Berlin, Federal Republic of Germany, 1986.

[83] Lamport, L., *Synchronizing Time Servers*, SRC report No. 18, December SRC, Palo Alto, CA, June 1987.

[84] Lamport, L., and Melliar-Smith, P. M., "Synchronizing Clocks in the Presence of Faults," *Journal of the ACM*, Vol. 32 (1), 52–78, January 1985.

[85] Lamport, L., Shostak, R., and Pease, M., "The Byzantine Generals Problem," *ACM Trans. on Prog. Lang. and Systems*, Vol. 4, (3), 382–401, July 1982.

[86] Leban, B., McDonald, D., and Forster, D., *A Representation for Collections of Temporal Intervals*, Proceedings of the Fifth National Conference on Artificial Intelligence (AAAI), pp. 367–371, Philadelphia, PA, August 11–15, 1986.

[87] Lee, I., and Davidson, S. B., "Adding Time to Synchronous Process Communications," *IEEE Trans. on Computers*, Vol. C–36 (8), 941–948, August 1987.

[88] Lehoczky, J. P., Sha, L., and Strosnider, J. K., *Enhanced Aperiodic Responsiveness in Hard Real-Time Environments*, Proceedings of Real-Time Systems Symposium, pp. 261–270, San Jose, CA, December 1987.

[89] LeLann, G., *Issues in Fault-Tolerant Real-Time Local Area Network*, IEEE Proceedings of the Fifth Symposium on Reliability in Distributed Software and Database Systems, pp. 28–32, Los Angeles, CA, January 1986.

[90] Levi, S.-T., *A Methodology for Designing Distributed, Fault-Tolerant, and Reactive Real-Time Operating Systems*, Ph.D. Dissertation, Department of Computer Science, University of Maryland, College Park, MD, April 1988.

[91] Levi, S.-T., and Agrawala, A. K., *Objects Architecture: A Comprehensive Design Approach for Real-Time, Distributed, Fault-Tolerant, Reactive Operating Systems*, CS–TR–1915, Technical Report, Department of Computer Science, University of Maryland, College Park, MD, September 1987.

[92] Levi, S.-T., Mossé, D., and Agrawala, A. K., *Allocation of Real-Time Computations under Fault-Tolerance Constraints*, Proceedings of the Ninth Real-Time Symposium, pp. 161–170, Huntsville, AL, December 1988.

[93] Levi, S.-T., Tripathi, S. K., Carson, S. D., and Agrawala, A. K., *The MARUTI Hard Real-Time Operating System*, The Fourth Israel Conference on Computer Systems and Software Engineering, Jerusalem, Israel, June 5–6, 1989.

[94] Liskov, B., and Scheifler, R., "Guardians and Actions: Linguistic Support for Robust Distributed Programs," *ACM Trans. on Programming Languages and Systems*, Vol. 5 (3), 381–404, July 1983.

[95] Liskov, B. H., and Snyder, A., "Exception Handling in CLU," *IEEE Trans. on Software Engineering*, Vol. SE–5 (6), 546–558, November 1979.

[96] Liu, C. L., and Layland, J. W., "Scheduling Algorithms for Multiprogramming in Hard Real-Time Environment," *Journal of the ACM*, Vol. 20 (1), 46–61, January 1973.

[97] Lundelius, J., and Lynch, N., *A New Fault Tolerant Algorithm for Clock Synchronization*, MIT Laboratory of Computer Science, Cambridge MA, June 1984.

[98] Ma, R. P., Lee, E., and Tsuchiya, M., *Design of Task Allocation Scheme for Time Critical Applications*, IEEE Proceedings—Real Time Systems Symposium, Miami Beach FL, December 1981.

[99] Ma, R. P., Lee, E., and Tsuchiya, M., "A Task Allocation Model for Distributed Computing Systems," *IEEE Trans. on Computers*, Vol. C–31 (1), January 1982.

[100] Mancini, L., "Modular Redundancy in a Message Passing System," *IEEE Trans. on Software Engineering*, Vol. SE–12 (1), 79–86, January 1986.

[101] Marzullo, K., and Owicki, S., "Maintaining the Time in a Distributed System," *ACM Operating Systems Review*, Vol. 19 (3), 44–54, July 1985.

[102] Mills, D. L., *DCNET Internet Clock Service*, RFC–778, Defense Advanced Research Projects Agency, Information Processing Techniques Office, April 1981.

[103] Mok, A., *Fundamental Design Problems for the Hard Real Time Environment*, MIT Ph.D. Dissertation, Cambridge, MA, May 1983.

[104] Mok, A. K., and Dertouzos, M. L., *Multiprocessor Scheduling in a Hard Real-Time Environment*, Proceedings of the Seventh Texas Conference on Computing Systems, pp. 5.1–5.12, Houston, TX, October 30–November 1, 1978.

[105] Molle, M. L., and Kleinrock L., "Virtual Time CSMA: Why Two Clocks are Better than One," *IEEE Trans. on Communications*, Vol. COM–33 (9), September 1985.

[106] Molloy, M., "Performance Analysis Using Stochastic Petri Nets," *IEEE Trans. on Computers*, Vol. C–31 (9), 913–917, September 1982.

[107] Mullender, S. J., and Tanenbaum, A. S., "The Design of a Capability Based Operating System," *The Computer Journal*, Vol. 29 (4) 289–299, August 1986.

[108] Nehmer, J., *An Object Architecture for Hard Real-Time Systems*, CS–TR–2003, Technical Report, Department of Computer Science, University of Maryland, College Park, MD, March 1988.

[109] Nelson, R., Haibt, L., and Sheridan, P., "Casting Petri Nets into Programs," *IEEE Trans. on Software Engineering*, Vol. SE–9 (5), 590–602, September 1983.

[110] Ostroff, J. S., and Wonham, W. M., *Modelling, Specifying, and Verifying Real-Time Computer-Embedded Systems*, Proceedings of the Eighth Real-Time Systems Symposium, pp. 124–132, San Jose, CA, December 1987.

[111] Owicki, S., and Gries, D., "Verifying Properties of Parallel Programs: An Axiomatic Approach," *Communications of the ACM*, Vol. 19 (5), 279–285, May 1976.

[112] Parnas, D. L., "On the Criteria to be Used in Decomposing Systems into Modules," *Communications of the ACM*, Vol. 15 (12), 1053–1058, December 1972.

[113] Parnas, D. L., "Designing Software for Ease of Extension and Contraction," *IEEE Trans. on Software Engineering*, Vol. SE–5 (2), 128–137, March 1979.

[114] Peterson, J. L., "Petri Nets," *ACM Computing Surveys*, Vol. 9 (3), 223–252, September 1977.

[115] Peterson, J. L., and Silberschatz, A., *Operating System Concepts*, Addison Wesley Publishing, Reading, MA, July 1984.

[116] Popek, G., "Issues in Kernel Design," (in *Operating Systems: An Advanced Course*, Bayer, R., Graham, R., and Seegmuller, G., editors), Springer-Verlag, Berlin, Federal Republic of Germany, 1979.

[117] Postel, J., *Internet Protocol*, RFC–791, Defense Advanced Research Projects Agency, Information Processing Techniques Office, September 1981.

[118] Postel, J., *Internet Control Message Protocol*, RFC–792, Defense Advanced Research Projects Agency, Information Processing Techniques Office, September 1981.

[119] Postel, J., *Transmission Control Protocol*, RFC-793, Defense Advanced Research Projects Agency, Information Processing Techniques Office, September 1981.

[120] Quirk, W. (editor), *Verification and Validation of Real Time Software*, Springer-Verlag, Berlin, Federal Republic of Germany, 1985.

[121] Ramamrithan, K., and Stankovic, J., "Dynamic Task Scheduling in Hard Real-Time Distributed Systems," *IEEE Software*, Vol. 1 (3), 65–75, July 1984.

[122] Randel, B., "System Structure for Software Fault Tolerance," *IEEE Trans. on Software Engineering*, Vol. SE–1 (2), 220–232, June 1975.

[123] Reed, D. P., "Implementing Atomic Actions on Decentralized Data," *ACM Trans. on Computer Systems*, Vol. 1 (1), 3–23, February 1983.

[124] Reisig, W., *Petri Nets*, Springer-Verlag, Berlin, Federal Republic of Germany, 1985.

[125] Ricart, G., and Agrawala, A., "An Optimal Algorithm for Mutual Exclusion in Computer Network," *Communication of the ACM*, Vol. 23 (1), 9–17, January 1981.

[126] Rit, J., *Propagating Temporal Constraints for Scheduling*, Proceedings of the Fifth National Conference on Artificial Intelligence (AAAI), pp. 383–388, Philadelphia, PA, August 11–15, 1986.

[127] Saltzer, J., "Naming and Binding of Objects," (in *Operating Systems: An Advanced Course*, Bayer, R., Graham, R., and Seegmuller, G., editors), Springer-Verlag, Berlin, Federal Republic of Germany, 1979.

[128] Schneider, F. B., Gries, D., and Schlichting, R. D., "Fault Tolerant Broadcasts," *Science of Computer Programming*, Vol. 4, 1–15, North Holland, 1984.

[129] Schwan, K., Bihari, T., and Weide, B., "High Performance Operating System Primitives for Robotics and Real-Time Control Systems," *ACM Trans. on Computer Systems*, Vol. 5 (3), 189–231, August 1987.

[130] Schwan, K., Bo, W., and Gopinath, P., *A High Performance, Object Based Operating System for Real-Time, Robotics Applications*, Proceedings of Real-Time System Symposium (IEEE), pp. 147–156, December 2–4, 1986, New Orleans, LA.

[131] Sha, L., Lehoczky, J. P., and Rajkumar, P., *Solutions for Some Practical Problems in Prioritized Preemptive Scheduling*, Proceedings of Real-Time System Symposium (IEEE), pp. 181–191, December 2–4, 1986, New Orleans, LA.

[132] Shankar, A. U., and Lam, S. S., *Time Dependent Communication Protocols, Tutorial: Principles of Communication and Networking Protocols*, S. S. Lam (editor), IEEE Computer Society, 1984.

[133] Shankar, A. U., and Lam, S. S., *Time-Dependent Distributed Sytems: Proving Safety, Liveness and Real-Time Properties*, technical report CS–TR–1586, Department of Computer Science, University of Maryland, College Park, MD, December 1985.

[134] Shin, K., and Ramanathan, P., "Clock Synchronization of a Large Multiprocessor System in the Presence of Malicious Faults," *IEEE Trans. on Computers*, Vol. C–36 (1), 2–12, January 1987.

[135] Skeen, D., *Nonblocking Commit Protocols*, Memorandum No UCB/ERL M81/11, Electronic Research Lab, College of Engineering, University of Berkeley, CA, March 1981.

[136] Skeen, D., and Stonebraker, M., "A Formal Model of Crash Recovery in a Distributed System," *IEEE Trans. on Software Engineering*, Vol. SE–9 (3), 219–228, May 1983.

[137] Stallings, W., *The DOD Communication Protocol Standards*, SIGNAL, Vol 40. (8) 29–34, April 1986.

[138] Stallings, W., *Local Networks*, second edition, Macmillan Publishing Company, New York, NY 1987.

[139] Stankovic, J. A. (editor), *Real-Time Computing Systems: The Next Generation*, March, 1987 CMU Workshop on Fundamental Issues in Distributed Real-Time Systems, Carnegie Mellon University, Pittsburgh, PA, November 23, 1987.

[140] Stankovic, J. A., and Ramamrithan, K., *The Design of the Spring Kernel*, Proceedings of Real-Time Systems Symposium, pp. 146–157, San Jose, CA, December 1987.

[141] Stankovic, J., Ramamrithan, K., and Cheng, S., "Evaluation of A Flexible Task Scheduling Algorithm for Hard Real-Time Systems," *IEEE Trans. on Computers*, Vol. C–34 (12), 1130–1143, August 1987.

[142] Stoyenko, A. D., *A Case for Schedulability Analyzable Real-Time Language*, IEEE Fourth Workshop on Real-Time Operating Systems, pp. 120–124, Cambridge, MA, July 1987.

[143] Stoyenko, A. D., *A Schedulability Analyzer for Real-Time Euclid*, Proceedings of Real-Time Systems Symposium, pp. 218–227, San Jose, CA, December 1987.

[144] Stoyenko, A. D., and Kligerman, E., "Real-Time Euclid: A Language for Reliable Real-Time Systems," *IEEE Trans. on Software Engineering*, Vol. SE–12 (9), 941–949, September 1986.

[145] Tanenbaum, A., and Von Renesse, R., "Distributed Operating Systems," *ACM Computing Surveys*, Vol. 17 (4), 419–470, December 1985.

[146] Taylor, D. J., and Seger, C. J., "Robust Storage Structures for Crash Recovery," *IEEE Trans. on Computers*, Vol. C–35 (4), 288–295, April 1986.

[147] Tokuda, H., Wendorf, J. W., and Wang, H.-Y., *Implementation of a Time Driven Scheduler for Real-Time Operating Systems*, Proceedings of Real-Time Systems Symposium, pp. 271–279, San Jose, CA, December 1987.

[148] Tripathi, S., and Chang, S., *A Clock Synchronization Algorithm for Hierarchical LANs— Implementation and Measurements*, Technical Report TR–86–48, Systems Research Center, University of Maryland, College Park, MD, 1986.

[149] Vanderlin, D., "Toward a Real-Time Executive Standard," *Unix World*, pp. 75–81, April 1988.

[150] Vilain, M., and Kautz, H., *Constraint Propagation Algorithms for Temporal Reasoning*, Proceedings of the Fifth National Conference on Artificial Intelligence (AAAI), pp. 377–382, Philadelphia, PA, August 11–15, 1986.

[151] Voges, U., et al., "SADAT—An Automated Testing Tool," *IEEE Trans on Software Engineering*, Vol. SE–6 (3), 286–290, May 1980.

[152] Voltz, R. A., and Mudge, T. N., "Instruction Level Timing Mechanism for Accurate Real-Time Task Scheduling," *IEEE Trans. on Computers*, Vol. C–36 (8), 988–993, August 1987.

[153] Watson, R. W., "Distributed System Architecture Model," (in Lampson, B. W., Paul, M., and Siegert, H. J., editors, *Distributed Systems: Architecture and Implementation–an Advanced Course*, pp. 10–43), Springer-Verlag, Berlin, Federal Republic of Germany, 1981.

[154] Wirth, N., "Toward a Discipline of Real Time Programming," *Communications of the ACM*, Vol. 20 (8), 577–583, August 1977.

[155] Zave, P., "The Operational Versus The Conventional Approach to Software Development," *Communications of the ACM*, Vol. 27 (2), 104–118, February 1984.

[156] Zhao, W., and Ramamrithan, K., *Distributed Scheduling Using Bidding and Focused Addressing*, Proceedings of Real-Time Systems Symposium (IEEE), pp. 103–111, San Diego, CA, December 3–6, 1985.

[157] Zhao, W., and Ramamrithan, K., *A Virtual Time CSMA Protocol for Hard Real-Time Communication*, Proceedings of Real-Time System Symposium (IEEE), pp. 120–127, New Orleans, LA, December 2–4, 1986.

[158] Zhao, W., Ramamrithan, K., and Stankovic, J., "Scheduling Tasks with Resource Requirements in Hard Real-Time Systems," *IEEE Trans. on Software Engineering*, Vol. SE–13 (5), 564–577, May 1987.

[159] Zhao, W., Ramamrithan, K., and Stankovic, J., "Preemptive Scheduling under Time and Resource Constraints," *IEEE Trans. on Computers*, Vol. C–36 (8), 949–960, August 1987.

[160] Zhao, W., and Ramamrithan, K., "Simple and Integrated Heuristic Algorithms for Scheduling Tasks with Resource Constraints," *Journal of Systems and Software*, to be published 1987.

INDEX